TT 71-58007

AKADEMIYA NAUK SSSR
Institute Morfologii Zhivotnykh im. A. N. Severtsova

ACADEMY OF SCIENCES, USSR
A. N. Severtsov Institute of Morphology of Animals

VARIABILITY OF
MAMMALS

(Izmenchivost' Mlekopitayushchikh)

A. V. YABLOKOV

**Revised by the author for this edition
Scientific editor of translation : L. Van Valen**

*Nauka Publishers
Moscow,* 1966

Translated from Russian

Published for the Smithsonian Institution and the
National Science Foundation, Washington, D.C.
by Amerind Publishing Co. Pvt. Ltd., New Delhi
1974

Translated and Published for the Smithsonian Institution,
pursuant to an agreement with
The National Science Foundation, Washington, D. C.
by Amerind Publishing Co. Pvt. Ltd.,
66 Janpath, New Delhi 110001

Translator : Dr. Jayant Honmode
General Editor : Dr. V. S. Kothekar

Available from the U. S. Department of Commerce
National Technical Information Service
Springfield, Virginia 22161

Printed at Prem Printing Press, Lucknow, India

FOREWORD

Phenotypic variation is the raw material for natural selection, yet a century after Darwin it is an almost unknown subject. To a considerable extent this may be true because even to see the significance of studying variation within populations (rather than taking it as given) requires an appreciation of several ordinarily separate disciplines: morphology, ecology, genetics, developmental biology, and to some extent systematics and paleontology. Other disciplines are also sometimes important, but these are central.

Darwin wrote more on variation than on any other subject. Since his time, there has been almost no one of intellectual power in western countries who has known all the central subjects adequately to make much progress. In the USSR, however, Schmalhausen (to use the ancestral spelling of his name rather than the direct re-transliteration Shmal'gauzen) was such a person. His major book, *Factors of Evolution*, is, because of its original treatment of variation, perhaps as important as any book on evolution since Darwin. Despite a translation in 1949, Schmalhausen's book is not well known in western countries, perhaps because of prejudice against Russian work, perhaps because of Dobzhansky's introduction to the translation. This introduction damned the book by praising some minor achievements rather than the central theme. And, contrary to the introduction, the translation deleted some of Schmalhausen's unorthodox insights. Some of his insights, such as the distinction between r and K selection, have been rediscovered or absorbed into western science; others have not.

Yablokov's book documents part of Schmalhausen's approach with respect to mammals and makes some general theoretical advances. Taken together, the books may hopefully be of some importance in re-directing western research onto the subject of variation. The subject is unexpectedly recondite when looked at seriously, and its exploration is still mostly by travellers going elsewhere.

The Russian scientific tradition differs from ours in various ways. I have tried to retain this as well as the characteristic flavor of Russian writing. Except for occasional misprints and the like in the Russian version, I have made no changes from that version. The few apparent mistakes in the original don't seriously detract from the book. I caught some important mistranslations, but as I have not re-translated the book others presumably remain. Yablokov has gone over the revised translation and suggested some improvements. The published Russian version and the translation differs in some matters of substance because of changes by Yablokov in the interim, but comments on single passages should nevertheless be based on both versions.

Vaclav Laska, the Slavic bibliographer at the University of Chicago, went over the entire bibliography with me. He made a number of corrections as well as greatly helping with the references themselves. Katherine Rylaarsdam also helped with bibliographic matters. Almost all the references should now be clear, if not easily accessible, to western readers. Quotations from English sources, or from books translated into English, are wherever possible given as these versions rather than as re-translations of the sometimes garbled translations into Russian.

In addition to Yablokov's book and those of Schmalhausen and Paaver, in his bibliography, I append here a chronological and probably incomplete list of book-length treatments of variation after Darwin. I exclude special topics with large literatures of their own: heredity, mimicry, agricultural aspects, pathology, and human behavior; and books that also treat other subjects than variation and so are better known.

Bateson, W. 1894. Materials for the Study of Variation. London: Macmillan. 598 pp.

Pringsheim, H. 1910. Die Variabilität niederer Organismen. Berlin: J. Springer. 216 pp.

Deecke, W. 1920. Der Wert der Variationsstatistik für die Paläontologie. Ber. Naturf. Ges. Freiburg i Br., 22: 7-218.

Pelseneer, P. 1920. Les variations et leur hérédité chez les Mollusques. Acad. Roy. Belgique, Classe Sci., Mém. in-8° (2) 5: 1-826.

Hammar, J. A. H. 1932. Über Wachstum und Rückgang. Leipzig: Akademische Verlagsgesellschaft. 539 pp.

Robson, G. S., and O. W. Richards, 1936. The Variation of Animals in Nature. London: Longman and Green. 425 pp.

Colyer, F. 1936. Variations and Diseases of the Teeth of Animals. London: John Bale, Sons and Danielsson. 750 pp.

Ludwig, W. 1936. Das Rechts-Links Problem im Tierreich und beim Menschen. Berlin: J. Springer. 496 pp. (Reprinted 1970, Springer-Verlag).

Williams, R. J. 1956. Biochemical Individuality. New York: J. Wiley. 214 pp.

Olson, E. C., and R. L. Miller, 1958. Morphological Integration. Chicago: Univ. Chicago Press. 317 pp.

Berry, R. J. and H. N. Southern (eds.), 1970. Variation in Mammalian Populations. Symp. Zool. Soc. London. 26: 1-403.

L. VAN VALEN

INTRODUCTION

Toward the beginning of the 20th century, with the development of Darwin's theory, problems confronting the evolutionary studies about the formation of ways of evolutionary growth of organs could be considered as understood on general lines (Haeckel, 1894-1896; Huxley, 1858; Gegenbaur, 1898-1901; Severtsov, 1912, 1914; and many others). But studies on the mode of growth of individual organs (morphological interrelations) must serve as only a preface to causal researches on phylogenesis (Severtsov, 1939; p. 58). However, the study of the mechanism of evolution could not be carried out till the foundation was laid: availability of a large number of new facts, the development of new concepts and theories in such fields of biology as the studies of fine and ultra-fine structures in living creatures, and a composite scientific approach to animal behavior and genetics.

But in the period of the "modern synthesis of all these sciences" that followed (Dodson, 1960; Huxley, 1942), the morphological trend in research was not the dominant one as in the past but played a subsidiary role. As such, morphology, which was at one time the chief instrument for understanding phylogenesis, presently fell aside in deciding the general evolutionary questions. Each of the new trends in morphology probing the secrets of structures of living organisms to greater and greater depths (ultraviolet and electron microscopy, histology and cytology, neurology, etc.) had only one principle: to know more about everything small.

This fact, in its own way, led to the situation that evolved by the middle of the 20th century: morphology developed into many independent lines and became an experimental science, and while aspects of medical morphology were attaining foremost importance in their development, evolutionary morphology and comparative anatomy were relegated more and more toward secondary importance.

Morphology in the past studied organisms and all of comparative anatomy was based on these studies. This course was an historic necessity and facilitated drawing general conclusions of great importance: to establish the very fact of evolution and to form the general structure of the genealogical tree of the present animal kingdom. But following this course it was impossible to understand how evolution occurs.

One of the chief achievements of present theoretical biology is the development of the concept of population as an elementary evolutionary unit. This most important fact, substantiated by voluminous data in genetics (Chetverikov, 1926; Wright, 1931; Dubinin, 1931; Dubinin and Romashov, 1932; and others), ecology (Sumner, 1909-1932; Elton, 1927; Pearl, 1939; and others), paleontology and general biology (Schmalhausen, 1939; Simpson, 1941, 1944; Mayr, 1942; Beklemishev, 1960, 1964; and others), is absolutely inadequate until it takes into account vertebrate morphology.

This poses highly specific problems because the study of the structure of a particular specimen is not adequate to characterize in detail the group of animals under study.

In response to these new requirements a new trend has appeared in morphology in the last decade. It is based firstly on comparative anatomy, secondly on quantitative ecology, and thirdly on population genetics. This trend is known as "population morphology".

The basis of this trend is the study of the population as an evolutionary unit by morphological methods. Here, too, the study of variability, the material basis of the evolutionary process, attracts more and more attention from morphologists of all animal groups.

A question arises: Is it correct to study phenotype without studying genotype? In other words, can a morphologist who, as a rule, is concerned with the study of phenotypic variability discuss evolutionary processes? To this question, George Gaylord Simpson (1944) gave a good answer. He showed that the question of whether a given trait is inherited does not exhaust its significance for evolution:

"No morphological character is inherited as such. The ultimate morphological expression of the same hereditary factors differ markedly. The particular expression, among several possible expressions, developed in a given individual does not affect the potentialities passed on to its descendants. It certainly affects the fate of the individual and therefore helps to determine whether that individual will have descendants" (Simpson, 1837; p. 62; 1944, p. 30). For a morphologist, this discussion has great importance because it allows him to confidently consider that the morphological and phenotypic variability under study has a direct relation with the evolution of the group (Cannon, 1959; Yablokov, 1963b). In the morphological approach to the study of the evolutionary process, it is also important to note that the so-called "small" morphological variations are usually correlated with significant specializations in the activity of the organism (Olenov, 1961) and a variation in an individual trait usually indicates a variation in the condition of the whole organism (Sinskaya, 1948). Finally, there is no reason to believe that variability in one type of organs will be governed by one rule and variability of other organs by another. Most general properties of variability, as a phenomenon, will no doubt be similar for the variability of the length of the tail and for the variability in the number of cells in the cerebral cortex. Of course, in the living being there are organs with relatively greater or lesser importance, but the relativity of any organ, emerging from the multi-functionality of organs, diversification in the function of each organ during ontogeny, and insufficient understanding of the functional importance of individual organs and their structure (Sokal and Sneath, 1963), brings all the organs into equality when studying general properties of variability (in the same way as the general laws of heredity can be studied equally in viruses, *Drosophila*, and peas).

It would appear that the brilliant successes achieved by mathematical and population genetics in the 1930's have come very close to unfolding the exact and important aspects of the mechanism of evolution. But the problem appeared to be much more difficult: the research workers had to discover the complicated phenomena in the formation of a population as a dynamic structure, then their relationships in similar populations of diverse organisms, which together form a self-developing system, a bio-geocenose. Only recently have the research workers begun to understand clearly the different channels or links through which the development of any population is controlled (Schmalhausen, 1958-1965); only now we begin to actually understand the importance of this differential approach toward the study of various forms of natural selection (Berg, 1964a, 1964b). It appears that the general understanding of the complex picture of genetic variation in populations determined by the action of selection, mutation, and stochastic (genetico-automatic) processes (Belyaev, 1962; p. 111), is insufficient to explain almost exclusively on this basis genetical problems and the role of the so-called "non-hereditary" variability in evolution (Kirpichnikov, 1935, 1940; Lukin, 1936; Kamshilov, 1939; Dobzhansky, 1937; and others). It mainly helped to show the inadequacy of only the genetical approach. Now it is clear that this trend has promising contacts of a genetical approach to the study of the evolutionary processes with morphological and ecological points of view. Now, as never before, the problem of the intermingling of these approaches has become acute; without it the future fruitful growth of the evolutionary concept appears to be at a standstill (Blair, 1964)

In the present work, an attempt has been made to make an advance in one particular problem against this common background of association of many sciences in the study of evolution, i.e., the study of the characteristics of population morphology in the class Mammalia.

It was considered important to collect every fact about the variability of different systems of organs and the structure of mammals. This has been done in Chapter II. On the basis of an analysis of variability at various taxonomic levels in one specially studied group of Pinnipedia, an attempt has been made to clarify the general characteristics of variability of a group at different taxonomic categories (Chapter III). The entire collected data showed the inadequacy of the existing classifications of variability as a whole and has permitted us to suggest a new scheme of classification of the phenomenon of variability (Chapter IV). In the concluding chapters of this work (Chapters V and VI), an attempt has been made to throw light on various general questions related to the process of "micro-evolution" operating at the level of a population (a concept introduced by Timofeev-Ressovskii, 1939, 1958, 1965a, 1965b).

All this taken together indicates the inadequacy of existing studies on the phenomenon of variability and defines the general structure of the present work. That is why, because the starting point is the problem of variability as such, the ecological analysis of evolving structures is given only in a most general form in the majority of cases.

The importance and the necessity for such formalized (in the initial stages) study of variability, has been recognized by many research workers (Alpatov and Boschko-Stepanenko, 1928; Simpson and Roe, 1939; Bader, 1955; Bader and Hall, 1960; Roginskii, 1959; and others), who have noted many similar situations: these have been dealt with in detail at appropriate places in the work.

The selection of mammals and not any other vertebrates or invertebrates for the present research is not accidental. In this highly developed class of the animal kingdom, the patterns of evolutionary growth which are of interest to us must be acting in a most evident way, perhaps because "evolution produces new forms" (Berg, 1959).

Among mammals, it was of interest to study many ecologically different forms. In this regard, it was thought necessary to examine critically some sharply divergent groups, for example groups of aquatic mammals and Chiroptera, which have undergone substantial morphological adjustments in the course of adaptation to the environment, and which therefore have adaptations not characteristic of other mammals. An examination of these groups, perhaps, will be most fruitful as compared to the "typical" terrestrial mammals, morphologically nearer to the ancestors for all mammalian forms. The proposed work is a beginning of such analysis and has been carried out on original data from Pinnipedia and Cetacea of the USSR, as well as on data obtained by other research workers on all principal groups of mammals.

Data on population morphology of mammals are accumulating at a very fast rate. This situation shows once again the necessity for generalization, theoretical comprehension, and the formation of specific working hypotheses for future planned and intensive studies on populations by morphological methods.

In biology, as it becomes a more and more perfect science, there arises a necessity to use clearly defined concepts. Hence, in the beginning it is important to define exactly as far as possible the basic terminology necessary for a uniform treatment of the theoretical basis of the problems under study.

1. *Variability* is sometimes understood as a process of appearance of qualitative differences as well as the presence of such differences (Simpson, 1948). Specific use of the concept of "variability" should be made only for stating the fact of qualitative differences. In our work, the definition of variability has been used as suggested by George Gaylord Simpson: *the presence of differences among individuals within a breeding population.*

It is clear from the definition that the variability examined under such a plan, appears not as a property of the individual organism but as a property or characteristic of the population.

2. *Population* in the present work may be understood as a group of individuals in which panmixis occurs and which is genetically isolated from similar such groups for more than one generation.

3. *Selection* (in the most general sense) is understood to be a result of interaction between individuals of the evolving species and the changing environment (Schmalhausen, 1939; p. 77. Also, see note in Chapter IV of the present work).

4. *Environment* is understood as all that surrounds the population (organism) and related in any form to the continuance of its life functions; geographical and climatic conditions, food, competitors, behavioral interactions, etc. When examined in such generality, the organism or the population can be taken as a part of its own environment (Simpson, 1948).

5. *Trait* is understood as any characteristic of the organism and of the population as a whole which can be studied and expressed in quantitative units.

6. *Structure* in the present work refers to a component part of an individual organ or a system of organs; for example, phalanges or fingers as structures of hands, blood corpuscles as structures of blood, different groups of cells as structures of individual organs and systems, etc.

A number of researchers, mainly the staff of the Institute of Developmental Biology, Academy of Sciences, USSR (Moscow), took part in the collection and initial preparation of the material reported in this work. Professor S. E. Kleinenberg was the initiator of many discussions that took place in the laboratory and which continued during many months of field work in the Arctic and Pacific Oceans. Dr. G. A. Klevezal', Dr. V. M.

Bel'kovich, and V. I. Borisov rendered me invaluable help in the collection of the material and V. Ya. Etin in the processing of this material.

Credit in the publication of this work, first of all, goes to those criticisms and discussions in which the following scientists took part: N. V. Timofeev-Ressovskii (whose great erudition and personal respect mainly determined the formation of my viewpoints), N. N. Vorontsov, V. I. Tsalkin, B. S. Matveev, S. S. Schwartz, members of the laboratory colloquium and the scientific council of the Institute, members of the seminar on morphology at the zoological museum of Moscow State University, and the members of the inter-sectional seminar on evolutionary problems at the Moscow Society of Naturalists, where, in recent years, various parts of this work were discussed.

In the process of working on separate chapters, I took advice from Y. I. Starobogatov, Academician I. I. Schmalhausen, corresponding member AN SSSR D. K. Belyaev, K. K. Chapskii, T. G. Sarycheva, K. K. Flerov, Ya. L. Glembotskii, and G. D. Polyakov; and critical observations were made by K. A. Yudin, K. K. Chapskii, corresponding member AN SSSR G. V. Nikol'skii, A. A. Lyubishchev, N. P. Naumov, V. M. Makushok, and B. N. Shornikov.

I express my sincere and deep gratitude to all the above-mentioned research workers.

I dedicate this work to my friend, wife, and constant helper—Eleonora Dmitrievna Bakulina.

*   *   *

Since I finished the first edition of this work, there have appeared a large number of new papers on the intraspecific variability of mammals. In the introduction to the first edition, I mentioned the possibility of having omitted much work worthy of inclusion, but now I *unavoidably* have to omit many interesting studies in this area without even mentioning them. This is because of the technical unfeasibility of surveying thousands of studies in one book, and because in some recent studies new (and at times very interesting) data give us nothing new in principle with respect to the intraspecific population variability of mammals.

It is quite evident that for the specialist on some relatively small group of mammals (or on some part of the anatomy), his particular subject will in many cases be absent from this book. However, I hope that in neighboring pages he will find information on the variability of other groups of mammals (or parts of the anatomy), unfamiliar to him in detail, a feature desirable for broad comparison and deep analysis.

This book has data on fundamental matters: an account of intraspecific phenomena (more exactly, intrapopulational), phenotypic variability of mammals. The study of the variability of the phenotype is a necessary step in any kind of deep study of population variability. This work, I hope, shows some degree of direction in the development of "population morphology"; it can therefore be of interest to more people than specialists in the study of mammals. It seems to me that the population-morphological (or, more broadly, the "phenotypic") approach permits accurate analysis of large populations. This approach has been made first to morphological material, but such populations also occur, now more and more frequently, in genetical, ecological, and ethological analyses of species, and give a means of studying current problems of biology.

After the publication in Moscow, in 1966, of the first edition of this book, I have obtained information from various comments and answers to requests from many people. I thank these people, and among them especially P. F. Rokitskii (Minsk), V. S. Smirnov (Sverdlovsk), E. Olson (Chicago), B. M. Melnikov (Moscow), Ya. I Starobogatov (Leningrad), Yu. T. Artem'ev (Kazan), C. A. Long (Stevens Point), and others. Many of these observations were helpful for the present version of the book. Besides these items, I have added some other data and rather condensed accounts of some general principles.

I am glad that publication of this work in English will make it more accessible to workers from many countries, and express my most sincere and deep gratitude to Professor L. Van Valen for his initiative in the translation of this book and editorial work on it.

A. V. YABLOKOV
Moscow   Institute of Developmental Biology
November, 1972   Academy of Sciences of the USSR

CONTENTS

Chapter I

GENERAL APPROACHES TO THE STUDY OF VARIABILITY

Method for Complex Analysis of Mammalian Variability

An absence of a general framework for the collection of data to study population morphology has been increasingly felt in the last few years. This necessity is all the more felt because until recently data on quantitative variability of mammals were used only in such zoological disciplines as taxonomy, zoogeography and genetics. This continued through many decades with the same traits, usually skull measurements and some body measurements, being studied. Such a situation is of historical significance.

In the 19th or at the beginning of the 20th century, the attention of researchers was centered on the formation of the family tree of the organic world in general and, as far as mammals were concerned, to the construction of a general phylogenetic classification of mammals and an inventory of the world fauna. Such an inventory was prepared, and by the end of the 19th century a general classification was formulated. The researchers in comparative anatomy (which by now had lost much of its importance in the evolutionary approach) continued and intensified efforts to bring to light minute details. In the beginning of this century, this approach to comparative anatomy in phylogenetic research reached its final expression, through the formation of a theory of organogenesis, in the works of A. N. Severtsov—a morphologist and evolutionist. Afterwards, comparative anatomy became closer to ecological morphology, the aims and objectives of which differed to a considerable degree from the former aims of classical comparative anatomy.[1]

---

[1] In this country, this transition is specially noticeable in the growth of morphology in the past 20-25 years, which was stimulated to a great extent by the spread of Neolamarckism.

The methods of comparative anatomy, which initiated quantitative morphology, now served only as additional working methods in the mixed fields of biology. As a result of this, comparative anatomy looked qualitatively impoverished because of a strong restriction to only a few traits of organisms, but at the same time it was enriched through the quantitative methods which facilitated deeper studies under a new light. Such a situation, naturally, was well suited to all the contiguous sciences and continued for the whole first quarter of our century. That is why even until the 1950's not a single broad system of analysis of quantitative variability was worked out.

Many works on the taxonomy and genetics of mammals, which dealt with either very few traits or (in taxonomy) a great number of partial traits not possessing the required quantitative value and not comparable with other traits in other systems, would exemplify what has been said above. To obtain sources of data, for example, on the variability of the intestinal length, quantity of hemoglobin, variability of hair cover, etc., one had to look not into works on zoology or on comparative anatomy but into works on physiology, hematology, commerce, etc., and any accidental appearance of such information in zoological literature reduced its value to zero.

These conditions led researchers who conducted studies on the structure of mammals, to develop a better method for the complex analysis of variability in the morphological structure of mammals. F. Sumner (1906-1908) used morphological indices (excluding skull measurements) for different traits (Sumner, 1908) for characterizing populations of mice; afterwards, the same author increased the number of traits to twelve (Sumner, 1919-1932). The research of F. Sumner, and similar works of other scientists, was carried out in accordance with population genetics. Afterwards, in an attempt to find out more useful criteria for the similarities and differences of animal groups, taxonomists began studying not the individual traits but their whole complexes (Huxley, 1940; Terent'ev, 1959; Mayr *et al.*, 1956). Finally, the works of S. S. Schwartz and his co-workers (1954-1965) revealed the possibility of a complex quantitative approach to the study of ecological and morphological characteristics of mammals and other vertebrates.

The distinguishing character of all these works (with the exception of works like that of S. S. Schwartz, based not on morphological but ecological aspects) happens to be an attempt to obtain a larger number of traits not for the characterization of the organism as a whole, but for a deeper genetical study of the population, or a more objective study of the taxonomy of the group.

At present, we are witnesses to a new era in the development of quantitative morphology and comparative anatomy. These morphological approaches, in combination with population genetics and quantitative ecology, seem to be more and more important for solving a number of evolutionary problems.   Population morphology, arising as a result of such interactions, has the aim of obtaining an objective characterization of populations as elementary evolutionary units.   For this, a wide and complex calculation of the variability of all the systems of organs of the members of a population is needed.   In a number of cases, it is as yet difficult to fulfil this condition because of the absence of an objective and a feasible method of investigation.   But there is no doubt that the very posing of the problem should help in working out such methods.

Principles of Selection of Traits

It is desirable to take the broadest possible sample of variability in traits of organisms forming a population to study the nature of morphological variability.   This has to be seen from two basic points of view:

1.   Study of all traits in population is desirable but impossible; and

2.   During the study of the general control of variability, a single approximation is possible and necessary (reasons for this have been given in the introduction).

It can logically be assumed that the optimum solution to the problem of selecting the number of traits to study for population variability, lies somewhere between the number of organs of animals, and the general number of functions regulated by these organs.   Both limits are highly uncertain and depend on the level of our knowledge.

George Gaylord Simpson (1948), with reference to studying the rate of evolution, observed that the most serious difficulties in solving his problems were as follows:

1.   Selecting traits;

2.   Presenting them all in a measurable form capable of being expressed in comparable units; and

3.   Imparting to them corresponding weights to obtain a general mean value (Simpson, p. 43).[2]

These very difficulties arise during the study of variability.

While measuring the length of intestines in a population of wild mammals—a quite exact trait—we may obtain insufficiently correct biological data for the population as a whole.   It would appear that the particular categories studied do not feed in the same manner, as was revealed from the analysis of food of other members of the same population (the problem of non-characteristic and "unclean" selection), but on the other hand the length of intestines will be a good trait for the selection of animals

[2] Here and afterwards, this work of G. G. Simpson has been cited according to the Russian edition, 1948.

of the same age and sex from an animal population fed on similar rations for a long time, for example, for characterization of an experimental population of mice in a vivarium. We can see from this example that it is necessary to decide in advance what types of variability to analyze and then, depending on the aim of the investigation, to separate the traits showing the kind of variability to be studied. (For classification of variability, see Chapter IV).

One of the basic necessities for the study of measurements is that their calculations and determination should be easy. It is difficult, practically, to compare the variability of external characters of the body with the strength of the muscles and speed of movement, but it is easy and valid to compare wild animals for variability of color, body proportions, and meristic traits.

It is not proper to study variability in number of eyes or extremities, but in insects the number of facets in the compound eye may be a good trait for study; similarly, the number of parapodia in polychaete worms. In Carnivora or ungulates, it is not proper to study the number of fingers and the number of phalanges in each finger, but it would be good to study these traits in cetaceans. At the same time, in ungulates and Carnivora, it may be useful to study the variability of parameters in individual elements of extremities, e.g., linear measurements, weight, form of long bones, and size of articulated surfaces.

During the selection of traits for comparison, it is necessary to take into consideration the importance of the function of differently measured characters of this or that organ, because as seen below (Chapter V) the character and magnitude of variability depends on the character of a trait. This means that in order to obtain the most objective estimate of the variability of any organ, it is important to consider heterogeneous traits (linear, weight, meristic, volume, etc.) characterizing this organ from different angles.

Summarizing in a nutshell the proposed approaches to selecting traits for comparison, it can be said that it is necessary to select the following types of traits:

1. Those which will correspond best to the type, form, and appearance of the variability under study;
2. Those which may be easily studied and determined;
3. Those related to most different systems of organs;
4. Those characterizing one and the same organ from different sides.

Framework of Analysis of Morphological Variability of Mammals

On the basis of data obtained on variability in mammals, it seemed possible to make a general arrangement of characters appropriate to most mammals. The given arrangement should be broadened, corrected, and detailed in future.

Integument

Hair cover: Number of hairs of different types in a unit area on different body parts*.[3] Measurements of hairs of different types on different body parts.

Vibrissae: Number of vibrissae on different body parts, and within a part by group*; measurement of vibrissae*.

Skin as such: Number of layers of epithelial cells in the stratum corneum, stratum granulosum, stratum lucidum, and stratum spinosum of epidermis; cell measurements; number of dermal papillae and collagenous fibers in a unit area on different body parts*; number of sweat and sebaceous glands in a unit area on different body parts; general thickness of individual layers of skin*; dermatoglyphic ridges on extremities*.

Color: Colorimetric character of body surface*, size of dark and light parts*, number and disposition of spots*, quantity of pigment in a unit area.

Skeleton

Axial skeleton: Number of vertebrae by divisions (thoracic, lumbar, sacral, caudal)*. Number of sternal ribs* and asternal ribs*, number of segments in sternum, number of cartilagenous bones (in cetaceans), linear measurements of all parts of the skeleton[4] (scapulae*, vertebrae*, hyoid bone*, etc.).

Extremities: Measurement of skeletal extremities, pectoral and pelvic girdles, characteristics of disposition and form of metacarpal and metatarsal bones*, number of phalanges and digits (for cetaceans)*.

Skull: Condylobasal length, basicranial length, occipital length*, length of palate*, length of upper toothrow*, mastoid width*, width of brain cavity*, maximum width of zygomatic arch*, width of nasal passage*, width of palate*, width of snout near canines*, width of occipital condyles*, length of auditory meatus*, width of auditory meatus*, length of nasal bones*, width of nasal bones*, least distance between orbits*, height of skull*, length of lower jaw*, height of lower jaw behind molars*, number of teeth in upper and lower jaws*, weight of skull*, volume of skull*, volume of brain cavity*, diameter of largest tooth, height of canines, length of molars*, width of molars*. For some orders of mammals, this arrangement

[3] The traits used in this work have been asterisked (*).

[4] Basic qualities required for the traits are maximum homogeneity and demarcation by fixed points, this gives an opportunity to obtain similar results even if the measurements are taken by different researchers. Such an experiment was conducted in our collaborative work (Yablokov and Serzhent, 1963) and showed full agreement in the data obtained.

will have to be changed, for example for cetaceans (Kleinenberg *et al.*,
1965).

Digestive system
Intestine: Length as a whole and by parts*, diameter, weight of intestine*, weight of stomach*, volume of intestine and stomach*, number of
different types of glands in a unit area of intestinal surface in different
parts*, histological characters of mucus membrane and mesentery*.
Tongue: Histological characters of mucus membrane, number and
arrangement of different types of sensory organs* (papillae).

Respiratory system
Trachea: Number of rings*, measurements.
Lungs: Measurements, number of lobules, number and measurements
of acinus and alveoli.

Urogenital system
Kidneys: Measurements*, size of pyramids, length of ureters, volume
of urinary bladder*, quantitative histological characters of urethra.
Spermatozoa: Measurements and form*, number of spermatozoa in
a unit volume of ejaculation.
Measurements of testis, vas deferens, ovaries, fallopian tubes, uterus.
Glands of internal secretions: Measurements, weight, and quantitative
histological characters of liver, adrenals, thyroid, and parathyroid glands*,
Hypophysis*.

Nervous system
Central nervous system: Measurements of the brain* and its different
parts, form and disposition of sulci and gyri. Histological characters of
gray and white matter (number of cells of different types*, number of cell
layers in different parts of the brain).
Cranial nerves: Measurements, number of plexuses, number of rootlets,
characters of spinal cord, characters of sense organs*.

Circulatory system
Heart: Measurements and weight*, histological characters.
Arteries and veins: Positions of main trunks; histological characters
of walls; number of capillaries, arterioles, venules, in different parts of
the organism.
Blood-producing organs: Measurements of spleen*, quantitative histo-
logical characters of spleen and bone marrow.
Blood: Characters of corpuscles* and plasma.
This is a general list of the traits that can be obtained through modern

laboratory and field techniques in the study of qualitative and quantitative variability of mammalian morphology.

On the whole, it seems possible even now to obtain quantitative data on approximately 150 different traits of organs of different systems. Even in a greatly abbreviated case where only the most simple traits are selected (without histological and anatomical details), the researcher must try to pinpoint at least 35-45 traits in order to give a far better picture of the morphology of the population under study than would be possible with only 10-15 as usual.

Methods of Analysis of Data

The general methods of estimating variability, widely known among biologists, are used while studying population morphology (Plochinskii, 1960; Rokitskii, 1961; and others). Some of them are briefly described below:

a) It is obvious that the simplest measure of the magnitude of variability of a sample in a given trait is the observed range (Lim)[5]. However, this method happens to be the least perfect, because the extreme values of a sample depend greatly on the sample size, which is itself subject to sharp variations; and what is most important, with this measure the characteristics of the distribution of variation within the sample are not clear. Finally, the comparison of the range of variability can be carried out only within one species or in very closely related taxa for which the mean of the trait under study is similar.

b) The coefficient suggested by R. L. Berg (1964a)—the ratio of maximum value of a trait of a sample to its minimum value—serves as the latest modification of this old method of estimation of variability:

$$\frac{X_{max}}{X_{min}} .$$

The resultant coefficient, which is dimensionless, allows a comparison of traits of different absolute values and also of heterogeneous traits. However, even by use of this coefficient, it is not possible to determine the

[5] Here, and henceforth, the so-called "normal" distribution, expressed by a Gaussian curve, has been considered. In nature, the variation of traits cannot always be expressed by a "normal" distribution. Apart from the "normal," some other different types of distributions could be encountered in nature, of which the binomial distribution and the Poisson distribution are the foremost. But it is known in biological statistics (Beili, 1964) that in large samples the binomial distribution and the Poisson distribution approach normality. This means that even if the researcher encounters such types of distributions and at times does not consider them, the usual analysis for the normal distribution allows proper results in such cases anyway.

characteristics of the distribution of variation within the sample and the effect of sample size is unchanged.   It is evident that this coefficient can be very widely used during some specialized investigations.   The simplicity of its calculation considerably lessens the analysis of the data.

c)   A better method of expressing variability is the estimation of the standard deviation:

$$\sigma = \sqrt{\frac{\Sigma \ (x-\bar{x})^2}{n}} \ .$$

Certain researchers, for example, A. A. Lyubishchev (1923), G. V. Nikol'skii and V. A. Pikuleva (1958) prefer this method of estimation of variability to other methods.   The standard deviation (sigma) is in fact capable of exactly characterizing the whole variation of samples by showing the degree of inclination in the cumulative distribution curve.   Comparison of variability of different traits or traits with different measurement units is absolutely impossible because sigma is a dimensioned statistic.

d)   The "Profile Method" of S. R. Zarapkin is an interesting development; in this method, different populations are compared not by the absolute but by the relative value of sigma (Zarapkin, 1934).   This method, no doubt, is very useful for carrying out comparisons of variability of different populations within a species or among closely related types and is worth developing further.   In the present work (Chapter III), an attempt has been made to modify this method slightly.

e)   The most widely used method for determining variability is the estimation of the so-called coefficient of variation.   This is obtained by dividing sigma by the arithmetic mean and is expressed in percentages:

$$c.v. = \frac{\sigma \cdot 100}{\bar{x}} \ .$$

The coefficient of variation is considered the best and most widely used index for characterizing the range of individual variation in one or diverse traits (Alpatov, 1956, p. 374 ; Haldane, 1955).

The basic advantage of a coefficient of variation lies in the fact that, in addition to completely characterizing the amount of variation, it happens to be a dimensionless index and allows a comparison of variability of large and small organs of different species, variability of completely different organs, and variability of differently measured traits of one and the same organ.   The relative ease of estimating the coefficient of variation for original data, as well as for data collected from the majority of detailed publications related to morphological characterization of a population, is nonetheless important.   It is not proper to consider the coefficient of variation as an ideal index.   One of the main shortcomings is its incapability of showing the degree of asymmetry in the distribution under study. With opposite indices of asymmetry, the coefficient of variation may remain unchanged in magnitude.

Another shortcoming of a coefficient of variation has been noted by J. B. S. Haldane (1955). With samples of the usual size investigated, significantly smaller than the general population, lesser variability is obtained. This situation arises especially during the investigation of very small samples, consisting of only a few individuals. These observations seem completely justified. However, one should remember that in the estimation of coefficients of variation for different traits of one and the same population, we obtain completely comparable data.

f) The study of variability is not confined to the methods of its estimation mentioned above. Analysis of distributions with the help of the *F* statistic of Snedecor can be very helpful in morphological investigations. This method is good for the comparison of different populations with one species, as shown by B. Sturgen and N. Popovich (1961).

One promising method of estimating variability has been proposed by Ya. I. Starobogatov. This method consists of a direct ratio of variances (σ^2) estimated as with standard deviations. With the use of this method, as well as with the use of a coefficient of variation, obtaining dimensioned figures is avoided and at the same time the index obtained expresses the basic properties of the distribution curve of the trait—range of variation in the trait and degree of spread of the curve.

g) Experience has shown that for the study of variability of the polymorphic type (including epigenetic polymorphism), there is a possibility of successfully utilizing a number of methods based on comparisons of frequencies of class, without resorting to each statistical analysis of data in the way generally understood for variation by zoologists. First of all, it is possible to use the chi-square of Person and the Lambda statistic of A. N. Kolmogorov and N. V. Smirnov. These methods as used in biological research have been given in the works of N. A. Plochinskii (1960). It is of interest to note, as observed by P. F. Rokitskii (1964), that statistics of this type can be used not only for polymorphic variability but also for the general case of quantitative variability. These statistics have been investigated by us in one case, in the study of mammalian color (Yablokov and Etin, 1965), and in addition, prospects of combined use of these statistics have been put forth in this work (for details, see Chapter IV).

h) Simple determination of the number of aberrant individuals for a given trait in a population, relative to a given number of individuals, is the other method of estimating morphological variability in population morphology (Gershonson, 1946), for example per 1,000 or 1,000,000 individuals; this is similar to the methods used in genetics for evaluating the number of mutations per given number of gametes.

i)   Graphical methods are quite important in the study of variability; by their use the number of arbitrary assumptions of the statistical formulas is reduced to a minimum.   The normal curve is based on the assumption that the number of possible states of variation is practically unlimited and the curve on both sides of the mean intersects the base line only at infinity. But all the natural populations, however large they may be, have numerical end values for variants.   As a rule, this assumption does not play a great role during work on rather small samples from natural populations.   But it is possible to imagine a case where it is necessary to consider this situation so that the biological significance of the statistical result obtained is not lost.

Graphical methods are very handy to use because of their considerable clarity.   Transfer of data to a histogram opens the possibility of bringing to light trends in recurring frequencies of different classes.   A scatter diagram also is a graphical method of expressing quantitative variability. This has been described by E. Mayr *et al*. (1956) and examples of its use are given in some biological works (Sarycheva, 1948; Yablokov, 1963b). When the amount of data is not sufficient for statistical representation, an opportunity to derive conclusions through comparing the variability of homogeneous traits in adjoining groups is possible in some cases.   Another advantage of the scatter diagram is that it offers a possibility to compare not only two characters, but three or more.

In this work, the problem of the study of correlation between traits has intentionally not been touched, though it is of great importance in the general analysis of the structure of variability (Terent'ev, 1959; Berg, 1964a, 1964b).

From this short review of the different methods of estimation and expression of variability, it can be seen that, generally, all usual methods of variation statistics are used in population morphology.   The distinctive feature of researches in the field of population morphology is not in specific methods of data analysis but in the very approach to the data, with an aim of presenting the character of a population as a unity.   Mention must be made of the fact that the use of statistical methods in population biology is in harmony with the general trend of modern natural science, which is making the whole of biology an exact science.   P. F. Rokitskii (1964) is right in saying that ". . . though difficulties are experienced in the application of biological principles with these methods (this means mathematical methods—A. Ya.), their inclusion in the armory of zoologists is absolutely necessary.   Only extensive use of these methods on material of different types will insure a determination of the practicability of their use, permit an evaluation of the significance of individual methods, and reveal the degree of sensitivity of the criteria obtained on their basis" (pp. 86-87).

The Statistical Significance of Differences

The importance of evaluating the degree of significance of differences between comparable distributions of traits in case of different populations does not need a special justification. As is generally used in various investigations, the significance of differences between comparable indices is estimated with the help of the t statistic according to the formula:

$$t = \frac{x_1 - x_2}{s_d} \, ,$$

where, given a sufficiently large sample size (generally more than 25 specimens)

$$s_d = \sqrt{s_{x_1}^2 + s_{x_2}^2} \, ,$$

and with the comparison of smaller sample sizes

$$s_d = \sqrt{\frac{\Sigma_1 (x_1 - \bar{x}_1) + \Sigma_2 (x_2 - \bar{x}_2)}{(n_1 - 1) + (n_2 - 1)} \cdot \left(\frac{n_1 + n_2}{n_1 n_2} \right)}$$

(Rokitskii, 1961; formulas 23 to 25).

It is important to draw attention to the fact that the statistical significance of results obtained through mathematical analysis of biological material cannot always be estimated unconditionally on the basis of these or any other mathematical formulas. The complexity of the biological system so much surpasses the statistical methods that I am deeply convinced there is no possibility of analyzing them through intricate expressions of probability figures or through Student's area of the probability curve (t). The other exception to the absoluteness of the results of statistical analysis is in the fact that statistical methods analyze *quantitative* differences, and during a comparison of different populations in biology, we want to get an answer as to the presence or absence of *qualitative* similarities.

One can completely agree with the opinion of B. Sturgen and N. Popovich (1961) who say that "unfortunately, we as yet do not make use of objective criteria in evaluating qualitative differences in the mysteries of natural life through mathematics" (p. 575).

In the material collected by us on the morphology of Pinnipedia, there are data which show that significant differences were observed through the use of statistical methods between certain biologically homogeneous characters in different samples. One of the reasons for such a situation may be the considerable deviation of the distribution curve for the given

trait under study in a natural population from the "normal" distribution—
to which alone the usually used statistical calculations arc faithful.[6]

Some mathematicians have come to the conclusion that the laws of
calculations of probability cannot be used for higher forms of movement
of matter without considering the practically infinite quantity of information
available about the state of such higher forms of movement. Explaining
this point of view, E. Borel' (1964) writes: "It seems fallacious to use the
laws of estimation of probability for the mystery of formation of crystals
from more or less super-saturated solutions. At least, it is not possible
to examine such problems of probability without estimating certain properties
of matter: properties which facilitate formation of crystals" (p. 104). And,
in the conclusion of the review of the possible uses of the theory of probability
with cosmogonical problems and problems of biology, Borel' writes: "It
seems that even in this field, the results given by us may not help much
at present" (*Ibid.*).

In these excerpts nothing is said about probability and significance
in the evaluation of differences between two populations, but it is important
to pose the question in principle.

It can be assumed that the significance of the differences will be
dependent not only on the magnitude of the given trait but also on those
concrete relations through which this trait influences the life of the population. In other words, significance of differences according to the t value
may depend on the force of natural selection for the given trait.

The modern concept of intensity or force of selection does not represent
a regularly applied vector of constant magnitude (Schmalhausen, 1946).
It is already clear that during short time intervals, intensity of selection
will vary in relation to the changes in the state of the organism as part of
the population on the one hand, and of the whole population as a part of
the biogeocenose on the other. Practically, this means that the intensity
of selection changes even at different times of the day, not to mention times
in a year, and in different years, etc.

Another way of approaching the solution to the problem of biological
significance of differences, is the comparative analysis of not one but a
number of paired traits. Examples of such trends will be given in this work.
Here I will cite only one example taken from the work of F. Sumner (1909).
On the basis of the data given by this author, coefficients of variation of
body weights of male and female mice living for a long time in hot or cold
rooms were calculated. A comparison of values shows that, in three
instances, statistically significant results were obtained between females
in hot and cold rooms at the age of six months, and between males and
females of 2.5 months in one series, and in the other series at six months

[6] See footnote 5 on p. 7.

in a hot room (respective *t* values 2.0, 2.1; and 2.7). However, the sum total of the data obtained contradicts the conclusions about the actual significant differences in the first group of these animals (already in seven-month-old females there is no difference at all: $t=0.22$). All this leads to the conclusion that the statistically significant results obtained may be due to some unrecorded conditions of sampling and analysis of the material, in different years, and in different experimental populations. But the second conclusion, about the differences in variability between males and females in the hot room, seems to be convincing, not because the differences in all series are similar (variability is higher in males) and sufficiently high, but because the same type of variability (increase in the variability of males rather than variability of females) is observed in all series of the other room also. A comparison of these data shows that differences in the variability of males and females is much more significant in the hot room and less in the cold room (but biologically significant, though not statistically).

While summarizing, it can be underlined that the value of *t* in biological experiments may serve only as orientation to the factual material obtained by the researcher.

Optimum Size of Sample

The question of non-conformity of the "normal" curve with the specific conditions present in natural populations, has been discussed above. From this, a practical conclusion having a direct bearing on the collection of material on variability of morphological structure in populations follows, namely, a conclusion about the optimal size of sample.

Usually, in zoological works where statistical methods of investigation are used, it is emphasized that for obtaining objective data, analysis of sufficiently large series is necessary. The minimum number of individuals is also usually indicated—25 to 30 or, better, 40 to 100 items (E. Mayr *et al.*, 1956; P. F. Rokitskii, 1961; and others). Generally, there is no mention of the maximum sample size. I. I. Schmalhausen (1935) observed that 50 measurements are enough. Comparable indications are rarely found in other works and this leads to the fact that usually the researchers use hundreds of measurements, hoping to obtain the most exact value of a simple arithmetic mean, of sigma, and of a coefficient of variation. Because of this the volume of analytical work considerably increases, which acts as a hindrance in the use of exact quantitative methods in biology.

What is the accuracy of data obtained from a small or large sample from a population? Does any optimum size of sample exist for the investigations of variability; if so, would a numerically large sample be necessary to obtain useful data, or would a small one be enough in order to avoid extra analytical work? Let us analyze the data in Table 1 to answer these questions, where statistics characterizing the body length of the white whale and the Greenland or harp seal are given with reference to sample size.

Table 1. Comparison of statistics (length of body in cm) of large and small samples from one population

n	$\bar{x} \pm s_{\bar{x}}$	$c.v. \pm s_{c.v.}$	n	$\bar{x} \pm s_{\bar{x}}$	$c.v. \pm s_{c.v.}$
MATURE MALES OF WHITE WHALE (*Delphinapterus leucas*) Okhotsk Sea (1958)			MATURE FEMALES OF GREENLAND SEAL (harp seal) (*Pagophilus groenlandicus*) White Sea (1961)		
25	447.0 ± 5.04	5.64 ± 0.81	25	183.2 ± 1.42	3.86 ± 0.55
50_1	454.4 ± 3.28	5.11 ± 0.51	50_1	185.8 ± 1.07	4.08 ± 0.41
50_2	446.5 ± 3.62	5.75 ± 0.58	50_2	182.7 ± 1.00	3.85 ± 0.39
100	450.5 ± 1.55	3.44 ± 0.34	100	184.1 ± 0.75	4.08 ± 0.29
			200	181.7 ± 0.57	4.44 ± 0.22
			400	183.7 ± 0.40	4.35 ± 0.15

The results of this comparison show that:

a)   The estimated mean of the body length of the white whale did not change when the sample changed from 25 to 100 individuals, i.e., during a four-fold quantitative increase in the observations (and time spent on the analysis of data);

b)   The value of coefficients of variation in the body length of the white whale remains the same during three samples—25, 50_1, and 50_2 and the value of the sample of 100 specimens is statistically significantly lower ($t = 3.45$);

c)   The mean body length of the Greenland seal did not vary according to data collected from 25 and 400 specimens, but shows significant statistical change between samples of 200 to 400 specimens; and

d)   The value of the coefficient of variation of the body length of the Greenland seal practically does not change during all samples.

It seems possible to derive a general conclusion that for obtaining sufficiently exact characterization of a population, the sample need not exceed 50 specimens.   This conclusion, naturally, applies only to sufficiently homogeneous samples (same sex, same stage of growth, obtained at the same time from the population, and with random sampling), and is open to further experimental confirmation.

Accuracy of Measurement and Individual Errors of the Researchers

The question of optimum accuracy during sampling is of great importance in the difficult investigations of large series of material and is ubiquitous in the study of population variability.

As a result of many measurements of different organs and structures, I arrived at an empirical rule. The measurements should be taken with an accuracy equal to the individual error of measurements. This individual error can be determined easily as a result of certain successive measurements. For example, during measurement of body length of one and the same seal calf, the following data were obtained: 46.7, 48.3, 47.8 cm. It is clear that the accuracy of measurement in the given case does not exceed 1.00 cm, which is due to many reasons not completely controlled by the researcher, i.e., similarity in stretching the measuring scale, position of hands or of the animal in relation to the observer, degree of attention, the presence of side disturbances, etc. All the remaining measurements in this sample have to be done to the accuracy of 1.00 cm without calculating the tenths of a centimeter.

Another example: During the measurements of the length of a skull, the following results were obtained: 351.6, 349.8, 352.3 mm. In this case, it is not necessary to measure the tenths of a millimeter in further measurements of skulls of the same type.

Such a conclusion is based not only on the greater simplicity and comfort while accuracy remains maximal, but also because the measurements taken with more accuracy are incapable of providing more accurate results in the final analysis of the data.

It is well known from the investigations of taxonomists that one and the same measurement, taken on one and the same material by different individuals, may give different results (P. Jewell and P. Fullagar, 1966). This fact must be taken into consideration during the study of population variability. Special experiments conducted by F. Sumner (1927) some 30-odd years ago have not lost their importance and must be remembered. The first series of experiments were concerned with comparing the results of measurements recorded by different investigators.

Three qualified zoologists measured one and the same series consisting of ten characters of deermice (*Peromyscus maniculatus*). The results of twice-repeated measurements are given in Table 2.

As seen from the data, the differences between results obtained by different investigators are pronounced and, in addition, it is also observable that the individual peculiarities of each investigator's measurements are likewise carried through. For example, investigator I obtained, as a rule, measurements of greater magnitude (six out of ten of his measurements are maximum); investigator III obtained measurements of average magnitude.[7]

---

[7] It is important to note that in all these cases, the coefficient of variation of the trait is absolutely the same for all the investigators; this again denotes the objectivity and usefulness of this index for comparison of heterogeneous data.

Table 2.   Results of measurements (in mm) of the same series of *Peromyscus maniculatus* **by different investigators (Sumner, 1927; Table 1)**

	Investigator	Body length	Length of tail	Body length without tail	Foot length	Ear length
First day	I	164.7	74.9	89.8	19.62	16.52
	II	156.3	70.9	85.4	19.65	16.20
	III	158.6	70.2	88.4	19.70	16.31
Second day	I	163.9	74.4	89.5	19.59	16.12
	II	163.7	72.2	91.5	19.30	15.70
	III	164.1	71.1	93.0	20.00	15.94

In another series of experiments, F. Sumner (1927) showed clearly how important it is to obtain maximum homogeneity in conditions while obtaining factual data.   Table 3 shows how the time that elapsed from the moment of death of an animal influences the value of measurements of its body.

It is very clear that while collecting data from the same population, even if one and the same investigator measures the animal 15 minutes after death, and in another population after two or more hours, then, even though measurements of the living animals were absolutely identical, the data obtained will be different.

Table 3.   Results of measurements (in mm) of the same series of mice at different times after death (Sumner, 1927; Table 2, p. 181)

Time after death	Total length	Tail length	Body length	Foot length	Ear length	Body weight
EXPERIMENT I						
0	166.65	76.95	89.70	20.455	16.950	—
15 minutes	166.70	76.90	89.80	20.440	16.975	—
45 minutes	165.85	77.05	88.80	20.395	16.865	—
2 hours	164.10	75.80	88.30	20.425	16.845	—
EXPERIMENT II						
0	165.05	72.75	92.30	19.695	17.175	21.34
26 hours	164.40	72.65	91.75	19.700	16.955	20.97

Moreover, if some animals of the same population are measured 15 minutes after death and others after some hours and the values obtained are combined, then the mean value thus obtained will not properly represent the natural conditions even though each of the measurements carried out was highly accurate and the individual error of measurement would not affect the results.   It is clear from the example given that the length of an animal can be measured accurately to 1 to 2 mm and the length of the feet and ears accurately to 0.1 mm; it is unnecessary to measure body weight with accuracy over 0.5 g.

Another clear example showing the importance of reasonably accurate measurements is given in the work of M. Alexander (1960). It was observed that the skull measurements in one and the same population of muskrats varied according to the time of the year. A significant difference was observed in the value of measurements of skulls freshly obtained, those recently obtained by museums, and those preserved for a long time in storage. The main reason for such changes was also determined. Seasonal changes altered the humidity level at different times of the year in the storage area of the American Museum of Natural History. In the final manifestations, these changes reached up to 1.5 percent and considerably increased the individual error which, as was observed by us, is nearly 0.5 percent from the value of the measurements (i.e., for linear measurements). The investigator may derive wrong conclusions during a strict comparison if the possibility of collecting wrong data is not considered when selecting skulls to be measured at different times.

Looking at these examples as a whole, an empirical rule could be formed: The accuracy of measurements should not be higher than possible errors which may be due to the investigator and also related to the nature of the material.

Coefficient of Variation as an Index for the "Population-Environment" System

The possibility of using different methods for estimating variability from a formal viewpoint was discussed above with a view to deciding how far a given method is capable of completely expressing the aspects of variation. But while studying variability with an aim to understanding the relationship of processes of variability to processes of micro-evolution, a question arises inevitably about the extent to which one or another method expresses the relations arising during the process of growth of a population.

Should the coefficient of variation act as an index indicating the relationship within the "environment-population" system? A direct answer to this question was not traced in the literature on variability. To a certain extent this can be explained because, as rightly noticed by G. D. Polyakov (1961), in the majority of cases where variability of some traits was investigated in zoological works, variability was mentioned only as an additional character of the trait. Such a situation, of course, is unjust. Variability, expressed by a coefficient of variation, can and must be used in zoological works as a separate and important index; but for this, it first has to be proved that there is a relationship between changes of this coefficient and changes in the intensity of natural controlling factors.

That such a relationship exists can be proved by arranging data on changes in coefficients of variation in the changing relationships between the group of growing organisms and environment to show, for example:

a)   The changes in the coefficient of variation in one population in different seasons, and different years, under common ecological conditions;

b)   The changes in the coefficient of variation for one and the same trait in groups of different growth rates, each with the same relation to the environment at each stage of growth; and

c)   Constancy of coefficients of variation with homogeneous ecological factors.

Of course, none of the given situations can serve as a final proof of a relationship between the coefficient of variation and changes in the "environment-population" system, but on the whole, these data should provide an answer to acceptance or non-acceptance of this coefficient for ecological investigations of a population.

Change of coefficient of variation
in different years and seasons

Considerable seasonal variation in coefficients of variation in iodine concentration of the inner and subcutaneous fat of the muskrat (*Ondatra zibethica*) is known (Schwartz, 1960). A. V. Pokrovskii (1962) showed clear seasonal change in the coefficients of variation in sexual maturity of female lemmings (*Lagurus lagurus*). Analysis of data put forth by L. G. Krotova (1962) indicates considerable seasonal variation in the coefficients of variation for traits like absolute weight of adrenals, width of their cortex, ascorbic acid content in the adrenals, glycogen in the liver, and sugar in the blood of the water vole (*Arvicola terrestris*). Data on changes in coefficients of variation for a number of traits in a population of moles (*Talpa europaea*) studied for a number of years in different climatic conditions are given in the work of K. Ya. Fateev (1962).

Weights of organs vary from year to year and these variations not only attain high statistical significance ($P < 0.01$) but also show a general tendency toward reduction of magnitude in the coefficient of variation from 1958 to 1960.   Many examples other than those given above are available on the differing magnitudes of coefficients of variation for different traits depending on season and year, and will be given in a large number in the present work.   This may, to my mind, provide a satisfactory basis for belief in the existence of a specific relationship between magnitude of this coefficient and interrelationships with the "population-environment" system.

Change in the coefficients of variation
for different age groups

Data on coefficients of variation for tail length of mature and new-born males and females of the Greenland (harp) seal (*Pagophilus groenlandicus*) found in the White Sea in the Autumn of 1961 are given below. It seems that the coefficient of variation for new-borns is somewhat higher than for mature animals.

	Mature	New-born	$t_{ad-juv,}$	P
Males	4.3±0.31	6.3±0.80	−2.29	<0.02
Females	4.4±0.22	7.3±0.93	−3.02	<0.01

Similar data on change in coefficients of variation in different age groups can be found in the work of V. B. Scheffer (1962), where length and weight of embryos and new-borns of fur seals (*Callorhinus ursinus*) have been examined. Measurements and weights every ten days show that at the end of the embryonic period, the coefficient of variation for length and weight of body of embryo fur seals regularly declined (Figure 1). Moreover, these changes occurred simultaneously in males and females. The latter point increases the significance of this conclusion.

Model data on changes of coefficients of variation with age are given in the work of Ya. Hromada and L. Strnad (1962) on variability of weight and volume of skulls for two types of monkeys (*Macaca rhesus* and *M. cynomolgus*); similar data are also given in the work of V. S. Smirnov (1962) on studies of variability in skulls of arctic foxes (*Vulpes lagopus*). Regular changes of coefficients of variation with age have been observed in large numbers by H. D. King (1923) during studies on the variability of body weight in gray rats, and by John Carmon et al. (1963) for deermice (*Peromyscus polionotus*).

All these data emphasize a sufficiently clear possibility that there exists a specific

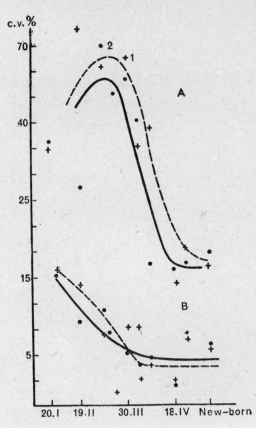

Figure 1. Magnitude of coefficient of variation of (*A*) weight, and (*B*) body length of embryos and new-born fur seals—(*1*) Males, and (*2*) Females (Scheffer, 1962).

relationship between coefficients of variation and change of external conditions in which a population propagates.

Constancy of coefficient of variation in adaptively homogeneous traits

The conclusion about the direct relationship of a coefficient of variation with the "environment-population" system is also confirmed by an analysis of functionally homogeneous traits in a population. Van Valen (1962), who studied variability of length and breadth of the molar teeth on the upper and lower jaws of deermice (*Peromyscus maniculatus*), confirms this observation on the great constancy of variability in these ecologically homogeneous structures (Table 4).

Table 4.   Variability ($s.c. \pm s._{c.v.}$) **of measurements of** *Peromyscus*
(**Van Valen, 1962**)

Trait	Upper Jaw			Lower Jaw		
	M^1	M^2	M^3	M_1	M_2	M_3
Breadth of tooth	3.6±0.36	3.4±0.34	4.3±0.43	4.2±0.42	3.2±0.32	4.2±0.42
Length of tooth	4.3±0.43	3.9±0.39	5.1±0.52	4.1±0.41	4.1±0.41	4.4±0.45

Table 5.   A comparison of coefficients of variation in the number of vibrissae on the lip group in the Greenland seal and the ringed seal (**Mature females**)

Line	Greenland seal (*Pagophilus groenlandicus*) Newfoundland			Ringed seal (*Pusa hispida*)		
	Right	Left	t	Right	Left	t
1st	7.3±0.99	8.4±1.18	−0.7	8.1±0.95	9.9±1.20	−1.1
2nd	4.8±0.65	5.9±0.81	−1.0	5.6±0.66	6.0±0.70	−0.1
3rd	5.9±0.81	6.7±0.91	−0.7	6.6±0.78	5.5±0.64	0.8
4th	9.4±1.28	6.7±0.92	+1.7	7.6±0.90	7.1±0.84	0.4
5th	11.7±1.59	8.4±1.14	+1.7	11.0±1.30	10.7±1.30	0.1
6th	17.6±2.39	15.2±2.11	+0.8	17.0±2.00	19.4±2.29	−0.8
7th	37.3±5.07	35.4±4.91	+0.3	41.2±4.90	37.7±4.40	−0.5
8th	168.2±22.9	184.2±25.1	−0.5	533.3±62.8	65.0±7.7	7.3
Total	4.9±0.66	4.8±0.67	+0.01	6.0±0.70	6.0±0.71	+0.0

A comparison of coefficients of variation in the number of vibrissae on the lips of the Greenland seal, from the left and right sides, serves as a second example (Table 5, and Figure 2).

As seen from the data given, the two types of pinnipeds do not differ in the variation of right and left vibrissae. The 8th line is an exception in the ringed seal, but even this single exception can be well explained. The absolute number of whiskers in the 8th line is small—on an average only 0.03 on the right and 0.18 on the left. With such very uneven

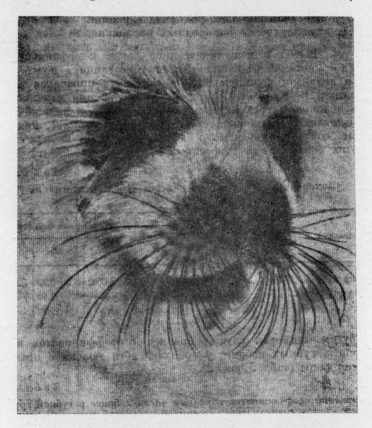

Figure 2. Snout of a young Greenland seal. The location of lip, nasal, and eye vibrissae is seen clearly. Author's photograph.

distribution (more than 80 percent do not have vibrissae at all in the 8th line), the statistical indices used by us in this instance cannot positively represent the existing condition because distribution of this trait does not fall under the "normal" distribution. On the whole, the data cited specifically emphasize that for functionally homogeneous structures in an organism, the coefficients of variation seem similar.

And so, all the three ways examined by us—analysis of coefficients of variation for functionally homogeneous structures, coefficients of variation in one population in different seasons and years, and coefficients of variation in different age groups—permit one to assume a specific relationship between the magnitude of coefficients of variation and evolutionary factors functioning in nature. This conclusion allows us further to look into the coefficient of variation as a sufficiently promising index of relationship in the "environment-population" system.

CHAPTER II

THE NATURE OF VARIABILITY IN DIFFERENT SYSTEMS IN MAMMALS

In the world literature on the study of mammals, there is a large quantity of data on the variability of organs and structures. However, these data are widely scattered, which limits their use for comparison with newly obtained material. On the other hand, the present need for knowing the nature of the variability of different organs and systems as a whole requires us to carry out a broad comparison of all systems and organs among mammals.

Until recently, no attempts were made to systematize the data on the variability of mammals or to discover the nature of variability in organs of different systems of these animals. The work of S. S. Schwartz (1960) is an exception; here considerable factual material on the variability of weight of internal organs (so-called interior traits) for many types of amphibians, reptiles, birds, and mammals has been examined from an ecological point of view. Unfortunately, use of the coefficient of variation for relative values of traits (rather than absolute ones) makes it difficult to compare these data directly with data on other types of mammals and also on other systems of organs.

It is generally known that the variability of functional hard parts of skeletons in mammals lies between 3 and 10% (Simpson and Roe, 1939). In 1960, S. S. Schwartz showed that variability of "interior traits" (mainly relative weights of internal organs), though somewhat higher, does not exceed an average of 10 to 20%.

On the basis of extensive data on the structure of certain skull traits of horses in the evolutionary line *Hyracotherium-Mesohippus-Merychippus-Neohipparion*, G. G. Simpson (1948) concluded that ". . . variation differs surprisingly little from time to time for one trait within a group, for homologous variates in different groups, and for different analogous variates" (p. 135; 1944, p. 83. Data on variability of skeleton are also on the same page). It is possible that within such geological intervals, during millions and millions of years, variability of the structures of horse skulls changed insignificantly; but, while studying now living populations, it has to be conceded that variability of even one and the same trait of small mammals may change very significantly during some months. But in any case, this question concerning magnitude of variability is not very clear—as can be concluded from the quotation from Simpson above.

On the basis of a number of small experiments, R. S. Bader (1955), and later Ya. Ya. Roginskii (1959), came to the conclusion that the extent of difference in variation among non-homologous traits within a species is higher than the difference of variability among homologous traits between species; in other words, the difference in the variability of different organs within a species is higher than the difference in variability of one and the same organ for other species. But this conclusion was mainly based upon measurements of body and skeleton. None of the studies known to me answers the question of whether there is a specific variability for each large system of organs in mammals. This chapter will attempt to find an answer to this question on the basis of exact and factual data. To accomplish that end, every effort has been made to present the data available on variability of structures of different types of mammals in the form of coefficients of variation—the most convenient form for comparing diverse data.

These factual data include:

1. The author's data obtained specifically at the time of conducting these investigations (mainly on cetaceans and pinnipeds);

2. The raw data obtained from other researchers (based on variable populations) and further analyzed by us for standard deviations, means, standard errors, coefficients of variation and their errors

$$(\bar{x} \pm s_{\bar{x}}, \sigma, c.\ v. \pm s_{c.v.});$$

3. Data obtained as a result of previous data in the literature, with analysis of coefficient of variation and error $(c.\ v. \pm s_{c.v.})$, either on the basis of coefficients of variation already calculated or on the basis of standard deviations and mean arithmetical errors estimated by the authors.

Any review of this nature would invariably be incomplete. It is practically impossible to collect the large quantity of work already published and still being published on a great scale, on the variability of different organs.

But in spite of the incompleteness of the data cited, it is proposed to start such abstracting work now because no such review exists in the world literature. In order to attain strict systematization, the data presented herein on variability have been arranged in the following order: Marsupialia, Cetacea, Carnivora, Pinnipedia, Perissodactyla, Artiodactyla, and the rest of the orders of mammals.

Integument

Hair

As shown from the data analyzed by E. Z. Kogteva (1963) (Table 2 in the Appendix), the coefficient of variation for the length of summer and winter fur on different body parts of moles varies from 2.1 to 6.2%. The variability of summer fur is somewhat higher on the middle back but variability of winter fur is somewhat higher in the sacral region. A comparison of winter and summer fur shows that whereas the variability of guard hair, medullated hair, and underfur on the middle back varies typically in winter and summer (during winter the variability is half as much), there is little variability of length of different types of hair on the sacrum.

The variability of summer fur on the sacral region and the shoulder (scapular) region is higher in summer than in winter. The results show that in winter the variability of length in all types of hair on various parts of the body is, on an average, almost the same even for different types of hair (adaptive significance ?).

The variability of thickness of hair on different parts of the body of a seal in different seasons fluctuates from 0.5 (medullated, winter) to 3.1% (underfur, summer). The maximum variability for thickness in all seasons is characteristic of underfur.

In the work of A. Banerjee (1963) data are given on the variability of diameter and thickness of human hair. More than 40 series of measurements carried out on the different external traits of hair (straight, curly, soft, hard, silky, etc.) of different peoples in India, showed that the coefficient of variation is not directly related to any of the specific characteristics of hair and varies from 5.8 to 19.8%. (Most values are from 10 to 15%.)

In the work of E. Z. Kogteva (1963) mentioned above, there are data on the thickness and length of hair of the varying hare for different seasons of the year. Analysis of these data (Table 2 in the Appendix) shows that the magnitude of variation of thickness of hair on the sides has characteristically lower values—to 0.6%.

The comparison of coefficients of variation for thickness of hair on the back, on the sacrum, and in the belly regions in different seasons of the year shows that the variability of thickness of hair on the back differs from the variability of hair thickness on the rump and belly (the latter two being alike in this trait). In some instances the variability of thickness of hair on the back (for medullated hair of I and II categories) is higher; in others, it is less (for other medullated hair) than the corresponding values for the rump and belly. The coefficient of variation for thickness of hair on the back shows large seasonal differences (in three types of medullated hair) but the variability of hair thickness in the belly region does not differ by season. These conclusions are confirmed on general lines by the analysis of data on variability of thickness of hair for varying hare. Variability of all types of hair on the back is considerably lower on an average for this trait (2.9%; the range of variation being from 0.6 to 10.9%) than on the sacrum (4.0% on an average, with a range of 1.4 to 9.3%), and on the belly (4.2% average, ranging from 1.8 to 10.1%); the hair in the border region of the back is different in length from that on the sacrum and belly. Variability characteristics of these hairs are similar to each other.

The observations of E. Z. Kogteva (1963) on the variability of length of hair for different types of summer and winter fur on different body parts of the varying hare are interesting. There are no overall differences between different seasons for this trait and the slight differences (regarding length of directed hair on the rump, length of medullated hair of III category) can be explained, it appears, on the basis of improper collection of material. From this example, it can once again be seen that perfection of data on biological material is not possible through statistical analysis. A manifestation of overall trends in the character of structures is immensely more important than information on their various differences. Because we lack full details about the collection of the material, many additional factors which may not have been considered during these morphological investigations (i.e., time differences in procuring experimental animals, separate regions and micro-regions of their habitat, absence of information on age and sex of the populations, etc.), can be presumed to have affected the data obtained by E. Z. Kogteva (1963). In such cases, many rash conclusions based on formal interpretation of factual data can be avoided; these, in fact, indicate the insufficient "cleanness" of the sampling.

A considerable difference between characteristics of variation of hairs in winter and summer fur can be noted from the analysis of variability of length of different hair types on the varying hare. It seems that out of 18 comparisons between different types of hair on different body parts during the summer, there are no differences in the magnitude of variability in 10 cases. Yet, while comparing the same traits in winter, the number of clearly defined differences considerably increases. Therefore, it is possible to make a preliminary conclusion about great differences in coefficients of variation for length of different types of hair in the winter period. This conclusion does not confirm the results of investigations on the fur of moles (see above) but the differences in the ecological peculiarities of these species must be taken into consideration.

Finally, in the analysis of variability of hair length of different types, the considerable stability of variability of medullated fibers of I category and a lower variability of II category of underfur, needs special mention.

Analysis of data put forth by F. Sumner (1909) on mice shows that the magnitude of the coefficient of variation for the number of hair per unit area (11.7-17.7%) is considerably lower than the variability of weight of hair per unit area (23.6-26.8%). The magnitude of variability is such that a formal determination of differences in variability of animals maintained in hot or cold rooms, and likewise between males and females, cannot be done.

However, an ostensible trend to decreased variability for these parameters and a somewhat increased variability for number of hair in females can be observed in hot rooms. An analysis of the relative value of the trait—weight of hair in grams/(body length)^2—shows the same trend, that is, the variability is lower in the hot room. The relative variability occupies an intermediate position (19.5-21.7%) between variability of number of hair and their absolute weight in respect to the magnitude of the coefficient of variation.

The data of R. Huestis (1925) on variability of length of deermice (*Peromyscus*) show that variability of this trait varies in different subtypes and their hybrids from 5.5 to 7.0%; the variability of differently colored portions of hair, from 8.7 to 16.5%. However, the percentage variability of the number of hair for different types is high.

Hair type	Range of variability
A	4.5 to 10.4
B	15.9 to 47.0
C	24.6 to 62.4
D	25.5 to 59.5

The increased variability of number of hair for the last two types can be easily explained by the elementary relations between magnitude of a trait and its variability (see Chapter V); hair of these types is very sparse.

Data obtained on the basis of material analyzed from the work of E. V. Fadeev (1958) show that in the coypu (*Myocastor*), the variability of all types of hair in animals of different growth stages is very similar, beginning with 1.5 months of growth; it varies from 3 to 12.6% with an average of about 5 to 6%. (All observations were recorded in the beginning of December.) The variability for thickness of hair in the same samples is less pronounced: For the directed and medullated hair of I and IV categories, it does not go above 4.5% (average about 2%) but for the medullated hair of V category, it goes up to 10.5%, and for underfur up to 15.7% (Table 6).

28 Variability of Mammals

Data on variability of parameters of hair of Carnivora obtained from Kogteva's work (1963) referred to above, are given in Table 2 of the Appendix. The coefficient of variation of the raccoon-dog (*Nyctereutes procyonoides*) varies from 1.3 to 10% (average, about 5%) and thickness of hair of different types varies from 0.75 to 11.6% (average, about 3.5%). Variability of hair on different parts of the body differs: variability of length of medullated fibers of categories II to IV and underfur, and hair thickness in all underfur and medullated fibers of categories II to III, is different.

Table 6. Variability of length and thickness of hair of *Myocastor coypus* (**Calculated from the data of Fadeev, 1958**)

Age		c. v. of hair length			c. v. of hair thickness		
		40 Days	120 Days	7 Months	40 Days	120 Days	7 Months
Guard hair		3.8	7.2	12.6	1.1	1.5	1.1
Medullated	I	5.6	10.7	3.6	1.8	1.7	1.4
	II	6.6	6.2	4.2	1.3	1.3	2.1
	III	8.0	3.0	8.3	3.3	2.5	2.9
	IV	4.1	5.7	4.5	4.2	3.5	4.5
	V	9.0	5.1	6.2	1.5	10.5	6.3
Underfur		9.0	12.0	7.3	11.5	5.8	15.7

The results obtained from an analysis of data by M. A. Gerasimova (1958) on variability of hair measurements for sables, and the variability of length for all types of hair (guard, four categories of medullated, and underfur) is, on the average, about 5 to 7% (less in the guard hair and more in the underfur). Variability of thickness of hair for these same sables is considerably high; on the average, about 17% (maximum for categories III and IV of medullated hair). It is interesting that in populations transferred to a new environment (from the Barguzin reserve forest in the Tomsk region), the variability of length for almost all types of hair increased a little, whereas the variability of thickness did not show such a regular change.

Variability of wool weight of sheep (yearly clip) on an average was 17.5% from eight different farms (Popova, 1941). According to these data, variability of length of underfur of sheep averaged 31.3% (range, 20.6 to 49.4%); variability of medullated hair averaged 17.7% (range, 10.0 to 23.3%). It is seen that these results coincide with the observations of F. Sumner (1909) and R. Huestis (1925), and are considerably higher than similar observations on wild mammals investigated by E. Z. Kogteva (1963).

In the same work, E. T. Popova (1941) presents detailed data (based on an examination of several thousand sheep of different breeds) on a microscopical analysis of the fineness of different sorts of wool in crossbreeds of Lincoln sheep and local ones. Analysis of these data shows that the coefficient of variation for hair thickness of sheep is very much higher than the measurements obtained for hair thickness of seals and hares by E. Z. Kogteva (1963). Variability of thickness (fineness) of wool for crossbreeds averaged 40.9% (range, 26.1 to 50.4%), and variability of the same trait for local sheep was 52.3% (range, 48.4 to 59.7%).

It would appear that the given data are enough to estimate general outlines of variability in some parameters of the fur.

Vibrissae

Variability of other hair, like vibrissae, is directly related to the variability of parameters of the fur. The number of vibrissae on different mammals has not been studied enough, though, as shown by our work, vibrissae could prove to be very sensitive indicators in studies of certain natural populations. As shown by the investigations of A. V. Yablokov (1962, 1963a, 1964a), A. V. Yablokov and G. A. Klevezal' (1964), G. A. Fedoseev and A. V. Yablokov (1965), the variability of lip, nose, and eye vibrissae differ characteristically.

On the average, the least variability in number of hair is found in the lip region, about 5 to 6% (range, 2.7-10.1% for eight types of Pinnipedia). Two other regions—eyes and nose—have rather similar variability; for eye hair, the average is 15-20% (range, 1.6 to 37.8%); for nose hair, the average is about 20% (range, 13.7 to 78%) (Figure 3).

Variability less than 10% is characteristic for all the basic lines of vibrissae in the lip group, but in the last lines this variability may increase up to great magnitudes (500-1,000%).[1]

As the data on variability of vibrissae on different parts of the head for certain baleen whales (Figure 4) show, the coefficients of variation for number of vibrissae in three different groups (side of lower jaw, front of lower jaw, and upper jaw) are rather similar—20.6 to 32.4%.

Color

It will not be out of place to examine certain aspects of variability of normal coloration in this section on the structure of the integument (primarily, just those traits of color which can be quantitatively estimated, because quantitative variability of coloration and the phenomenon of epigenetic polymorphism are described in Chapter IV).

[1] In a number of cases no variability of nasal hair was observed (*c. v.* equals 0%). Hence, the nasal hair and the number of hair in the last line of the lip group are characteristic not of the Gaussian distribution, but of Poisson's distribution; and so, the peculiarities of variability for these structures in very general terms could be satisfactorily approximated by using distribution-free methods of analysis on the material.

It was determined by the works of S. S. Schwartz and his co-workers (Pokrovskii, Smirnov and Schwartz, 1962) that color, along with other

Figure 3.   Caspian seal on board a ship.   Functional zones of nasal and eye vibrissae are seen.   Author's photograph.

Figure 4.   Fin whale. Group of vibrissae at the end of lower jaw as seen from below. Kuril Islands (1954).   Author's photograph.

morphological traits, may be used successfully for an analysis of variability both among species and among subspecies. The index of variability for the degree of reflection in red light (measured by photometer) in 13 series of two subtypes, was about 3% (range, 2.0 to 3.7%). Another trait of coloration, the index of reflection in white light (whiteness), seems to be considerably variable—average 19.8% (range, 14.9 to 29.9%).

Substantial material on variability of the same traits in the red-backed and bank vole (*Clethrionomys rutilus* and *C. glareolus*) (Bol'shakov, 1962) reveals an analogous pattern. The variability index of color ranges from 3.3 to 3.6%, and variability of "whiteness" from 8.7 to 13.8%.

An analysis of colors for two subspecies of deermice carried out by F. Sumner (1924) is interesting. The coloration of the wild populations was studied under natural conditions and after 7 to 12 generations, and the color of two other populations was studied in the habitat of a third sub-species. This experiment offered a possibility of excluding specific biotic components of natural selection. On the whole, it seems that the variation in color of each subspecies is stable in the new surroundings even though a specific change takes place in it. In all cases, variability of different types of coloration seems to be very slight: black color, 1.4-2.9; white color, 5.9-10%; ratio of red to green, 7.7-18.0%.

In another work, F. Sumner (1923) presents absolute values of magnitude of variability of coloration in populations of deermice and their offspring in the first and second generations. From data of ten different experimental populations it is seen that each color trait has its own para-meters of variability.

Black has the least variability (average, 2.2%); white comes next (average, 10.1%); then the ratio of red color to green (average, 14.0%); the average for all color variations taken together is 19.9%.

These observations of F. Sumner substantiate his own data (1926) on variability of color of other species of the genus *Peromyscus*. In any type, body colors and the coefficients of variation for different traits are different. Red color varies among individuals of three subspecies from 7.6 to 9.2%, green from 5.3 to 12.1%, and the ratio of these colors varies from 8.0 to 10.8%.

On certain body parts of mammals, measurement of the area which is covered by one or the other color seems possible. For example, it is possible to measure the width of white spots on the tails of rodents. The coefficient of variation for this trait of *Peromyscus maniculatus*, estimated from Sumner's data (1924), is not large—12.9 to 14.6%.

Variation in the length of color regions of different types of hairs on agouti-colored mice differs for different types of hair; straight hair is 25.2 to 29.3% but zigzag hair is 3.8 to 13.3% (Table 7).

Table 7. Variability of size of yellow spots on different types of hair from different body parts of male mice (Original data from D. Galbraith, 1964)*

Shoulder		Middle of back		Sacrum	
$x \pm s_{\bar{x}}$	$c.\,v. \pm s_{c.v.}$	$\bar{x} \pm s_{\bar{x}}$	$c.\,v. \pm s_{c.v.}$	$\bar{x} \pm s_{\bar{x}}$	$c.\,v. \pm s_{c.v.}$
		ZIGZAG HAIR			
0.76 ± 0.01	11.8 ± 0.9	0.59 ± 0.003	3.8 ± 0.31	0.60 ± 0.01	13.3 ± 1.3
		STRAIGHT HAIR			
1.01 ± 0.03	25.2 ± 2.1	0.87 ± 0.03	29.3 ± 2.4	0.91 ± 0.03	28.0 ± 2.3

* In this work, additional data on five different types of hair for males and females are given.

A simple method of quantitative estimation of coloration, subjectively dividing all degrees of appearance of different numbers of spots on the skin of *P. maniculatus* into four groups (from 0 to 3) has been proposed by L. Dice (1938). The data obtained on the mean value of variability in this trait for eight different populations from Arizona show that it strongly varies between 14.9 and 72%, averaging about 36% (Table 53).

In the same work, the author compares the variability of colors determined by photometric methods; moreover he has done so not for the whole skin as F. Sumner, S. S. Schwartz, and others have, but separately for the sides, chest, and back. This undoubtedly represents the natural conditions more exactly (Table 8).

Table 8. Coefficient of variation ($c.\ v. \pm s_{c.v.}$) **of photometric indices of body color of** *P. maniculatus* **(Estimated from data of Dice, 1938)**

Population	Red	Yellow	Green	Pale-blue	Violet-blue
			BACK		
I	20.8±1.4	22.3±1.5	18.8±1.3	23.1±1.6	22.6±1.5
II	17.4±1.8	20.5±2.1	17.6±1.8	18.8±1.9	21.8±2.2
III	18.2±1.0	19.7±1.1	20.8±1.1	21.6±1.2	23.2±1.2
IV	21.1±1.7	20.4±1.7	22.3±1.8	22.5±1.9	22.2±1.8
V	26.2±2.4	25.2±2.3	30.9±2.9	30.8±2.8	31.1±2.9
VI	24.8±3.8	25.4±3.9	28.6±4.4	29.9±4.6	32.1±5.0
VII	24.1±1.9	24.9±2.0	28.1±2.2	30.5±2.4	31.4±2.5
VIII	7.9±1.2	12.7±1.9	12.1±1.8	15.5±2.3	18.0±2.6
			SIDES		
I	12.3±0.8	13.2±0.9	13.0±0.9	17.2±1.2	17.4±1.2
II	13.2±1.3	13.7±1.4	13.3±1.3	16.0±1.6	16.4±1.7
III	13.2±0.7	12.7±0.7	15.2±0.8	15.0±0.8	15.3±0.8
IV	12.1±1.0	11.9±1.0	14.7±1.2	13.8±1.1	14.7±1.2
V	16.6±1.5	16.3±1.5	18.3±1.7	21.3±2.0	26.1±2.4
VI	13.8±2.1	14.6±2.3	13.4±2.1	19.0±2.9	19.2±3.0
VII	12.8±1.0	14.8±1.16	15.9±1.3	20.5±1.6	20.4±1.6
VIII	11.0±1.6	11.3±1.7	13.8±2.0	14.9±2.2	15.6±2.3

An analysis of these data shows that the magnitude of the coefficient of variation closely approaches the means for variability of colors in other mammals—11 to 32%. Comparing the variability of all populations reveals that some populations have comparatively low indices of variability (12.7 to 12.2%) whereas the variability of coloration in other populations is higher (24.1 to 36.1%). On the whole, it appears that the variability of back color is considerably higher than the variability of color on the sides of the body, and that variability of red, yellow, and green shades is lower than variability of pale-blue and violet-blue colors. Without knowing the living conditions of the animal, it is not possible to understand the adaptive value of such differences, but there is no doubt that an analysis of variability, as in the given case, would help an ecological analysis carried out by the same author.

By using the same method of differential estimation of coloration on different body parts with the photometric method, D. Hayne (1950) obtained data on the absolute variability for red, green, and bluish-violet shades in the color of the back for nine populations of *Peromyscus polionotus* from Florida and Alabama. The results of analyzing data show that variability of red varies in different populations from 16.5 to 66.2%; variability of green, from 11.1 to 65.3%; and variability of bluish-violet, from 17.2 to 67.9%. In other words, no significant differences in the variability of different shades of colors were observed. But it is clear from the investigations of L. Dice (1938) that a particular magnitude of variability is characteristic for each population taken separately; thus the traits of the ninth population are highly variable (65.3 to 67.9%) while the second population is the least variable (11.1 to 21.2%).

R. Boolootian (1954) presents data on the percent of red pigment in the color of three subspecies of kangaroo rats (*Dipodomys nitratoides*). It is observed that the variability of quantity of red pigment in different populations is slight—on an average, 9.9% (8.7 to 11.5%). The variability of color of feet in deermice seems to be much greater. Calculations made from the data of F. Sumner (1924) show that variability of this trait in one subspecies of *P. maniculatus* is 35.4 to 39.2%, and in another 75.5 to 77.9%.

To conclude this section on the variability of coloration, the data obtained can be summarized as follows: Notwithstanding the comparatively high indices of variability of color (up to 60-70%), these indices have characteristically quite a low mean variability—to the level of 10 to 20%. At the same time, it is very important that the nature of the variability of coloration seems to be inherent in the given population as a specific trait; and for the magnitude of variability of color within the species, gradations can be discovered from populations with lower values of variability (5-15%) up to populations with maximum variability (60-70%). Such behavior in coefficients of variation of color (perhaps determined by the influence of controlling factors of evolution) makes the study of variability in color shade a very promising method for the study of finer differences within a species (see also Chapter V).

Variability of colors expressed not only by shades but by the magnitude of area occupied by a particular color field (3.8-29.3%) and the number of spots on a body surface (on an average, 35%) are characterized by clustered values.

Skin

Data on the magnitude of variability for skin thickness, thickness of epidermis, thickness of the stratum corneum of the epidermis, and thickness of the reticular layer of skin in sheep of various breeds are included in the detailed work of M. Tumurzhav (1964). The coefficient of variation for thickness of the epidermis in six flocks of sheep in Mongolia differs a little for new-born, six-month-old, and mature animals: new-born, 13.5-18.8%; mature, 9.07-23.65%. The same picture emerges when comparing the whole skin: new-born, 5.3-9.2%; six-month-old, 7.9-11.8%; and more mature, 6.8-10.1%.

The coefficient of variation in thickness of the stratum corneum varies from 4.3 to 18.7%. But the variability of the reticular layer is somewhat higher: new-born, 19.2-24.2%; six-month-old, 11.1-20.8%; and mature ewes, 18.7-27.1%.

These data can hardly be taken as characteristic for mammals. The possibility remains that these traits of domestic animals differ considerably from similar animals under natural conditions. However, attention is drawn to the fact of a considerable constancy in coefficients of variation in the samples of different age groups, and to the possible use of such aspects of fine histological structures for characterizing variability of the skin.

The general weight of skin may also serve as a good parameter for this system. It appears that variations in the variability of skin weight for the northern fur seal (*Callorhinus ursinus*) are insignificant for males at the age of three and four years. The variability within 13 selected animals of this age (but of different body lengths) varied only from 6.5 to 13.6% (Scheffer, 1962).

In a different species of marine mammal, the white whale (*Delphinapterus leucas*), variability of skin weight is 14.8%. It is interesting to note that the variability of skin weight in these two cases seems to be very low, whereas the reader may remember that traits concerning weights normally have a very high variability.

Skin derivatives

Original data on the number of plates of the nine-banded armadillo (*Dasypus novemcinctus*), are given in the work of Newman (1913). The variability of this trait in four groups, based on age and sex, was surprisingly constant:

	$\bar{x} \pm s_{\bar{x}}$	$\sigma \pm s_\sigma$	$c.\,v. \pm s_{c.v.}$	n
Adult females	559.0 ± 1.26	14.0 ± 0.89	2.50 ± 0.23	56
Males, their offspring	558.6 ± 0.65	15.4 ± 0.48	2.74 ± 0.13	224
Adult females	559.8 ± 1.34	15.3 ± 0.95	2.74 ± 0.25	56
Females, their offspring	559.1 ± 0.57	13.0 ± 0.41	2.74 ± 0.13	224

It is known that in this species of armadillo the four offspring are always monozygous quadruplets. To study variability of traits in such cases gives a unique opportunity for evaluating genetical components of a common phenotypic variability.

The number of rings of scales on the tails of mice appears to be a satisfactory trait for genetical investigations (Law, 1938). Calculations show that the variability of this trait in 28 samples from different populations varies from 2.2 to 17.8%. It is interesting to note that some populations clearly differ from others in the magnitude of variability, as in the analysis of certain color traits. Lower values of variability in the number of rings on the tail are characteristic of one line (2.2-3.0%) in four series, and comparatively higher values of variability are characteristic of another line (10.8-17.8%). Very homogeneous values of the coefficient of variation in the number of rings on the tail were observed by us for two populations of coypu (*Myocastor coypus*) which had acclimatized for two years in the Caucasus and Central Asia—from 5.9 to 8.6 (for four series) (Yablokov and Etin, 1968).

It is well known that baleen plates of whales grow as derivatives of the integument. Variability in the number of fringes on a unit length of the edge of a baleen plate is similar in different species, 18.1-26.9% (see Table 50). Finally, data on variability in the number of dermatoglyphic ridges are available for man—35.4 to 43.2% (Van Valen, 1963); and moreover, they are highly correlated with simple interdependence (see Chapter V). Variability of this trait in males is somewhat less than that in females.

General conclusion on the variability of integument

Looking at the variability of different organs, and the characteristics of the traits of the integumentary system, a typical and wide degree of variability in different structures is noticed. It could be said with confidence that the variability of parameters of hair in the majority of mammals is 5 to 10%, while the variability of shades of colors determined by photometrical methods averages 10 to 20%. Variability of histological parameters of the skin has typically similar figures. But on the other hand, behind these mean values, the possibility exists of obtaining surprisingly homogeneous and low variability indices as well as comparatively higher variability.

It is important that the variability of almost all the traits of skin structures are characterized by different values in different populations. This means that the traits related to the skin could be important indicators in studying variability of environment and genetics for all kinds of populations. And, on the whole, it can undoubtedly be said that the study of quantitative morphological peculiarities of the integumentary system is one field in the general study of population morphology of mammals which is still very little explored.

Skeleton

Skull

It was necessary to select some homogeneous material which could be used for a comparison with unrelated species from a great number of studies devoted to the structure of mammalian skulls.

The data obtained are given according to systemic traits in Tables 4 and 5 in the Appendix. It appears that in the majority of mammalian orders the following measurements have usually been used in the study of the variability of the skull; condylobasal length of the skull; length of mastoid; width of the skull at the mastoid and jugal; width between the eyes; width of rostrum; length of palate; height of skull; length of tooth row (usually upper); and length of mandible. Certain data obtained or cited in the tables are based on investigations of a large number of populations within one species; for example, the data of F. Clark (1940) on *peromyscus* concerning variability in a number of structures for 30 different populations; the data of D. Hoffmeister (1951) on 14 populations of the same species; the data of B. Kurtén and R. Rausch (1959) on 26 different samples of the grizzly bear (*Ursus arctos*); the data of V. N. Pavlinin (1962, 1963) on variability for 11 different geographical and sex groups of sables (*Martes zibellina*); the data of V. N. Bol'shakov and S. S. Schwartz (1962) and S. S. Schwartz (1962, 1962a) on variability for 10 or more populations of bank voles (*Clethrionomys glareolus*), lemmings (*Lagurus lagurus*), etc.

All the data collected comprise 57 different species; they are concerned with more than 370 different individual samples (according to age, sex, geography, etc.) and have been obtained from the following 9 mammalian orders: Insectivora, Chiroptera, Ungulata, Primates, Lagomorpha, Cetacea, Carnivora, Pinnipedia, and Rodentia. It is thought that these data as a whole are sufficient to characterize precisely the nature of the variability in linear traits of skulls in all groups of mammals.

As seen from the data in Tables 4b and 5 in the Appendix, the variability of traits of the skull in such orders as Insectivora, Ungulata, and Chiroptera has a wide range. Comparative data are presented in Tables 4a and 4b. For the class as a whole, the variability of condylobasal length varies from 0.4 to 6.8%; the mastoid width from 1 to 8.3%; width of molars, 0.4 to 9.6%; width between eyes, 1.5 to 8.3%; width of snout, 0.9 to 10.6%; length of tooth row, 1.0 to 10.6%, etc. (Table 5, Appendix).[2]

---

[2] The data in the Table show that in roughly eight cases of different traits, the variability was very high, up to 41%. Possibly in these samples errors of calculation have been made, or the samples were made without due consideration for the necessary requirements. It is also quite possible that in individual cases the variability of skeletal features can be quite high. In any case, strictly speaking, we do not have as yet data that preclude such an assumption regarding the possibility of a sharp rise in variability in individual populations under special conditions of evolutionary factors.

Data for all parameters of variability for all the orders studied, are summarized in Table 5. It seems that the overall variability of all the given traits of mammals varies from 0.2 to 12.0%, averaging about 2 to 5%. The magnitude of the linear variability of the skull as determined by the given data is not related to the size of species nor to its systemic position, and the range of variability is similar for all the traits of the skull under study.

There are no differences in the range of variability of condylobasal length, the length of the lower jaw, and the length of the palate. However differential analysis of variability of different traits is possible if fairly uniform series of samples, taken from one order or one species, are available. The data of J. Dynowski (1963) on the skull of the house-mouse (*Mus musculus*) show that for the three groups of mature males and females studied, the least variability occurs for braincase width, width between eyes, and length of cranial cavity. The most variable traits were length of palate and condylobasal length of skull.

According to the data of F. Clark (1940) the width of skull in *Peromyscus maniculatus* seems to be the least variable measurement; the most variable was the length of lower jaw. The length of lower jaw happens to be the most variable trait also for two other species of *Peromyscus* which were studied by F. Clark namely, *P. leucopus* (eight populations) and *P. eremicus* (four populations). However, the length of the skull seems to be the least variable for *P. leucopus*, while in *P. eremicus* (like *P. maniculatus*), the width of the skull varies least. Thus it can be said that width of skull is usually least variable and length of lower jaw most variable in the genus *Peromyscus*.

The data of T. Peshev and G. Georgiev (1961) show that for ten populations of field mice (*Apodemus sylvaticus*) the variability of condylobasal length of skull is somewhat lower than the width at the jugals. Z. Gebczynska (1964) shows that in four out of six groups of mature field voles (*Microtus agrestis*) the variability of condylobasal length is more than the variability of width of skull. On the other hand, S. S. Schwartz (1962) finds that the variability of the condylobasal length in *Lagurus lagurus* seems very small. Likewise, V. N. Pavlinin (1962) observed that low variability of condylobasal length was characteristic of eight samples of sables; the most variable traits of the measurements for these samples of sables were length of tooth row and width between eyes.

Data on the variability of Pinnipedia in 17 samples of skulls of different species confirm the known facts about the least variability of the condylobasal length (Table 4c, Appendix). After this come (in ascending order of coefficients of variation) braincase width, length of lower jaw, height of skull, length of palate, length of upper tooth row, width of snout, and width between eyes.

According to the work of V. A. Dolgov (1963), condylobasal length in three species of shrew (*Sorex*) from the Oksk collection was also the least variable measurement; after it (in order of increased variability) came length of tooth row, width of skull, height of skull, and width between eyes (see Table 4b, Appendix).

Summarizing the results of the analysis of the extensive data (comparatively speaking) presented in Tables 4 and 5, it can be noticed that the general belief that the condylobasal length of the skull is always the least variable trait among the measurements of the skull, can only be accepted with great reservation. In fact, in the majority of cases, the mean values of variation in the condylobasal length in different samples are a little lower than those of variation in other measurements. But due to the number of exceptions, this rule deserves guarded acceptance and cannot be taken as always correct in all conditions.

The data already available are indicative of the different nature of variability in different species. This means that the time has come to pose the question of the necessity of studying the special characteristics of variability in each species and family, etc; such a study may prove the necessity for studying the special features of growth in all groups.

And finally, before beginning the analysis of variability in skull measurement, it must be underlined that however homogeneous these may be even within one species (for example, during a comparison of variability of hair), a complex interrelation of parameters of variability of one and the same trait is found within one population. Sometimes it happens that the variability of trait sharply differs in males and females, and in young and mature animals. Such conditions make it difficult to analyze the variability of a trait and makes us speak with great reservation about the overall variability of that given trait in a given population. Some qualifications must be made such as "variability characteristic of aged males or aged females"; in some cases, details mentioning year and season of birth of the animal have to be given so as to depict the somewhat different nature of variability among certain samples.

In complete agreement with the known elementary regularities (Chapter V), the variability of width of skull considerably exceeds in magnitude the variability of most other measurements.

Variability of weight of the lower jaw of the muskrat (*Ondatra zibethica*) is 10.5±0.48% (Latimer and Riley, 1934); of human beings, 17.1±1.18% (Lowrance and Latimer, 1957). The nature of the magnitude of variability of weight of the whole skull in certain mammals is as follows:

Macaca rhesus	10.4±20.1%	(7 groups)	Hromada and Strnad (1962)
Macaca cynomolgus	15.7±31.6%	(6 groups)	,, ,,
Ondatra zibethica	14.1±0.75%		Latimer and Riley (1934)
Homo sapiens	16.6±1.15%		Lowrance and Latimer (1957)

According to Hromada and Strnad (1962) variability of the volume of the skull has somewhat lower values (7.3 to 13.7%) for 13 different groups of two species of *Macaca*.

An estimation of variability for epigenetic polymorphism is necessary while studying the skull of mammals, just as it is necessary for the majority of organs and systems. Many examples of this variability are given in the works of R. Berry (1963, 1964), R. Berry and A. Searle (1963) and others. (See the section on "Epigenetic polymorphism" in Chapter IV.) One example showing prospects for using methods of study of epigenetic polymorphism in separate structures of the skull can be cited here.

It is known (Straus, 1962) that a great taxonomic and phylogenetic value has been attached to the interrelationship of fissure (*s. mylohyoideus*) and foramen (*f. mandibulare*) during the investigations on primates. During the study on the variability of these traits, it was observed that the fissure and foramen were found in very different combinations within a population of one species and did not characterize either the species or large systemic groups (Figure 5). But the investigations showed at the same time that the nature of the distribution for different types of fissure and foramen in each species may serve as a typical characteristic of a population (Table 9).

Table 9. Occurrence (in percentages) of four basic types* of dispositions of *Fissure mylohyoideus* in some primates (Straus, 1962)

Genus	Type of disposition				Genus	Type of disposition			
	I	II	III	IV		I	II	III	IV
Tupaia ..	82.1	17.9	—	—	*Papio* ..	73.2	20.7	6.1	—
Homo ..	27.6	3.4	10.3	58.6	*Colobus* ..	53.1	40.6	6.2	—
Galago ..	25.0	—	—	75.0	*Pongo* ..	23.2	38.7	36.6	1.4
Tarsius ..	6.3	—	3.1	90.6	*Pan* ..	8.9	32.5	51.2	7.3
Aotus ..	13.8	24.1	55.2	6.9	*Gorilla* ..	70.6	19.0	9.2	1.2
Ateles ..	9.4	56.3	6.2	28.1					

* For character of types, see Figure 5.

Unfortunately, in the cited investigations the characteristics of species and not of populations have been obtained, but there is no doubt whatsoever that clear-cut differences can be found in the frequency of occurrence of different types of fissure structures even in different populations of one species.

Dental system

Variability in the parameters of the dental system is close to the

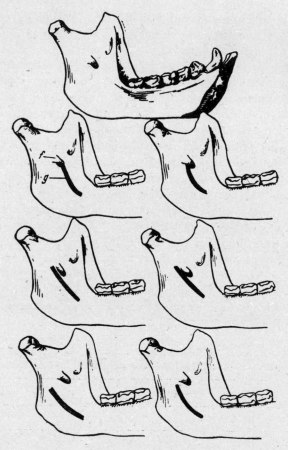

Figure 5. Inner surface of lower jaw of mature orangutans
with different varieties of relationship between fissure (*s. mylohyoideus*)
and foramen (*f. mandibulare*) (Straus, 1962).

variability of the structure and measurements of the skull. A review of
different investigations carried out for 17 species of mammals shows that
characters of the dental system like measurements of the incisors, canines,
premolars, and molars of the upper and lower jaw, and similarly the
number of teeth in cetaceans (and some pinnipeds), have characteristically
rather low variability values (Table 10).

As shown in the data presented in the work of L. Freedman (1963),
variability of different teeth differs considerably in magnitude. (Length
and breadth of teeth in male and female baboons in three different populations were studied.) Canines appeared to be most variable in the upper
jaw (mean coefficient of variation, 12%), and the molars were the least
variable (mean coefficient of variation, 4.8%); linear variability of

incisors is a little higher than the variability of premolar measurements. Variability of corresponding teeth in the lower jaw is in the same order. It is interesting to note that while the magnitude of variation of molars, premolars, and incisors is almost identical between the upper and lower jaws, the variability of the canine of the upper jaw is somewhat higher than for the one on the lower jaw. But the differences among the types of teeth in their coefficients of variation is, perhaps, not characteristic of mammals in general.

Table 10. Summarized data on variability ($Lim_{c.v.}$) of linear measurements and number of elements of the dental system in some mammals*

	Incisors	Canines	Premolars	Molars	No. of teeth[†]
Upper Jaw	6.2-14.6 (4)	5.9-26.5 (6)	2.3-14.8 (40)	2.0-9.5 (60)	
					3.9-17.4 (22)
Lower Jaw	5.2-10.4 (16)	4.8-19.8 (6)	4.1-10.1 (23)	2.9-17.0 (68)	

* Primates, Lagomorpha, Carnivora, Cetacea, Pinnipedia, Chiroptera, Rodentia, Ungulata. Number of samples studied are given in parentheses.
[†] For walrus and dolphins.

In the work of R. S. Bader (1955), carried out on a large number of fossil ungulates belonging to ten species of the subfamilies *Merychyinae* and *Merycochoerinae,* it has been shown that the coefficients of variation of measurements of premolars and molars are not different. This fact confirms the general conclusion that in each case the value of the coefficient of variation is controlled mainly by ecological and not by stochastic determinants. The differences in the magnitude of variability of tooth measurements for two ecologically different species of Black Sea dolphins (Table 11) could hardly be explained by accidental reasons.

Table 11. Variability ($c.v. \pm s_{c.v.}$%) of length of teeth of adult male and female dolphins of the Black Sea (Analyzed from the data of Kleinenberg, 1956)

Genus		Male	Female
Delphinus delphis	..	8.4±1.38	7.9±1.02
Tursiops truncatus	..	12.4±2.77	14.8±2.23
t_{1-2}	..	—1.29	—2.87

It is natural to assume that diverse modes of feeding (there is direct information on this) and different methods of using teeth bring about such variability through selection.

On the whole, variability of the dental system completely corresponds to the variability of skull measurements. It may be said that, as a rule, the variability of measurements for individual teeth (not canines) is in the range of 4-10%, though considerable deviations are possible. Perhaps the study of such variable traits in the dental system may point to specific conditions occurring during such important functions as the capture of food, defence from enemies, etc. in the life of species in the process of evolution.

The study of the dental system is also necessary in the context of epigenetic polymorphism. Examples of such work can be cited for various orders of mammals. Zejda's work (1960) presents data on the simple form of M^3 of the bank vole (*Clethrionomys glareolus*) and some interesting aspects of its distribution in Czechoslovakia (Figure 6). Determination of the distribution of color on the molars of the common shrew (*Sorex araneus*) may serve as a good way to characterize individual populations of this species (Markov, 1957). It was possible to distinguish populations of martens and sables (Pavlinin, 1963) according to the appearance of additional teeth, protuberances, grooves, and the form of the external and internal sides of M^3. Definite population differences have been observed (Stein, 1963) in the occurrence of different abnormalities in the dental system in moles (*Talpa europaea*).

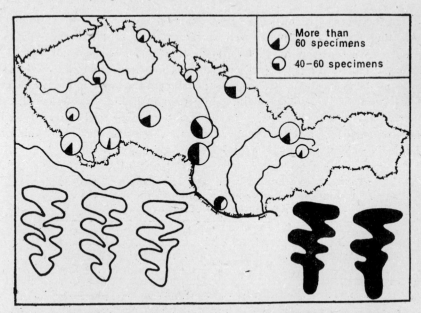

Figure 6.   Frequency of occurrence of "simple" (*black*) and "complex" (*white*) form of the third upper molar of the bank vole in different populations in Czechoslovakia (J. Zejda, 1960).

These examples show how much unexpected and interesting information can be had from the study of variability in seemingly well-studied and simple dental systems.

Post-cranial skeleton

Unfortunately, because of a number of methodological and technical difficulties in the study of the anatomy of mammals, the main part of the skeleton, as such, receives little attention.

In analyzing the linear variability of the post-cranial skeleton, it may be noted that the latter is distinguished by an extremely low amount of variability, chiefly lying in the range of 3 to 5%. This is especially noticeable when compared with the linear measurements of the skull, which are more labile. So far, this fact has not been examined by investigators who, as a rule, consider theoretical possibilities for measurements of the skull only.

D. S. Webb's data (1965) on the variability of the post-cranial skeleton (linear measurements of vertebrae and the pectoral and pelvic girdles) in *Camelops hesternus* (a North American Pleistocene species) are noteworthy. Out of 101 coefficients of variation estimated in this study, 51 were not above 4.8%, 92 did not exceed 8.5%; and only 9 coefficients of variation seemed to be in the range of 9.0-14.9%.

The number of ribs seem to be a good trait for characterizing different populations. The analysis of data by A. Shaw (1929) shows that the variability in number of ribs for a population of domestic swine—male and female—is $4.0 \pm 0.24\%$ to $4.2 \pm 0.26\%$. Results obtained by us on variability in number of ribs for different pinnipeds are given in Table 12.

Table 12. **Magnitude of variability** $(c.\ v. \pm s_{c.v.};\ Lim_{c.v.})$ **of number of ribs**

Species		Ribs	
		Sternal	Asternal
Harp seal (*Pagophilus groenlandicus*)	..	0-8.7(10)*	3.8-21.4(9)
Bearded seal (*Erignathus barbatus*)	..	0.0	2.2 ± 0.38
Hooded seal (*Cystophora cristata*)	..	0-4.9(8)	7.8-9.3(8)
Common seal (*Phoca vitulina*)	..	1.4 ± 0.14	17.5 ± 2.48
Ringed seal (*Pusa hispida*)	..	0-1.4(5)	0-4.2(5)
Baikal seal (*P. sibirica*)	..	0.0	5.6 ± 0.66
Coypu (*Myocastor coypus*)	..	0-4.3(4)	5.9-6.4(4)

* Number of samples carried out are given in parentheses. In this and other tables on samples of Pinnipedia, animals of the same sex and as far as possible of the same age, caught during one season (i e , 2 to 3 months) are included.

Variability of the number of vertebrae according to different divisions of the vertebral column is a very good trait for expressing the variability of the post-cranial skeleton for different populations and species.

Data obtained as a result of analyzing the material of L. Law (1938) of variability of caudal vertebrae in four lines of laboratory mice, show that variability of this trait ranges from 2.7 ± 0.42 to $6.2\pm0.93\%$ and is unrelated to the variability of tail length.[3] In another group of laboratory mice of other phenotypes, the variability of this trait seems to be more pronounced—from 2.9 ± 0.30 to $11.7\pm1.06\%$. It is interesting to note that out of eight lines, the variability of number of caudal vertebrae in males was lower than that in females in seven lines.

Hamburgh and Lynn's data (1964) on the variability of the number of caudal vertebrae in experimental populations of white rats are interesting. At the age of five days, the variability in number of vertebrae was considerably lower in the normal group than it was in those animals in which the growth of thyroid gland was artificially restricted (hypothyroidism). The values were, respectively: 5.0 ± 0.80 and $10.1\pm1.55\%$. In older animals, the situation was reversed: $9.0\pm1.64\%$ in control, and 9.9-2.9% in the hypothyroid animals.

Data on the variability in the number of vertebrae in certain mammals are given in Table 13.

Through the wide researches carried out by Latimer (1936-1959), it is clear that variability in the weight of the skeleton and the individual parts is considerable. From this work, the variability in general weight of skeleton is as follows:

Species		Number of samples
Rabbit ..	6.9-17.3%	6
Cat ..	13.3-21.3%	2
Man ..	12.7%	1

Variability in weight of individual elements of the skeleton is far more pronounced. In man the weight of parts (in descending order of magnitude of variability) like the hyoid bone, sternum, metacarpus, calvicle, patella, scapulae, radius, all ribs, and metatarsus, was observed to be particularly variable. The variability of the above-mentioned organs is 43.6 to 19.5% (data of Lowrance and Latimer, 1957).

While concluding this section about the variability of the post-cranial skeleton, mention of two specific interests in the study of organs of this system may be made. Firstly, the surprisingly small scope for variation of linear measurements in homogeneous samples. This reveals the constancy of skeletal traits and the possible potential of their use for the study of

---

[3] This observation is apparently not confirmed by the analysis of number of vertebrae in different types of tailless cats (Howell and Spiegel, 1966).

Table 13. **Variability of the number of caudal and thoracic
vertebrae of certain mammals (Number of samples
used is given in parentheses)**

Species	$\bar{x} \pm s_{\bar{x}}$ or Lim $\bar{x}$	$c.v. \pm s_{c.v.}$ or $Lim_{c.v.}$	Remarks
	Caudal		
Greenland seal (*P. groenlandicus*)			Own data
White Sea	13.4-14.0	7.8-10.2(3)*	,, ,,
Region of Yan-Maien	13.2-13.6	6.2-8.7(5)	,, ,,
Newfoundland Region	12.6-13.0	3.1-4.5(4)	,, ,,
Hooded seal (*Oystophora cristata*)	13.4-14.4	6.0-8.6(9)	,, ,,
Common seal (*Phoca vitulina*)	12.8±0.18	7.8±0.98	Adult females
Bearded seal (*Erignathus barbatus*)	11.9-12.3	6.7-8.0(2)	,, ,,
Ringed seal (*Pusa hispida*)	12.9-13.4	1.5-8.6(3)	,, ,,
Baikal seal (*P. sibirica*)	13.0±0.09	4.4±0.53	Males and females
Caspian seal (*P. caspica*)	12.1±0.28	9.3±0.58	Adult males
White mice (*Mus musculus albicans*)	31.6-32.1	2.3-2.8(2)	Sumner (1909), males
,, ,, ,, ,, ,,	—	2.9-11.7(16)	Law (1938), different lines
White rat (*Rattus norvegicus alb.*)	15.8-26.6	1.3-16.9(9)	Hamburgh, Lynn (1964)
Coypu (*Myocastor coypus*)	22.8-23.8	3.3-4.1(4)	Own data
	Thoracic and Lumbar		
Orangutan (*Simia satyrus*)	16.0±0.05	3.2±0.23	Males and females Schultz (1917)
Man (*Homo sapiens*)	17.0±0.02	1.2±0.08	Men and women Schultz (1917)
Pig (*Sus scrofa*)	20.5-21.3	1.9-2.3(2)	Males and females Freedman (1939)

precise problems in the field of population morphology. Secondly, the study of these parts of the skeleton is promising also for studies concerning epigenetic polymorphism; this has been well shown by Grüneberg (1950-1963) and Berry (1963-1964) on rodents. Other researchers (Dolgov, 1961; Ashton and Oxnard, 1964; Sikorska-Pivovska, 1965; and others) agree with this. In Figure 7 some traits which are used in the study of variability of the skeleton are clearly seen.

We see that the variability of linear measurements for the post-cranial skeleton usually varies from 3 to 5%. Variability of discrete traits is, on the average, higher (5 to 8%); and variability of characters comprising weight of organs is still higher (on the average, about 10 to 15%).

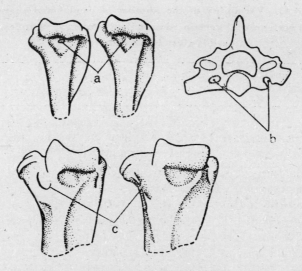

Figure 7.   Examples of epigenetic polymorphism in the skeleton of :
a—mouse *(Mus musculus) ; b*—guinea pig (*Cavia porcellus) ; c*—squirrel
(*Sciurus carolinensis*) (Berry and Searle, 1963).

Variability of Other Internal Organs

Masculature

Fewer data are available on variability of other internal organs of mammals than is available for the skeletal system as a whole.

Data on variability of weight (absolute and relative) for all musculature of rabbits of different genetical lines are presented in the work of Latimer and Sawin (1955). It was observed that variability of absolute weight of the musculature of males varies less than that of females: 14.7 to 17.2% in males and 11.7 to 21.5% in females, averaging about 15%. Variability of the relative weight of muscles (ratio of muscle weight to body weight) has values three times lower for males and females (3.9 to 5.5%); moreover, the variability of relative weight of musculature seems to be more a variable trait in males than in females: 3.9 to 5.5% in males, 5 to 5.4% in females. In one line out of three, females have higher coefficients of variation for absolute and relative weight. In one instance, these coefficients were higher for males and in another instance, variability of the absolute weight was higher in males but the variability of the relative weight was higher in females.

Characteristics of the musculature of the common cat have been examined in detail by Latimer (1944), who evaluated variability of the locomotor group of muscles separately for males and females (Table 14).

The variability of weight for the whole musculature of cats is a little higher than the variability of the locomotor group of muscles, and the variability of relative weights is appreciable—3 to 4 percent more than the similar values for rabbits. Among the lines studied (sufficiently large in number, homogeneous, and hence completely representative), a clearly greater variability of the absolute weight of muscles is observed in males, whereas the variability of relative weights is higher in females.

Table 14. Comparison of variability $(c. \, v. \pm s_{c.v.})$ **of absolute and relative indices in weight of skeleton and muscles of cats (From Latimer, 1944)**

| Organ | Coefficient of variation | | | | Absolute $t_{\substack{\land \\ \delta \, \female}}$ | Relative $t_{\substack{\land \\ \delta \, \female}}$ |
| | Absolute weight | | Relative weight | | | |
	Males	Females	Males	Females		
Skeleton	21.30±1.50	13.33±0.93	15.44±1.06	16.26±1.15	+6.06	—1.59
All musculature	27.93±2.03	23.95±1.74	7.02±0.48	8.11±0.56	+3.23	—0.13
Locomotor system	24.95±1.75	21.62±1.46	4.44±0.29	5.21±0.35	+4.84	—1.61

Based on the examples given above, it could be concluded that the relative weight of the musculature may be a good and constant index of a population since its variability in all instances is appreciably less than 10%, falling in line with the variability values of organs like the skull. But such a conclusion appears to be not absolutely correct. Other data available on the relative weight of musculature for other mammals (Tribe and Peel, 1963) show a considerable degree of variation for this trait. In six species of ungulates (sheep, gazelle, swine, etc.), variability of relative weight of musculature varies from 8.1 to 88.1%. The fact that the variability of relative weight in domestic ungulates appears to be directly proportional to the value of relative weight, attracts attention to these data. Regarding relative weight of musculature, *Bos indicus* is highest (32.5±2.0%). For this species, the highest variability of relative weight is also found. Sheep, which have the lowest relative weight of musculature (2.9±0.6%), also have the least variation for this trait (8.1±1.58%). In the same work of Tribe and Peel (1963), it was shown that in kangaroos (*Macropus sp.*) the relative weight of musculature is the least variable (3.4±0.68%) of any species studied.

On the whole, while characterizing the variability of weight of the musculature in mammals, it can be assumed that the variability can be 20% (ranging from 11.7 to 27.9%) and is considerably less in homogeneous samples for relative weight (up to 10%).

Only muscle weight has been used as a standard method of determining quantitative morphology in the study of muscular systems, while physiological traits have been used to a considerably less degree. Thus the methods used for the study of quantitative variability in epigenetic polymorphism appear to be necessary. References for such examples can be found in the works of S. Basu and S. Hasary (1960) on the study of muscles of anterior extremities in a large sample.

Brain and eye

Data are presented in the work of St. Reiniš (1964) on variability in number of glial and nerve cells in different layers of the cortex of the brain in rats of different ages. An analysis of these data shows (Figure 8) that the variability of nerve cells in rats from 1 to 25 days old adult animals, varies from 6.0 to 25%; the variability in number of glial cells varies from 12.7 to 44.5%. It is interesting that the variability in number of cells in the glia of the fourth layer takes a reversible trend with age. Variability in number of glial cells considerably increased

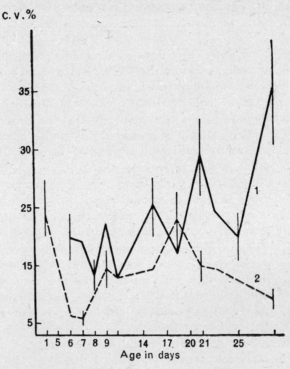

Figure 8.   Variability (*c. v.* $\pm 2s_{c.v.}$) of (*1*) glial and (*2*) nerve cells in the fourth zone of the cortex of rat brain (from Reiniš, 1964).

while variability of nerve cells decreased. Sharp peaks and depressions in the curve are seen in Figure 8, which may be explained perhaps by the unsatisfactory method of obtaining cross-sections exactly from one and the same part of the brain, and also perhaps by the fact that in different genotypes, developmental processes may proceed at different rates. However, the general conclusion is not changed. Such decrease in the variability of number of nerve cells in the brain cortex of adult mammals is well understood from the functional point of view. The control of morphological structures which facilitate correct decisions in all situations, must be very strict.

The variability in number of ganglia in the nerve plexuses ranged from $12.8\pm0.6\%$ to $20.6\pm0.9\%$ according to an analysis of the data of Sauer and Ruble, 1946.

Variability in the weight of the brain is comparatively not large. According to Brown, Pearce, and Van Allen (1926), the variability of the absolute weight of the brain in rabbits is 7.5-8.4% (three samples), and according to Latimer and Sawin (1955) it is 5.0-7.9% (six samples). One interesting fact, in the opinion of these authors, is that the variability of the relative weight of the brain (in proportion to body weight) appears to be considerably higher than the variability of the absolute weight (for all nine samples, 8.2 to 16.9%, average about 14%). Variability of the absolute weight of the brain of *Peromyscus maniculatus* (King, 1965) for one sample is 6.3%; data on the variability of brain weight for 27 different samples are given in the same work.

Data on the high variability of the relative weight of the brain are confirmed by material recently obtained on the brain of the pigmy ground squirrel (*Citellus pygmaeus*), where the variability of the relative weight of the brain varied from 12 to 42% (Schwartz, 1960).

According to A. Kramer (1964) the variability of the absolute weight of the brain in the gerbil (*Meriones unguiculatus*) is also quite low—3.8 to 5.0% (two samples); whereas the variability of relative weight (in mg/ 100g body weight) is considerably higher—15.7 to 23.6%.

The variability of parameters of the spinal cord of laboratory rabbits is characterized by moderate values. Variability of the absolute weight is 8.3 to 11.2% (six samples) and variability of the length is 3.2 to 4.9% (four samples); variability of corresponding relative values is 8.1 to 12.9% and 2.6 to 3.7% (Latimer and Sawin, 1955).

Thus the variability of nerve cells in the cortex of the brain in adult animals is less than 10%; variability of the absolute weight of the brain averages about 6 to 7%; and variability of the relative weight of the brain appears to be considerably larger, from 12 to 20 and up to 42%.

Variability of the absolute weight of the eyeball appears to be like that of the entire brain, i.e. 5.5 to 10.5% (seven samples of rabbits and guinea pigs) (Latimer, 1951, 1955). The variability of the relative weight of the eye, like the variability of the weight of the whole brain, appears to be quite high (8.5 to 14.8%) for the same samples.

The variability of the crystalline lens of the eye in deermice appears to be very high—up to 60% (King, 1965).

Glands

All the data on the variability of glands are for their absolute and relative weights.

Salivary glands. According to the data of Tribe and Peel (1963) the variability of the submandibular salivary glands in kangaroos (*Macropus sp.*) is 24.1%.

According to the data of A. Buchalczyk (1961), the variability of relative weight of salivary glands in the common shrew (*Sorex araneus*) varies from 3.6 to 28.7% (20 samples); higher values of the coefficients of variation are characteristics of the submandibular gland (18.0 to 28.7%), and for the parotid gland it is less (3.6 to 19.2%). Variability of the weight of these glands in relation to each other varies little, 1.3 to 2.6% (10 samples). Variability of absolute weight of the salivary gland of *Meriones unguiculatus* is 11.2 to 2.5% (2 samples) according to Kramer (1964), and the variability of the relative weight for this organ is 18.8 to 20.5%.

Pancreas. The variability of absolute weight for the pancreas in captive foxes (*Vulpes vulpes*) ranges from 10.4 to 34.3% (4 samples, Fateev *et al.*, 1961). The variability of relative weights of these glands in the same samples is, on the average, lower: 11.7 to 27.0%. The variability of absolute weight of the pancreas in rabbits is rather high but is maintained on the same level, 22.1 to 30% (6 samples, Latimer and Sawin, 1955). Relative weight variability for the same gland in the same samples is 19.4 to 25.9%.

The variability of weight for the pancreas of *Meriones unguiculatus* ranges from 27.4 to 29.2% according to Kramer (1964), whereas the variability of relative weight is somewhat less, 26.3 to 26.4%.

Relative weight variability for the pancreas of the pigmy ground squirrel (*Citellus pygmaeus*), according to data by S. S. Schwartz (1960), varies widely—in the range of 13.7 to 46.8% (6 samples). In the Caspian seal (*Pusa caspica*), the variability of absolute weight of this gland is 26.1% but for the white whale (*Delphinapterus leucas*) it is only 1.7%.

On the whole, the variability of absolute weight of the pancreas for different mammals ranges from 10.4 (not considering the data on the white whale) to 34.3%, averaging about 25%. Variability of the relative weight of this organ is somewhat less, 11.7 to 46.8%, averaging about 20%, but the scope of variation in relative variability is greater.

Liver. In insectivores, the variability of absolute weight of the liver is quite high compared to the variability of weight of other organs. In the European mole (*Talpa europaea*) the variability of absolute weight is 13.7 to 32.5% (four samples); the relative weight varies to a lesser degree, 15.4 to 22.4% (six samples) (Fateev, 1962); for three lines of the pigmy ground squirrel, 15.4 to 21.4%; for the common shrew (*Sorex araneus*), 10.8%; and for *Neomys fodiens*, 12.3% (Schwartz, 1960).

Similar values of variability for absolute and relative weights of the liver are observed in other mammals: 5.0 to 24.2% for absolute weight in foxes, and 6.3 to 24.1% for relative weight in the same four samples (Fateev *et al.*, 1961); 22.1 to 31.8% for absolute weight in rabbits, and 20.4 to 27.9% for relative weight in the same nine samples (Brown *et al.*, 1926; Latimer and Sawin, 1955); 10.4 to 41.9% for absolute weight in 15 samples of six species of marine mammals; 17.5 to 21.8% relative weight in pigmy ground squirrels (Schwartz, 1960); 9.7, 8.9, and 12.4% respectively for *Microtus oeconomicus*, red-backed voles (*Clethrionomys rutilus*), and water voles (*Arvicola terrestris*) (Schwartz, 1960); and finally 21.2 to 27.3% for other samples of muskrat (*Ondatra zibethica*) (Schwartz, 1962).

The variability of absolute weight of the liver in *Meriones unguiculatus*, according to A. Kramer (1964), is 28.8 to 32.3%, and the variability of relative weight is a little less, 21.0 to 23.3%.

On the whole, the range of variability for absolute weight of the liver is 5.0 to 41.9% (average, 25 to 30%) and that of relative weight is 6.3 to 27.9% (average, 15 to 20%).

Thyroid gland. In kangaroos, according to Tribe and Peel (1963), the variability of absolute weight of the thyroid gland is 24.1% and that of relative weight is 21.2%. The variability of the thyroid gland of *Neomys fodiens* varies from month to month (Table 15).

Table 15. Variability of the weight of the thyroid gland in
Neomys fodiens **in various months (Calculated from the data of Bazan, 1956)**

Sex, Month	$\bar{x} \pm s_{\bar{x}}$	$c.\,v. + s_{c.v.}$	n	Sex, Month	$\bar{x} \pm s_{\bar{x}}$	$c.\,v. + s_{c.v.}$	n
Male				*Female*			
July	75.1± 7.4	50.2± 7.0	26	July	76.1±11.1	56.4±10.3	15
August	65.9±17.7	71.0±19.0	7	August	72.1± 9.4	56.6± 9.2	19
September	63.4±11.6	60.6±12.9	11	September	63.2±10.4	70.1±11.7	18

Similar values of variation for this trait in rabbits are presented by Brown *et. al.*, (1926) namely, 56.2 to 70.3%. The relative weight of the thyroid gland in the latter case for three samples was 61.4 to 62.3%. Data presented by Latimer and Sawin (1955) for rabbits (six samples) differ considerably from the foregoing observation; they obtained an absolute weight variability of 22.3 to 40.6%, and for relative weight, 18.1 to 27.9%. The values of absolute and relative variability of weight of the thyroid gland in the guinea pig (*Cavia porcellus*) are close to the last mentioned values—29.9 and 31.5% respectively (Latimer, 1951).

The last example differs from previous ones in that the variability of relative weight of the thyroid gland appeared somewhat greater than the variability of absolute weight. It is difficult to say why it should be so but the fact that in the samples under study (*C. porcellus*) the relative weight variability for the adrenals and for the hypophysis was also higher, attracts attention (see below).

Variability of weight for the thyroid gland in *Meriones unguiculatus* was given by Kramer (1964) as 23.8 to 24.8% and the variability of relative weight as 20.4 to 38.2% (for two samples).

On the whole, the variability of absolute and relative weight for thyroid glands in mammals is exceedingly high and is respectively 22.0 to 71.0% and 18.1 to 62.3%.

Spleen. Variability of absolute weight of the spleen in moles (Fateev, 1962) ranges from 25.8 to 43.2% and the variability of relative weight in the same four samples is from 25.3 to 30.2%. Variability of absolute and relative weights of the spleen in rabbits seems to be close to these figures: respectively 30.8 to 51.5% and 26.3 to 55.5% (for nine samples of rabbits) (Brown *et al.*, 1926; Latimer and Sawin, 1955). A still greater range of variability for absolute weight of the spleen is characteristic for our pinnipeds and cetaceans: from 28.1 to 84.2% (ten samples, six species) (Table 7, Appendix). Finally, the data of Newson and Chitty (1962) show a similarly large range of variability in absolute values for the field vole (*Microtus agrestis*), 50.5 to 80.3% (Table 16).

Table 16. Coefficient of variation ($c. v. \pm s_{c.v.}$) **of weight of spleen of** *Microtus agrestis* **(Calculated from the data of Newson and Chitty, 1962)**

Sex	Population I	Population II	t
Males ..	60.3± 9.5	50.5± 8.9	—1.40 (I)
Females ..	80.3±10.7	76.9±11.4	—1.84 (II)

Variability of weight of the spleen in *Meriones unguiculatus* is very high, 58.7 to 65.5%; variability of relative weight is 68.1 to 78.7%.

From the data presented, it is seen that the variability of the spleen is exceedingly high, i.e., 25.8 to 84.2% for absolute weight, and 25.3 to 78.7% for relative weight. In the majority of the species studied the average variability of absolute weight of the spleen is close to 35 to 45%.

Adrenals. In the above-mentioned nine samples of rabbits, the variability of absolute weight of the adrenals varies from 29.6 to 43.3% and quite clearly differs from the material presented by Brown *et al.* (1926) and Latimer and Sawin (1955). The variability of these samples appeared to be comparatively high (40.1 to 43.3%) in the case of the first author and quite low (29.6 to 34.1% for six samples) in the case of the other authors. Variability of the relative weight of the adrenals in rabbits in the second work was 35.9 to 40.7%, and in the third, 20.0 to 36.7%; on the average, this is less than the variability of absolute weight in both cases.

According to Latimer (1951), the variability of absolute weight of the adrenals for porpoises is 29.4 and for the relative weight is 31.2%. The variability of absolute weight of right and left adrenals of chinchillas is 22.7 and 24.7%. L. G. Korotova's findings (1962) on the variability of weight and fine structure of the adrenals in the water vole (*Arvicola terrestris*) is interesting. The variability of absolute weight for the adrenals of males and females appeared to be very similar—25.0 and 25.5%; but the variability of relative weight in the same groups of animals was from 15.5 to 28.6%. In the same data, the variability of the thickness of the adrenal cortex was 18.2%, thickness of the *zona fasciculata,* 34.3%, and thickness of the *zona glomerulosa,* 32.5%.

Adrenal weight of *Meriones unguiculatus* varied from 18.3 to 22.9% according to Kramer (1964) and 26.1 to 31.5% (relative weight). Data on the weight of the adrenals of *M. hurrianoes* follow these values closely (Prakash, 1964).

McKeever and Quentin (1963) showed that in the mongoose *Herpestes auropunctatus* the variability of the absolute width of the *zona glomerulosa* ranged from 26 to 80.8%; the *zona fasciculata,* 39.9 to 49.6%, and the *zona reticularis* from 80.8 to 122.9%.[4] The variability of relative thickness (in relation to the thickness of the cortex) varied in three groups of animals as follows : *zona glomerulosa,* 43 to 94%, *zona fasciculata,* 28 to 33%, and *zona reticularis,* 57 to 63%.

The average variability for absolute weight of the adrenals is a little less than the variability for weight of the spleen, liver, and thyroid glands : 18.3 to 43.3% (average, 25 to 30% for absolute weight, and 20 to 30% for relative).

Hypophysis. The variability of absolute weight of the hypophysis of rabbits ranges from 18.5 to 34.1% (nine samples); the variability of relative weight is from 19.8 to 26.9% (Brown *et al.,* 1926; Latimer and Sawin, 1955). The variability of absolute and relative weights of the

----

[4] These figures were obtained by the author from graphs and do not represent great accuracy.

hypophysis in guinea pigs ranges from 17.2 to 18.1 (H. Latimer, 1951). Finally, the variability of absolute and relative weights of the hypophysis in the chinchilla (*Chinchilla laniger*) is 24.6 to 40.9% and 26.4 to 39.9% respectively.

The magnitude of variability of weight of the hypophysis of *Meriones unguiculatus* is close to these figures: 23.4 to 29.4% for absolute weight, and 26.1 to 27.4% for relative weight (Kramer, 1964).

All the data presented on variability of the hypophysis show the similarity of the magnitude of variability of absolute and relative weights of the hypophysis—on an average, about 25%.

Other glands. Data are available to show that the variability of absolute and relative weights of the pineal body (epiphysis) in rabbits practically coincide; they are respectively 26.7 to 32.5% and 27.7 to 34.0% (Brown *et al.*, 1926). Similarly, the variability of absolute and relative weights of the thymus in rabbits coincide with these figures, being 35.7 to 38.4% and 35.6 to 36.6% (according to Brown). The variability in length of the metatarsal gland in 12 samples of *Odocoileus hemionus* ranged from 3.2 to 22.2%, averaging about 11% (Anderson, *et al.*, 1964).

For the Harderian gland in rabbits, the variability of absolute weight ranged from 12.7 to 31.0% and of relative weight from 14.9 to 29.4% (for six samples; Latimer and Sawin, 1955).

Bhatnagar and Taneja (1960), and similar data in other works, revealed that the variability of milk quantity in one lactation of a cow does not vary much in different seasons of the year, 2.7 to 3.7% (five seasons). This characterizes the activity of the mammary gland; data on the variability of secretions in other glands do not exist.

Digestive tract

A number of works present material on the variability of number of vallate and foliate papillae on the tongue of elephants and certain other mammals. A partial reference appears in the work of Kubota Kinziro (1967); unfortunately, the data presented indicate only the presence of variability, so an exact analysis of its parameters is not possible.

Length of whole digestive tract. The variability of the length of the whole intestinal tube varies within narrow limits in different species: in moles (Fateev, 1962), from 8.1 to 18.7%; in rabbits (Latimer and Sawin, 1955), from 6.0 to 11.8%; in rats, from 11.6 to 12.8%; in white whales (our data; see Table 8 in the Appendix), 4.2%; in captive foxes (Fateev, 1961) from 6.5 to 27.8% and (per Sokolov, 1941) from 5.4 to 8.6%. In minks (*Mustela vison*) the variability of gut length ranges from 11.2 to 13.6% and, in certain pinnipeds, from 5.3 to 16.0% (from our data, Table 8, Appendix). The variability of length of the gut in gerbils ranges from 7.7 to 8.3% (Kramer, 1964).

It can be concluded that on an average, the variability of length of the whole digestive tract in the majority of mammals comes to about 10 to 12% (ranging to 4.2 to 27.8%).

The relative value of variability of the gut varies within close limits—from 2.3 to 28.4%. The maximum value of variability is in female foxes (Fateev, 1961), and the minimum is in pigmy ground squirrels (Schwartz, 1960). The relative variability of the gut in insectivores is seen from that of the shrews *Sorex araneus* and *Neomys fodiens*, which have 11.1 and 12.9% respectively (Schwartz, 1960).

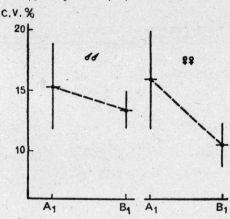

The variability of length of the small intestine in kangaroos (Tribe and Peel, 1963) is 25.8%; the length of this in female foxes varies from 6.7 to 9.4%. The variability of length of the small intestine in three species of pinnipeds—Baikal seal, Greenland seal, and hooded seal (total, eight samples)—ranges from 2.0 to 16.4%. The length of the small intestine and the total length of the intestines of both new-born and immature animals have the greatest values of variability in the samples of pinnipeds studied.

Figure 9. Value of coefficients of variation of intestinal length in (*A*) new-born, and (*B*) adult males and females of hooded seal *Cystophora cristata* (from the Greenland Sea, 1962).

It is clearly seen from Fig. 9 that variability of length of the intestines of the hooded seal (*Cystophora cristata*) considerably decreases with age. The variability of length of the small intestines in gerbils is moderate, 9.8 to 10.5% (Kramer, 1964).

The variability in length of the large intestine is rather high in the above-mentioned species of pinnipeds; the variability in the same seven samples was 15.0 to 58.0%; in kangaroos, 29%; in foxes 9.3 to 9.7%. It may be generally accepted that the variability in length of the large intestine is about 12 to 15%, whereas the variability of length of the small intestine is close to the value of variability for the length of the whole digestive tract, 8.0 to 12.0%.

The variability in length of the large intestine in gerbils is high: 10.1 to 22.2% (Kramer, 1964).

The length of the esophagus in three species of pinnipeds varies from 4.4 to 13.1% (Table 8, Appendix).

The length of the stomach is more variable in the same three species of pinnipeds—8.3 to 15.7%.

The weight of intestines appears to be quite a variable trait, ranging from 11.8 to 21.3%. It is interesting to note that in rabbits the relative weight of intestines is a more variable trait than the absolute weight.

The weight of the stomach is characterized by still higher values of coefficients of variation—from 10.7% in foxes to 24.8% in white whales, 33% in *Histriophoca fasciata*, and up to 51.8% in moles (Table 8, Appendix).

Data obtained by E. A. Sokolov (1941) on the volume of the stomach and intestines in mice can be presented while concluding this section on the variability in parameters of the gut. Variability of volume of the stomach in minks is 6.1 to 12.9% and in foxes 9.1 to 16.6%; the volume of the whole gut in minks is 9.7 to 10.5% and in foxes 12.5 to 12.6%. These data show the relatively small variation in the coefficient of variation in traits like volume of intestines. It must be noted that these data differ somewhat, however, from those of Tribe and L. Peel (1963) on varia- bility of weight of the stomach and large, small, and blind sections of the intestine (26.8 to 56.8%). But, of course, a direct comparison should not be made between these two sources as it is likely that both represent natural conditions.

The following list is a characterization of the average values of variability in parameters of the intestinal tract of mammals :

		Mean value $c. v.$	$Lim_{c.v.}$
Length of:			
Total gut	..	8-12	4.2-27.8
Small intestines	..	8-12	4.5-25.8
Large intestines	..	12-15	9.3-58.0
Esophagus	..	about 10	4.4-13.1
Stomach	..	11-13	8.3-15.7
Weight of intestine	..	about 25	11.8-46.1
Weight of stomach	..	about 30	18.2-51.8
Volume of stomach	..	—	6.1-56.8
Volume of intestine	..	15-25	9.7-46.0

Of course, it is not possible to take the data presented as final. How- ever, it can be specifically said that insofar as the mean values of linear variability are concerned, the intestine is like organs of other systems (such as the nervous system and the skeleton); i.e., it has a characteris- tically low variability and hence may be widely used in the investigations concerning population morphology.

Lungs and trachea

A comparison of values of variability characterizing the weight of lungs in different mammals (five species of pinnipeds: white whale, fox, rabbit, mole, and gerbil) in all 27 samples given in Table 9 of the Appendix, shows that the variability of this trait varies considerably from 15.5%

Name

(for one sample of rabbit) to 63.7% (for the sample of the Caspian seal). However, the majority of the coefficients of variation fall between 20 and 30%. The relative weight of lungs (percent of body weight) varies from 8.3 to 48.7%.

A convenient trait for studying population morphology of mammals is the number of rings in the trachea. The choice of this trait is based on the fact that it has a very low variability (Table 17).

Table 17. Variability in number of rings in the trachea
(Adult males)

Species		$\bar{x} \pm s\bar{x}$	$c.v. \pm s_{c.v.}$	n
Greenland seal (*Pagophilus groenlandicus*), Yan-Maien region	..	42.7±0.47	9.4±0.78	72
Common seal (*Phoca vitulina*)	..	69.4±0.54	3.8±0.55	24
Hooded seal (*Cystophora cristata*)	..	38.2±0.52	9.9±0.96	53
Ringed seal (*Pusa hispida*), Pechora Sea	..	91.5±0.87	5.8±0.67	37
Baikal seal (*P. sibirica*)	..	78.7±0.55	4.4±0.86	13
Caspian seal (*P. caspica*)	..	89.4±1.12	5.8±0.89	21
Coypu (*Myocastor coypus*)	..	88.9±0.28	6.3±0.7	42

In 36 samples of pinnipeds, the variability of this trait did not exceed 10.4% (3.2 to 10.4%) and averaged from 5 to 7% (Table 9, Appendix).

So the variability of generally used traits of the respiratory system is characterized by the following values :

Trait		Mean values $c.v.$	$Lim_{c.v.}$
Weight of lungs	..	20-30	15.5-63.7
Trachea : number of rings	..	5-7	3.2-10.4

Blood

It is generally assumed that the morphological picture of the blood may serve as a good index for the general condition of animals. Unfortunately, there are few data on the variability of blood parameters as such. From those available, it may be concluded that the variability of the quantity of hemoglobin in the blood may differ considerably from species to species; for example, from 1.6% in ewes (Kushner, 1941) to 26.1% in water voles (Schwartz, 1960). However, differences in variability are considerably restricted within a species (Table 18).

Variability of hemoglobin content of the blood in three groups of ewes appears to be close, 1.6 to 2.3% (Kushner, 1941) and in three groups of deermice (*Peromyscus leucopus*) 4.5 to 7.5% (Salander, 1961).

The same is true with variability in the number of erythrocytes.

Table 18. Coefficient of variation $(c.v. \pm s_{c.v.})$ **for quantity of hemoglobin in males of field voles** (*Microtus agrestis*) **in two nearby populations in different years (Calculated from the data of Newson and Chitty, 1962)**

Data	Males		Females	
	"Forest"	"Road"	"Forest"	"Road"
1956				
December	5.7 ± 1.03	—	4.5 ± 0.87	—
1957				
March	5.7 ± 0.78	4.6 ± 0.82	6.7 ± 0.98	5.8 ± 0.98
	5.0 ± 0.98			
May	5.1 ± 0.85	8.9 ± 1.63	6.9 ± 1.06	8.3 ± 1.38
September	8.2 ± 0.90	11.8 ± 2.15	8.1 ± 1.08	—
December	4.3 ± 0.75	6.9 ± 1.22	6.5 ± 1.23	11.9 ± 1.8
1958				
March	9.4 ± 1.84	5.3 ± 0.95	7.4 ± 1.45	7.1 ± 1.59

In the pigmy ground squirrel (*Citellus pygmaeus*) the variability of this trait ranges from 16.2 to 22.6% (three samples), and in muskrat (*Ondatra zibethica*), it is 20.6%, according to S. S. Schwartz (1960); but it is only 2.3 to 3.1% (three samples) in ewes according to Kushner (1941).

For the most part, the variability of number of erythrocytes and the quantity of hemoglobin in the blood varies in a limited range from 22.6 to 26.1%. This shows that after quick methods of determination for these traits in natural populations have been developed, they could prove to be good morphological indices for the study of peculiarities of animals in a population.

Variability in the total number of leucocytes varies in a more pronounced way [V. P. Kozakevich (1967) "Age and Seasonal Variability in Seven Samples of Susliks," C. K. Chai (1957) "Generational Variability in the Number of Leucocytes in Various Lines of Laboratory Rats," and others].

Unfortunately, until recently physiologists gave very little time to the study of variability of blood characters. Hence, many quantitative differences in blood among different species, families, and orders reported previously (review by P. A. Korzhuev, 1964) have to be examined in the future on a more factual quantitative basis.

Heart

There are a large number of works on the variability of the weight of the heart. Generally, variability of the absolute weight of the heart ranges from 7.8% (in one of the six groups of rabbits studied by Latimer and Sawin, 1955) to 44.3% (in one of the groups of moles studied by

Fateev, 1962) and even up to 70.9% in the Greenland seal (*Pagophilus groenlandicus*) (Table 10, Appendix).

Variability of the absolute weight of the heart in adult dogs was 24.9% (Latimer, 1961) and variability of the relative weight was 18.9%. According to the data of the same author, variability of the weight of the right ventricle was 25.5% and of the left ventricle was 25.0%; variability of the ratio of right ventricle to left ventricle was 11.2%. The relative weight of the ventricles (in relation to the weight of the whole heart) is the least variable (of the right, 7.5% and of the left, 6.5%).

Variability of the absolute weight of the heart in gerbils is 15.9 to 21.7% (Kramer, 1964) and the variability of the relative weight of the auricles (in relation to the whole heart) is 14.6 to 21.5%.

It can be said that the variability of the absolute weight of the heart for the majority of mammals is about 17 to 22%. Variability of the relative weight of the heart in all instances is a little less than the variability of the absolute weight. For example, the variability of absolute weight for the heart of moles is 16.7 to 44.3% and the variability of relative weight is only 14.4 to 26.5% (in the same population and in the same four groups). Similarly, variability of the weight of the heart in six groups of rabbits ranged from 7.8 to 19.4%, and variability of the relative weight in the same groups was 7.2 to 12.1%.

On the whole, it is clear that the variability of the relative weight of the heart is, on the average, about 13 to 16% (ranging from 6.7 to 26.9%).

As shown by the work of James (1960), characters of the structure of the heart and the arrangement of its blood vessels can be successfully studied also from the point of view of epigenetic polymorphism.

Urogenital system

The weight of the kidneys varies greatly and its variability is close to that of the weight for glands. The lowest known variability of kidney weight occurs in one of the groups of the hooded seal (*Cystophora cristata*), with a value of 11.9%; the highest known variability was 44.4% in *Histriophoca fasciata* of the Bering Sea and 43.1% in *Ondatra* (Schwartz, 1962). Within a population and species considerable differences are observed in the magnitude of variability, i.e., 15.9 to 29.0% in five samples of Greenland seals; 24.2 to 43.1% in two lines of muskrats (Schwartz, 1962); and 11.4 to 21.7% in five groups of hooded seals (Table 10, Appendix).

On an average, the variability of absolute weight of the kidneys is 20 to 25%.

Variability of relative weight of the kidneys is a little less. This is clearly seen in cases where a comparison of a single trait for one and the same population is possible. Variability of absolute weight of kidneys in rabbits (Latimer and Sawin, 1955) was 17.4 to 22.0%; variability of relative weight of kidneys in the same group was 11.3 to 19.5%. Variability of absolute weight of kidneys in moles was 13.3 to 34.0%; their relative weight variability was 15.1 to 19.3% (Fateev, 1962).

The same tendency is seen in the weight of kidneys for gerbils; 14.8 to 17.3% was the variability of absolute weight, and 13.1 to 16.5% the variability of relative weight (Kramer, 1964). On an average, the variablity of relative weight of kidneys is 15% (ranging from 11.4 to 25.4%).

There are some data available on the variability of kidney measurements. In large animals like cetaceans, it is difficult to weigh such organs as kidneys or lungs. Hence, we proposed a method of investigating the linear characteristics of these organs (Kleinenberg, Yablokov *et al.*, 1964). It appeared that the measurements of length and width of kidneys of white whales have a very stable variability (Table 19).

Table 19.   Variability of measurements of kidneys of white whales
(Delphinapterus leucas) **in adult males**

Measurement			$\bar{x} \pm s_{\bar{x}}$	$c.\, v. \pm s_{c.v.}$	n
Length of Kidneys:					
Right	..	..	44.0 ±0.86	7.3±1.37	14
Left	..	..	43.6 ±0.79	6.8±1.28	14
Width of kidneys:					
Right	..	..	16.6 ±0.41	9.3±1.76	14
Left	..	..	17.2 ±0.45	9.7±1.83	14
Length of body	..	..	374.6 ±7.1	7.1±1.35	14
Weight of kidneys:	..	..	4.73±0.42	38.9±6.3	19
Right			2.33±0.20	38.2±6.2	19
Left			2.38±0.22	39.9±6.5	19
Length of body	..	..	397.6 ±8.0	8.8±1.42	19

Variability of the weight of the ovaries in chinchillas (*Chinchilla laniger*) and rabbits (Latimer and Sawin, 1955) is 38.2 and 56 to 62.7% respectively. Variability of the relative weight of the ovaries in rabbits appears to be somewhat greater, 50 to 63.8%.

Variability of testis weight in the same populations is 29.5 and 31.4 to 38.7% respectively, and that of relative weight in rabbits, 26.5 to 29.7%.

The variability of absolute weight of the ovaries in adult gerbils of the same age, according to Kramer (1964) is 29.5±5.9%, and variability of relative weight of the testis in two samples of gerbils is 9.3 and 15.1%. Variability of absolute weight of the testis in different age groups of house mice (*Mus musculus*) ranges from 9 to 30% (eight samples, Suroviak, 1965).

From the data obtained during investigations on white whales, the variability of the width of the urinary bladder was 8.8%; of the length of the urinary bladder, 16.1%; of the length of the urethra, 14.8%; of the length of the ureter, 11.6 to 13.6%. On the whole, the variability of linear measurements of the urinary tract of white whales is near 11 to 13%.

The variability of measurements for the urinary bladder in gerbils ranges from 20.2 to 20.9% for length, and from 25.7 to 25.8% for width (Kramer, 1964).

The variability of the weight of the gall bladder in rabbits ranges from 17.4 to 31.5% (absolute weight) and 13.3 to 22.3% (relative weight).

The measurements of reproductive organs of white whales have shown that the variability of the length of the vagina is 20.3%; of the length of the uterine cervix, 31.1%; and of the length of the penis, 11.6%. These values are appreciably higher than usual ones for the linear measurements of organs, which possibly is explained by varying physiological states of the reproductive organs of the females at the time of investigation. This assumption is supported by the fact that the measurements of the penis agree with other values of linear measurements for the urogenital system.

The variability of the weight of the urinary bladder in rabbits (Latimer and Sawin, 1955) ranges from 30.3 to 43.0% for absolute weight, and 29.2 to 31.0% for relative weight.

Some general conclusions on the values of variability for parameters of the urogenital system in mammals are given below :

Measurements		$\bar{x}_{c.v.}$	$Lim_{c.v.}$
Weight of kidneys	..	20-25	11.4-44.4
Relative weight of kidneys	..	15	11.4-25.4
Size of kidneys	..	7-8	6.3-9.7
Weight of ovaries	..	40	29.5-62.7
Weight of testes	..	30	93.0-38.7
Size of urinary pathways	..	15	8.8-25.8
Size of genital organs	..		
Females	..	—	20.3-31.1
Males	..	—	11.6
Weight of uterus	..	—	30.3-43.0

From the summarized data presented, it can be seen that the variability of weights of organs of the urogenital system is like that of the glands, while the variability of linear measurements is close to the variability of organs in the skeletal and nervous system. Unfortunately, weights, which are characterized by very high values of variability, are usually used in the study of the urogenital system of mammals; this poses a difficulty for the correct evaluation of the significance of variability for these or other organs.

The fact that all possibilities of obtaining an exact quantitative analysis of this system have not yet been exhausted, is shown by the study of the morphology of spermatozoa by Hughes (1964). According to his data, the variability of the length of the head of spermatozoa in rat kangaroos (*Potorous tridactylus*) is only $4.4\pm0.4\%$.

General conclusions on the magnitude of variability for internal organs

In summarizing internal organs, the following picture is obtained (Table 20).

Table 20.   **Mean values of variability for internal organs and structures**

Organs	Variability of weight	Variability of linear measurements
Muscles ..	20 (11.7-27.9)	—
Brain ..	6-7	Less than 10 (number
Pancreas, hypophysis ..	25	of nerve cells)
Liver ..	25-30	
Adrenal ..	25-30	
Spleen ..	35-45	
Thyroid ..	30-50	
Intestine ..	15	8-12
Intestinal volume ..	10	
Lungs ..	20-30	
Trachea ..	—	5-7 (number of rings)
Hemoglobin ..	Usually about 10	
Number of erythrocytes ..	—	10-15
Heart ..	17-22	
Kidneys ..	20-25	7-8
Ovaries, testes ..	30-40	
Urinary and genital systems ..	—	15

As seen from the figures given, the minimum values of variability of weights are those of the nervous system and sense organs (5 to 10%), followed by the intestine (10 to 15%). The greatest variability of weight is characteristic of the thyroid gland, spleen, and testis and ovaries, 30 to 50%; variability of weight of muscles, and the majority of glands in the mammalian body, falls in the range of 20 to 30%.

The variability of linear measurements is more homogeneous. Variability of number of rings in the trachea, measurements of kidneys, and number of nerve cells in the cerebral cortex of adults is less than 10%; while length of intestine, number of erythrocytes, and measurements of the urogenital system give values from 10 to 15%.

These conclusions provide good material for researches in the field of population morphology for mammals, pointing to the potential prospect of their utilization for characterizing groups of linear measurements and weights of the intestine and parts of the nervous system.

Variability of Body Measurements and Weights

While comparing the variability of general measurements of the body, it is necessary to select some of the comparable measurements generally used during the investigations of the majority of mammals. This task has been made somewhat easy because most of the data given below are on rodents or insectivores, and their measurements generally comprise body length, tail length, length of foot, and length of ear. These very measurements are usually used during studies on other mammals. The pinnipeds are an exception; they have been compared among themselves according to specific measurements. The weight of the body has also been included in the general table (Table 1, Appendix).

The variability of body length in insectivores (Table 1a, Appendix) varies from 1.3% for *Sorex isodon* to 11.8% for *Sorex minutus* (Schwartz, 1960) and even up to 18.8% for *Neomys anomalurus* (St. Borowski and Dehnel, 1953). However, the average scope of variability is quite low—from 2 to 3% to 7 to 8%. Extensive data on certain species of insectivores allows a comparison of different groups belonging to one and the same population. Thus, an analysis of the work of St. Borowski and A. Dehnel (1953) and Zd. Puček (1956) shows that the variability of body length for 30 (!) groups of the common shrew *S. araneus* varies from 3.1 to 8.4% (Table 21); the variability of body length of *S. minutus* varies from 2.4 to 6.6% (data of 26 groups, Table 22); the variability of body length for 11 groups of *Neomys fodiens* ranges from 3.1 to 6.7% (Table 23).

On the whole, it is clear that the range of mean variability of body length in Insectivora is from 3 to 7%.

The variability of tail length in insectivores is, as a rule, higher than the variability of body length and ranges from 0.8 to 13% with an average of 5 to 8%; *Sorex araneus* is a single exception, from the data of Schwartz, 1960-1962 (Table 1, Appendix).

The variability of length of feet appears to be less than the variability for general body length in *Sorex araneus* (Schwartz, 1960), *Sorex minutus* (Dolgov, 1963; Schwartz, 1962), and the common hedgehog (Markov, 1957). The range of variation for the measurement in the groups investigated is from 1.7 to 8%, averaging about 3 to 4% (Table 1, Appendix).

The variability of ear length in Insectivora is appreciably high; 9.6% in the hedgehog according to G. Markov, 1957.

The variability of body weight for insectivores is much greater. Mean values and their range are considerably higher than for any body measurements—from 3.4 to 28.2% in *Sorex araneus*. On the average, this variability is higher than 10% and is usually about 12 to 13%, though in individual species the variability of weight is less than 10%; (for example, in three samples of the lesser shrew and two samples of the heterodont shrew,

Table 21.   Variability of body length for males and females of
Sorex araneus **in different years (Calculated from the**
data of Dehnel 1953, and Puček, 1956)

Month	$\bar{x}\pm s_{\bar{x}}$	σ	$c.v.\pm s_{c.v.}$	n	Remarks
April	71.0±0.44	3.03	4.3±0.43	48	
May	75.4±0.68	2.70	3.6±0.63	16	
June	74.4±0.68	3.61	4.9±0.65	28	
July	76.3±0.51	2.76	3.6±0.47	29	Born in 1946, caught in 1947.
August	76.5±0.55	3.06	4.0±0.51	31	
September	75.3±0.57	3.87	5.1±0.53	46	
October	73.0±0.75	3.61	4.9±0.73	23	
April	67.3±0.50	4.58	6.8±0.53	84	
May	73.3±0.63	3.71	5.1±0.60	35	
June	75.3±0.30	2.89	3.8±0.28	94	
July	75.3±0.44	3.32	4.4±0.41	57	Born in 1947, caught in 1948.
August	75.8±0.39	3.45	4.6±0.36	79	
September	75.6±0.37	3.17	4.2±0.35	73	
October	75.8±0.46	3.41	4.5±0.43	54	
June	78.3±0.51	3.86	4.9±0.48	58	
July	77.4±0.41	3.04	3.9±0.65	56	Born in 1948, caught in 1949.
August	76.0±0.54	4.62	6.07±0.28	74	
September	74.8±0.53	4.17	5.6±0.50	62	
July	68.4±1.31	5.56	8.4±1.36	19	
August	70.7±0.75	3.10	4.4±0.91	17	Born in 1949, caught in 1950.
September	70.7±1.21	4.54	6.4±1.21	14	
June	64.7±0.30	2.33	3.6±0.38	62	
July	62.8±0.25	2.80	4.5±0.28	124	Born in 1950, caught in 1951.
August	63.4±0.25	2.62	4.1±0.38	108	
September	63.1±0.38	2.60	4.1±0.42	47	
June	66.0±0.38	2.03	3.1±0.40	—	1954 (17)
December	64.4±1.10	4.78	7.4±1.20	19	
May	74.7±0.83	4.54	6.1±0.78	30	1955 (18)
September	72.9±0.69	3.77	5.17±0.67	30	

Table 22. Variability of body length of *Sorex minutus* **(Calculated from the data of Borowski and Dehnel, 1953)**

Month			$\bar{x} \pm s_{\bar{x}}$	σ	$c.\,v. \pm s_{c \cdot v.}$	n	Remarks
June	..	..	57.4±0.86	3.66	6.4±1.06	18	Born in 1946, caught in 1947.
July	..	..	58.1±0.58	3.03	5.2±0.71	17	
August	..	..	58.6±0.68	2.91	5.0±0.80	19	
September	..	..	48.4±0.69	3.15	6.5±1.00	21	Born in 1947, caught in 1947.
October	..	..	49.0±0.39	2.53	5.2±0.56	43	
June	..	..	58.5±0.19	1.19	3.4±0.23	111	Born in 1947, caught in 1948.
July	..	..	58.5±0.28	2.10	3.6±0.34	56	
August	..	..	58.6±0.36	2.22	3.8±0.42	41	
September	..	..	58.8±0.47	2.03	3.5±0.56	19	
June	..	..	51.4±0.49	1.83	3.6±0.67	14	Born in 1948, caught in 1948.
July	..	..	52.0±0.24	1.24	2.4±0.32	27	
August	..	..	50.7±0.32	1.87	3.7±0.45	34	
September	..	..	51.2±0.51	2.24	4.4±0.71	19	
June	..	..	59.1±0.45	3.22	5.4±0.54	51	Born in 1948, caught in 1949.
July	..	..	58.3±0.41	2.68	4.6±0.50	42	
August	..	..	59.1±0.41	2.56	4.3±0.49	39	
June	..	..	51.4±0.21	2.12	4.1±0.29	103	Born in 1949, caught in 1949.
July	..	..	51.4±0.20	2.27	4.4±0.27	133	
August	..	..	51.7±0.25	2.37	4.6±0.34	90	
September	..	..	51.5±0.27	2.26	4.4±0.38	68	
June	..	..	57.8±0.45	2.13	3.7±0.56	22	Born in 1949, caught in 1950.
June	..	..	52.4±0.34	2.45	4.7±0.46	51	Born in 1950, caught in 1950.
July	..	..	51.9±0.24	2.01	3.9±0.33	68	
August	..	..	51.6±0.21	2.00	3.9±0.29	93	
September	..	..	50.6±0.30	1.89	3.7±0.41	41	

and similarly, four samples of the common shrew studied by the same author, V. A. Dolgov—all from the Oksk collection).

In almost all instances when samples from six or more populations were investigated, the variability of body weight appeared to be of a very different character: from 8.7 to 28·2% in 23 samples of the common shrew (Table 24), from 9.0 to 14.9% in 13 samples of *Neomys fodiens* (Table 25), and from 5·7 to 23.8% in six samples of moles (Fateev, 1962).

On the whole, the variability of the body of insectivores is characterized by the following values :

Length			$\bar{x}_{c.v.}$	$Lim._{c.v.}$
Body	..	..	3-7	1.3-18.8
Tail	..	..	5-8	0.8-13
Foot	..	..	3-4	1.7-8.0
Ear	..	..	—	9.6
Body weight	..	..	12-15	3.4-28.2

Table 23. Variability of body length of *Neomys fodiens* **in different generations (Calculated from the data of Borowski and Dehnel, 1953)**

Month			$\bar{x} \pm s_{\bar{x}}$	σ	$c.v. \pm s_{c.v.}$	n	Remarks
June	..	..	86.1±1.04	5.09	5.9±0.85	24	
July	..	..	88.8±0.71	4.09	4.6±0.57	33	Born in 1948,
August	..	..	88.4±1.12	4.46	5.1±0.89	16	caught in 1949.
September	..	..	86.4±0.76	3.41	4.0±0.62	20	
August	..	..	80.8±0.67	2.92	3.6±0.60	18	
September	..	..	80.1±0.49	2.45	3.1±0.44	24	Born in 1949,
October	..	..	79.2±1.00	4.13	5.2±0.89	17	caught in 1949.
July	..	..	80.4±0.88	4.58	5.7±0.78	27	
August	..	..	80.6±1.05	5.44	6.7±0.92	27	Born in 1950,
September	..	..	80.3±0.91	4.57	5.7±0.80	25	caught in 1950.
October	..	..	81.9±0.75	4.47	5.5±0.64	36	

Data on the variability of body measurements for lagomorphs show that of the body measurements, the variability of body length is least (3.3 to 6.8%), and variability of ear length is greatest (13·8 to 15·1%) (Table 26).

Extensive research on the variability of body weight (in 47 samples of rabbits; Castle and Reed, 1936), allows one to determine that the upper limit of variability is similar in all groups investigated (about 16 to 20%), and the lower limit of variability ranges from 4·8% to 13·6%.

Table 24. Variability of body weight of *Sorex araneus* **in different years in one population (Calculated from the data of Borowski and Dehnel, 1953, and Puček, 1956)**

Month			$\bar{x} \pm s_{\bar{x}}$	σ	$c.\ v. \pm s_{c.v.}$	n	Remarks
August	..	..	7.05 ± 0.04	0.78	11.1 ± 0.44	322	
September	..	..	7.06 ± 0.07	0.89	12.6 ± 0.74	145	Born in 1947,
October	..	..	7.01 ± 0.11	0.95	13.6 ± 1.11	74	caught in 1948.
November	..	..	6.88 ± 0.13	0.73	10.6 ± 1.37	30	
June	..	..	10.7 ± 0.21	1.58	14.7 ± 1.35	59	
July	..	..	11.21 ± 0.15	1.10	9.8 ± 0.93	56	
August	..	..	11.02 ± 0.15	1.29	11.7 ± 0.96	75	Born in 1948,
September	..	..	9.85 ± 0.15	1.21	12.3 ± 1.10	62	caught in 1949.
October	..	..	9.22 ± 0.21	0.89	9.7 ± 1.61	18	
June	..	..	6.29 ± 0.05	0.67	10.7 ± 0.56	178	
July	..	..	6.57 ± 0.04	0.85	12.9 ± 0.41	504	
August	..	..	6.93 ± 0.04	0.90	13.0 ± 0.40	532	Born in 1949,
September	..	..	6.98 ± 0.09	0.93	13.3 ± 0.90	110	caught in 1950.
October	..	..	6.42 ± 0.15	0.86	13.4 ± 1.65	33	
June	..	..	9.92 ± 0.52	2.26	22.8 ± 3.70	19	
July	..	..	9.16 ± 0.59	2.58	28.2 ± 4.57	19	
August	..	..	9.82 ± 0.24	0.98	10.0 ± 1.71	17	Born in 1950,
September	..	..	9.45 ± 0.27	1.25	13.2 ± 1.99	22	caught in 1951.
October	..	..	8.71 ± 0.27	1.01	11.6 ± 2.19	14	
June	..	..	6.1 ± 0.10	0.53	8.7 ± 1.44	29	1954
December	..	..	6.4 ± 0.02	0.66	10.3 ± 1.72	18	
May	..	..	10.2 ± 0.27	1.47	14.4 ± 1.86	30	1955
September	..	..	9.8 ± 0.25	1.36	13.9 ± 1.79	30	

Table 25.   Variability of body weight of *Neomys fodiens* in different generations (Calculated from the data of Borowski and Dehnel, 1953)

Month	$\bar{x}\pm s_{\bar{x}}$	σ	$c.\ v.\pm s_{c.v.}$	n	Remarks
June	16.77 ± 0.36	1.72	10.3 ± 1.48	24	
July	16.98 ± 0.39	2.22	13.1 ± 1.61	33	Born in 1948,
August	16.97 ± 0.38	1.52	9.0 ± 1.53	16	found in 1949.
September	16.00 ± 0.40	1.79	11.2 ± 1.77	19	
August	12.64 ± 0.28	1.23	9.7 ± 1.62	18	
September	12.25 ± 0.37	1.83	14.9 ± 2.16	24	Born in 1949, found in 1949.
October	12.71 ± 0.39	1.62	12.8 ± 2.79	17	
June	11.38 ± 0.29	1.31	11.5 ± 1.78	21	
July	11.24 ± 0.29	1.49	13.3 ± 1.80	27	
August	12.19 ± 0.30	1.57	12.9 ± 1.75	27	Born in 1950,
September	12.54 ± 0.31	1.51	12.0 ± 1.74	24	found in 1950.
October	12.49 ± 0.30	1.80	14.4 ± 1.70	36	
November	13.32 ± 0.23	1.41	10.6 ± 1.21	38	

Table 26.   Variability of weights and body measurements of the black-tailed jack rabbit (*Lepus californicus*) (Original data by Bronson, 1958)

Trait	Males		Females	
	$\bar{x}\pm s_{\bar{x}}$	$c.\ v.\pm s_{c.v.}$	$\bar{x}\pm s_{\bar{x}}$	$c.\ v.\pm s_{c.v.}$
Body length	533.9 ± 1.5	4.2 ± 0.20	551.9 ± 1.7	4.5 ± 0.22
Ear length	107.0 ± 1.0	13.8 ± 0.66	106.4 ± 1.1	15.1 ± 0.73
Foot length	125.6 ± 1.0	11.8 ± 0.56	126.5 ± 1.1	12.7 ± 0.61
Tail length	73.1 ± 1.2	8.4 ± 1.16	78.1 ± 2.3	12.8 ± 2.1
Body weight	90.9 ± 0.6	9.8 ± 0.47	102.8 ± 0.8	11.3 ± 0.55

Detailed data on the variability of body measurements for the order Rodentia are available (Table 1, Appendix). In this table, data on the variability of body measurements and weight for more than four hundred different samples of 21 species are presented. Of course, the number of species studied is but a small part of the order, but these data no doubt reflect the real characteristics of variability for the group.

The range of variability of body length in rodents is great—from 0·5% in field voles (*Microtus agrestis*) to 12·9% in yellow-necked mice (*Apodemus flavicollis*) and even 21·0% for one of the 24 lines of laboratory mice.

However, in the majority of cases, the variability of body length ranges in different species of rodent from 3 or 4% to 6 or 8%, approaching 5% on the average (Table 1, Appendix).

Species with many samples can exhibit a large range of variability for body length even in one population of one species; (data on yellow-necked and forest mice of the genus *Peromyscus* and especially on mice of different populations under laboratory conditions). At the same time, natural data obtained on a number of samples in a species, show little scattering in values of coefficients of variation: 5.7 to 9.8% for field mice (*Apodemus sylvaticus*, eight samples); 3.7 to 5.6% for deermice (*Peromyscus leucopus*, Clark, 1940; eight samples); and 3.1 to 5.2% for nine samples of *P. maniculatus* (Table 27).

It is interesting to compare the three genera represented by the largest quantity of material on the variability of body length—*Apodemus, Peromyscus*, and *Mus*. It can be said confidently that the coefficients of variation for body length in the genus *Peromyscus* are the most stable and also the lowest—3.1 to 7.6% for 83 samples (Table 1, Appendix). The genus *Apodemus* takes second place in stability and value of variability, 5.1 to 12.9% for 34 samples. The genus *Mus* is characterized by the most scattered coefficients of variation—0.7 to 21.0% for 56 samples; very small as well as very high values of this index were found in the three families. Strictly speaking, such a comparison on the available material can only be conditional because most of the data on the genus *Mus* were based on experimental populations in laboratories, whereas the data for the other two genera were obtained from natural populations. But the differences between the genera *Peromyscus* and *Apodemus* are sufficiently clear so that a general conclusion can be drawn about the possible range of variability in the generic structure. In perusing the data on the variability of different taxa of pinnipeds (Chapter IV), such specificity in coefficients of variation is not observed. However, the data on pinnipeds are, at best, composed of 25 to 30 samples from each genus; hence, it is possible that if more extensive and homogeneous material could be studied, some weak patterns could be detected.

The values of variability for body dimensions of rodents approach 5% on the average, but the variability of tail length in all groups is, as a rule, high. The overall range of variability is also high: from 0.8% in one of the six samples of field voles studied, up to 26.5% in one of the samples of laboratory mice, and even up to 31.5% in one of the eight samples of field mice (Table 1, Appendix). On the average, it can be said that the magnitude of variability of tail length ranges from 8 to 10%. While analyzing the data on variability of tail length, it is interesting to see that the whole genus *Peromyscus* differs appreciably in having both constant and very low values of variability : 3.2 to 8.9%, averaging about 5%.

Table 27.   Variability of body length for some rodents

	$\bar{x} \pm s\bar{x}$	$c.\ v. \pm s_{c.v.}$	n	Remarks
		Apodemus flavicollis		
		(Original data from K. A. Adamczewska, 1959)		
August ..	100.0 ± 0.88	9.0 ± 0.63	103	Males
	97.0 ± 0.73	7.6 ± 0.53	102	Females
September ..	102.0 ± 0.48	6.7 ± 0.27	248	Males
	99.0 ± 0.40	6.8 ± 0.29	279	Females
October ..	103.6 ± 0.95	6.3 ± 0.65	46	Males
	96.6 ± 1.44	6.8 ± 0.83	33	Females
November ..	105.1 ± 0.64	5.7 ± 0.43	86	Males
	98.2 ± 0.70	6.4 ± 0.51	80	Females
		Peromyscus maniculatus		
		(Clark, 1940)		
Populations				
I	—	4.1 ± 0.46	—	Males and females of the same
II	—	4.2 ± 0.30	—	age produced in the labora-
III	—	6.2 ± 0.98	—	tory from one or two pairs
IV	—	4.2 ± 0.23	—	taken from each natural
V	—	4.5 ± 0.21	—	population
VI	—	5.1 ± 0.42	—	
VII	—	4.5 ± 0.24	—	
VIII	—	4.2 ± 0.49	—	
		P. maniculatus		
		(Original data according to Dice, 1938)		
Populations				
I	94.6 ± 0.38	4.3 ± 0.28	116	Males and females of about
II	94.6 ± 0.50	3.7 ± 0.37	49	one year of age
III	93.6 ± 0.50	5.2 ± 0.38	96	
IV	96.9 ± 0.41	3.6 ± 0.30	74	
V	93.3 ± 0.37	3.1 ± 0.28	61	
VI	93.5 ± 0.67	3.3 ± 0.51	22	
VII	95.8 ± 0.55	5.3 ± 0.41	84	
VIII	91.8 ± 1.26	4.6 ± 0.97	11	
IX	91.4 ± 0.75	3.9 ± 0.58	23	

The variability of absolute and relative tail length can be compared in two instances. The variability of absolute tail length in *P. maniculatus* (16 samples, Sumner, 1920) is 3.9 to 5.2%, while the variability of relative tail length is ostensibly lower, 3.2 to 4.8%. In the second instance, with house mice, the situation seems to be the reverse. The variability of absolute length of the tail in two samples ranges from 4.1 to 7.2%, whereas the variability of relative tail length in the same samples varies from 5.3 to 7.5% (calculated from Sumner, 1909).

During the analysis of data on variability of foot length in insectivores, a tendency was observed toward a lower variability for this trait than for body length. This feature is confirmed by more extensive data on rodents. The variability of foot length was not more than the variability of body length in a single group under study. On the whole, the variability of foot length ranges from 1.5 (for *Peromyscus maniculatus*) to 11.4% (for one out of five samples of bank voles, *Clethrionomys glareolus*, Table 1b, Appendix) and approaches 3 to 4% on the average. Even in the groups with many samples, a surprising similarity in variability of this trait in different samples is observed : 2.7 to 5.8% for 12 samples of yellow-necked mice (*Apodemus flavicollis*); 3.9 to 7.1% for another 12 samples of the same species; 3.5 to 6.9% for seven samples of red-backed voles (*Clethrionomys rutilus*); 2.5 to 3.6% for eight samples of *Peromyscus leucopus* (Clark, 1940); 2.5 to 4.1% for 22 samples of *P. maniculatus;* 1.5 to 3.1% and 2.5 to 4.0% for 16 and 30 samples respectively of the same species (Sumner, 1920; Clark, 1940).

Even in the genus *Mus,* where linear parameters vary so greatly, the variability of length of foot is very low and concentrated: 2.3 to 3.4% for four samples and 2.9 to 4.0% for six other samples (Table 1, Appendix).

A comparison of values of variability for ear length with values of variability for other body measurements seems to place the values for ear length between the low variability of foot length and the high variability of body length. The range of variability for this trait is quite restricted, from 2.7% (*Peromyscus maniculatus*) to 11.1% (*Clethrionomys glareolus*), with 5 to 6% as an average. In some cases, variability of ears is considerably less than variability of body length—for example, in some samples of deer-mice, *Peromyscus maniculatus,* and the house mouse (Table 1, Appendix). In other cases, variability of ear length is definitely higher than that of body length: common susliks (*Citellus citellus*), bank voles (*Clethrionomys glareolus*), and red-backed voles (*Clethrionomys rutilus*) (Table 1, Appendix). The genus *Peromyscus* has a low variability of ear length and other measurements.

The available data show that the variability for relative indices of body measurements of rodents is considerably higher than that of the similar absolute indices. Thus the variability of ear length in the house mouse varies from 2.7 to 4.4% and the variability of relative length of ear in the same sample varies from 4.9 to 6.1% (calculated from Sumner's data, 1909). A similar situation arises in the variability of foot length in the same samples; the variability of relative values appears to be considerably higher than the variability of absolute values.

As a rule, the variability of body weight in rodents is always higher

than the variability of linear measurements.   There is considerable variation in this trait in comparable samples and specimens : from 1.4% in
lemmings (*Lagurus lagurus*) (calculations from the data of A. I. Kryl'tsov'a,
1957) to 30.9% in a natural population of *Mus musculus* (estimated from
the data of J. Dynowskii, 1963).   The average values, inasmuch as they
can be determined from quite different types of data, approach 13 to 14%.
According to the data of K. Adamczewska (1959), J. L. Carmon *et al.*
(1963), F. Sumner (1909), and W. E. Castle *et al.* (1936), the variability among
individual groups belonging to a species is quite compact; for example,
in yellow-necked mice, 15.1 to 24.6% for eight samples; in house mice,
6.3 to 8.5% for eight samples, and 9.8 to 12.0% for another eight samples.
In other cases, within the limits of one species, very scattered values of
coefficients of variation for body weights are encountered: for example,
4.1 to 9.7% in 14 samples of field voles (*Microtus agrestis*) according to John
Newson and D. Chitty (1962); 8.9 to 28.2% for 84 samples of rats of different ages (King, 1923); 5.6 to 22.7% for 24 samples of house mice under
laboratory conditions, calculated from data by L. Law (1938); 1.4 to 12.0%
for nine samples of lemming (*L. lagurus*), calculated from data by A. I.
Kryl'tsov'a (1957).

On the whole, variability of measurements and body weight in rodents
can be defined according to the following mean values :

	$\bar{x}_{c.v.}$	$Lim_{c.v.}$
Body length	5	0.5-21.0
Tail length	8-10	0.8-26.5
Foot length	3-4	1.5-11.4
Ear length	5-6	2.7-11.1
Body weight	12-15	1.4-30.9

The last order for which there are extensive data on variability of
body measurements is the order Pinnipedia (Table 1, Appendix).   Data
on eight species, comprising more than 95 samples, showed that the variability is similar to that of the orders Rodentia and Insectivora; it is thought
that such tendencies are characteristic for each order as a whole.

Very detailed work is available for seals on the variability of body
length.   From the data presented in Table 1, it is seen that the variability
of body length varies quite widely, from 1.4 in one of the samples of *Pusa
hispida* to 18.7% in one of the two samples of the Baikal seal (*Pusa sibirica*).

Considerable variations in values of variability are not only found
among species, but even within species among different samples: 8.1 to
18.7% in Baikal seals, 3.1 to 7.4% in Greenland seals, 2.4 to 8.4% in Caspian seals, etc.   A group of four samples of *Pusa hispida* in the eastern seas
forms an exception, with 7.5 to 9.3%.   It is possible that such heterogeneous

coefficients of variation for length of pinnipeds result from insufficient homogeneity of age in the samples (see Chapter IV, the section on variability by age), a characteristic failing in the study of all large mammals with high longevity.

All other body measurements of pinnipeds differ from the measurements of terrestrial mammals and cannot be compared with them. It may be noted that the variability of all the rest of the body measurements studied in pinnipeds, appears to be higher than the corresponding values for body length—a situation which is similar to the one present in other orders of mammals.

The variability of body weight in Pinnipedia fluctuates greatly, from 5.0 to 11.3%; the last figure concerns the variability of weight of embryos in fur seals (Scheffer, 1962) and cannot characterize the variability of adult animals. Some data on adult animals show that the variability of body weight for Greenland seals is nearly 10%.

The variability of body length of ungulates and carnivores appears to be close to the variability for other orders studied, averaging about 3 to 5% (Table 1b). The variability of body length in a comparatively large group of sables (*Martes zibellina*) ranges from 1.7 to 3.8% in ten samples (calculated from the data of Kuznetsov, 1941a). Similarly, the variability of captive foxes is also low although it is for various types: from 2.3 to 7.9% (Fateev *et al.*, 1961). The variability of body measurements for mule deer (*Odocoileus hemionus*) appears to be low, 1.7 to 5.5% in 13 samples of different ages (Anderson *et al.*, 1965; Klein, 1964). The variability of body length for horned cattle is also not very great, 2.4 to 4.0% (Tsalkin, 1960).

The variability of body length of white whales (*Delphinapterus leucas*) does not differ from that of other mammals, ranging from 3.4 to 12.4% in 14 samples.

The weight of sheep, even under artificial conditions of rearing, does not exceed 20.7% in 39 samples (Popova, 1941). The variability of body weight for two populations of *Odocoileus hemionus* in 12 samples which controlled age and sex, varied from 8.9 to 34.7% (averaging about 16.5%) (Anderson *et al.*, 1965), and from 10.4 to 12.8% in a red deer population (*Cervus elaphus*) (Brna, 1964). This speaks for a considerable constancy of this trait in the main representatives of this group. The variability of body weight in captive foxes varied from 5.4 to 19.4% (Fateev *et al.*, 1961).

Before summarizing the data obtained on the variability of body weight for primates, it is to be remembered that the variability of body measurements probably ranges within the same limits. Instead of dwelling on the vast amount of anthropological data, I will turn to the recently published material of D. A. Zhdanov and B. A. Nikityuk (1964) on the variability of body height in a large number of Muscovites of similar age;

for 17 groups, the variability is very stable, from 3.0 to 3.8%. On the other hand, it is known (Schultz, 1926) that the variability of tail length in 11 species of higher primates ranged from 6.6 (in *Callithrix jacchus*) to 30.2% (in *Symphalangus syndactylus*).

The data presented on the variability of body parameters in various orders of mammals confirm some of the general findings of the researches on variability in the best studied orders, insectivores and rodents. These results are given below :

A. The variability of foot length in terrestrial mammals has the lowest value (body length in aquatic mammals) and then, in the ascending order of variability—body length, tail length, and finally, ear length.[5] The variability of body weight is higher than the variability of any linear body measurement;

B. Differences in variability are observed in all traits among different species and genera and, similarly, among different populations within one species. However, in a number of cases a specific magnitude of variability can be detected for a genus;

C. As a rule, the variability for relative values appears to be not lower, and in a number of cases higher, than the variability of absolute values for the same traits;

D. It seems that for all terrestrial mammals, the following values of variability, which are absolute values of variability (in percentages) in a sufficiently homogeneous sample, are characteristic:

Body lengh	..	..	..	4-6
Tail length	..	..	..	5-10
Foot length	..	..	..	3-4
Ear length	..	..	..	5-6
Body weight	..	..	..	12-15

E. A slightly higher variability of body measurements is characteristic of Pinnipedia and Cetacea.

General Character of Variability of Different Systems and Body Measurements of Mammals

After an inevitably short perusal of the variability of the basic system of organs and body measurements for different mammals, an attempt to

---

[5] Though variability of ear length appears to be one of the most variable of linear measurements, it appears that the range of variation in the variability value of this trait is quite constant. It is found that in many instances the minimum coefficient of variation is twice as small as the maximum one: for body length, it is 20 times; for body weight, 12 times; for tail length 9 times; for foot length, 7 times; and for ear length, only 2 times!

define the variability of different systems of individual organs is possible (Table 28).

Table 28. Average values of variability of structures, organs and body measurements of mammals

Organ, structure, measurement	Mean values of coefficients of variation			Remarks
	Linear	Meristic	Weight	
Hair	3-8	15	20	
Vibrissae	—	5-10	—	In cetaceans, nearly 20
Skin .	10-20	—	10-15	
Skull	4-6	—	15	
Teeth	5-10	10	—	Higher in molars and canines
Post-cranial skeleton	3-5	1	10-15	
Muscles	—	—	20	Relative weight is lower
Brain	—	10	6-7	
Glands	—	—	20-30	Spleen, thyroid, and ovary up to 50%
Gut	10	—	15	
Lungs, trachea	—	5-7	20-30	
Blood, heart	10	15	20	Relative weight of heart, 15
	Hemo-globin	Erythro-cytes	Heart	
Urogenital	10-15	—	20-35	
Body measurements	5-10	—	12-15	

It is important to emphasize again that the data presented in the Table must be looked upon as guidelines (greater details of the systems are given above). These guidelines show that the variability for organs of different systems and different measurable parameters within a system of organs differ considerably from each other. This is a trivial result. However, such a pattern of variability gives rise to conclusions which will change some widely-held viewpoints.

All organs can be divided provisionally into large groups in regard to variability.

The variability of organs in the first group is equal to, or less than, 10%; that for the second group is 10 to 15%; and that of the third group is at least 15%. The first group comprises (in order of ascending variability):

1. Linear measurements of the post-cranial skeleton,
2. Linear measurements of the skull,
3. Number of rings in the trachea,
4. Absolute weight of the brain,

    5.   Linear measurements of hair,
    6.   Linear measurements of teeth,
    7.   Linear measurements of the body,
    8.   Number of vibrissae.

The second group[6] consists of:

    1.   Linear measurements of the digestive tract,
    2.   Quantity of hemoglobin in the blood,
    3.   Number of elements in the post-cranial skeleton,
    4.   Number of elements in the nervous system.

The third group comprises:

    1.   Weight of the skin,
    2.   Weight of the post-cranial skeleton,
    3.   Body weight,
    4.   Linear measurements of the urogenital system,
    5.   Number of hairs,
    6.   Number of erythrocytes,
    7.   Linear measurements of the skin structures,
    8.   Weight of the skull,
    9.   Weight of muscles and heart, and similarly, weight of hair,
  10.   Weight and volume of the digestive tract,
  11.   Weight of lungs, stomach, the majority of glands, parts of the urogenital system,
  12.   Weight of the salivary gland, the thyroid gland, and the ovary.

    The list of organs in the first group should help in reconsidering to some extent the field and laboratory methods of researches on the variability of mammals. Out of all traits given in the first list, usually only two groups are studied—measurements of the skull and the body. The constant and sufficiently simple data like number of rings in the trachea, characters of the hair, and above all, the characters of the post-cranial skeleton (which are easily analyzed) have not yet attracted enough attention.

    Further, one of the objects of study in the field of population morphology of mammals is to collect data for determining limits and parameters of variability of all groups of systems for a single purpose. It is possible that in the near future it will be feasible to determine the degree of ecological plasticity in a species and the magnitude of its specialization with the help of a "Map of Variability" for one or another group of mammals. But, for the time being, it is important to carry out the study of animal ecology and the micro-evolutionary process of a population, with the help of an exact determination of the place of the population under study according to the location of an appropriate organ on the scale of variability.

    [6] The order of placement of traits in the second and third groups is affected at times by insufficiency of data.

Chapter III

AN ANALYSIS OF VARIABILITY OF POPULATIONS AT
DIFFERENT TAXONOMIC LEVELS WITHIN AN ORDER

For an evaluation of variability from the viewpoint of evolution, it is important to know the characteristics of variability for the same organs in representatives of different phylogenetically compact groups as well as in representatives of ecologically compact and diverse sets of species. During such an investigation, the necessity arises for a gradual comparison of variability for different populations within a species, within a genus, within a family, etc.

Data on the variability of traits in three populations of Greenland seals (*Pagophilus groenlandicus*) in the East Atlantic allow one to examine the question of variability for populations within a species. This same approach is useful in an examination of data on the morphology of ringed seals (*Pusa hispida*).

In the genus *Pusa*, a comparison of variability for the Baikal, Caspian, and ringed seals permits the comparison of variability within a genus.

A comparison of variability of traits for the Greenland seal and *Histriophoca fasciata* allows one to look into the problem of variability in related genera, and a comparison of variability between the genus of common seals (*Phoca*) and that of ringed seals (*Pusa*) helps to survey the problems of variability between less similar genera.

A comparison of variability of common seals and Greenland seals allows one to examine the variability of different groups in one subfamily, whereas a comparison of variability of the hooded seal (*Cystophora cristata*), bearded seal (*Erignathus barbatus*), and common seal permits one to examine the variability of different subfamilies. Finally, from the data on fur seals (*Callorhinus*), it is possible to compare two basic trunks in the order

Pinnipedia—the earless and the eared seals.

Thus, from this example of pinnipeds, a comparison of variability for groups within an order on different taxonomic levels seems possible.

Comparison of Variability of Populations within a Species

Variability of traits for three populations of Greenland seals of the East Atlantic

Greenland seals formed the very basis of the hunting industry in the East until recently. Three different places of hunting (White Sea, Yan-Maien region, and the Newfoundland region; Figure 23) facilitated the idea that three distinct populations of this animal existed; however, the degree of inter-dependence among these populations, and their origin, remained unknown until recently (Chapskii, 1961; Yablokov, 1962, 1963, 1963c; Sergeant, 1963). At the same time, it is necessary to know the degree of inter-dependence exactly for a rational utilization of stocks because all the populations intermix at places of summer migration and constitution of each group is uncertain. Hence, the industrial exploitation of each of the three regions should perhaps be different.

It must be noted that the variability of morphological structures did not attract the attention of researchers working on Greenland seals until our work was carried out. A comparison of absolute indices was done before [Khuzin, 1963; Yablokov, 1963; Yablokov and Serzhent (Sergeant), 1963; Yablokov and Klevezal', 1964; Yablokov and Etin, 1965; Kleinenberg *et al.*, 1965; and others], and hence instead of discussing these aspects here again, a direct analysis of indices of variability like the standard deviation and coefficient of variation may be made.

Comparison of the standard deviation. The standard deviation of a population (sigma) shows the degree of inclination for portions of a cumulative distribution curve characterizing the value of the trait and, it being a dimensioned number, allows a comparison of only those traits with similar absolute measurements (Chapter I). This situation creates an interest in comparing these indices for different populations with sex and age controlled.

The first stage of such a comparison is to compare the absolute values of the standard deviation for different populations. A graphical representation of the values of the standard deviation for a number of traits other than the skull, and also for the skull, in adult males and females of different populations, is given in Figures 10 and 11 respectively.

The values of the standard deviation are very close to each other in all populations for all the traits studied; individual variation does not exhibit a particular tendency.

Considering that the disposition of traits on the abscissa is arbitrary, we can continue to combine these traits within each group arbitrarily. (It is because the disposition of traits on the abscissa is arbitrary that it is not possible at times to join the points indicating value of sigmas; a histogram would have been the only solution. But, in view of the great

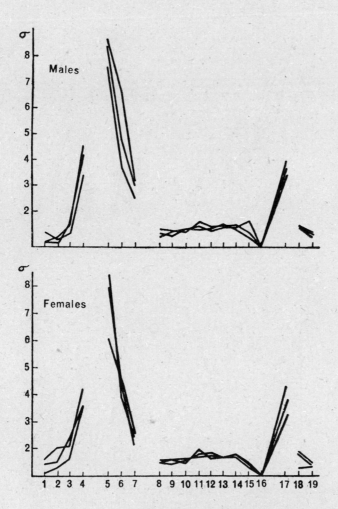

Figure 10.   A comparison of absolute values of the standard deviation for traits other than the skull in three populations of the Greenland seal (*Pagophilus groenlandicus*):

   On the abscissa: 1—*Number of sternal ribs;* 2—*Number of asternal ribs;* 3—*Number of caudal vertebrae;* 4—*Number of tracheal rings;* 5—*Body length;* 6—*Distance from the anus to the navel;* 7—*Distance from the anus to the opening of the urethra;* 8-16—*Number of vibrissae of lip according to rows;* 17—*Usual number of lip vibrissae;* 18—*Number of vibrissae of eyes;* 19—*Number of vibrissae of the nose.*

ease for examining the situation which the curve affords, and considering the conventional conditions of its construction, it is appropriate to use it.)

One of the methods for combining traits, where a gradual decrease of the standard deviation value for skull traits of the White Sea population has been taken as a basis, is shown in Figure 12. Specific conclusions can be derived from the analysis of standard deviations for males in this figure (Figure 12).

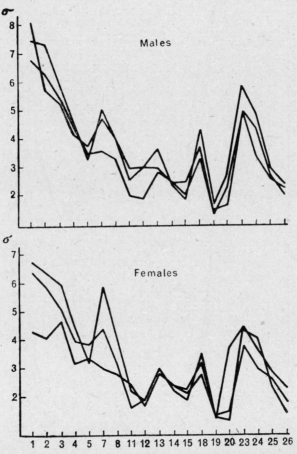

Figure 11. A comparison of absolute values of the standard deviation of skull measurements for three populations of the Greenland seal:

On the abscissa: 1—*Condylobasal length of skull;* 2—*Length of base of skull;* 3—*Length from occiput to nose;* 4—*Length of palate;* 5—*Length of upper tooth row;* 7—*Width of mastoids;* 8—*Width of brain cavity;* 11—*Width of palate;* 12—*Width of snout;* 13—*Width of occipital condyles;* 14—*Length of right auditory bulla;* 15—*Width of right auditory bulla;* 18—*Length of right nasal bone;* 19—*Width of nasal bone;* 20—*Width between eyes;* 23—*Length of right lower jaw;* 24—*Height of right lower jaw;* 25—*Length of tooth row of lower jaw;* 26—*Height of lower jaw behind molars.*

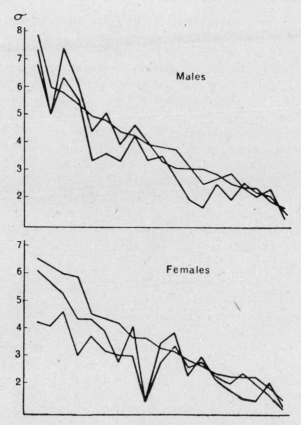

Figure 12. A comparison of absolute values of the standard deviation for skull measurements in three populations of the Greenland seal; skull measurements of the White Sea population are given along the abscissa in order of decreasing values of sigma.

1. The general features of the values of the standard deviation coincide in all three populations;

2. There is a similarity of behavior in the values of the standard deviation for the populations from the Yan-Maien region and the Newfoundland region but less when comparing either of these populations with the White Sea population. It is seen from Figure 12 that the change of the value of the standard deviation in the regions of Yan-Maien and Newfoundland is absolutely synchronized from the second trait to the ninth; and

3. The absolute value of standard deviation for the Newfoundland population is, as a rule, less.

An analysis of the transformed graph of the sigma values for skull measurements of females, leads to additional observations. The absolute values for the population of the White Sea exceed those of the Yan-Maien region (in 13 measurements out of 19). The main similarities between the Yan-Maien and Newfoundland populations in the configuration of the curves are from the third trait to the fifteenth inclusively.

And so, on the basis of an analysis of absolute values of the standard deviation for the traits under study, a comment should be made on: 1) the similarity in the variability of traits for all populations, 2) the great similarity between the populations of Yan-Maien and Newfoundland region, and 3) the comparatively lower variability for a number of traits in the Newfoundland population than for the other two populations.

For a further analysis of the standard deviation, let us use the method proposed by S. R. Zarapkin (1934-1939) to analyze the differences among populations of insectivores. The Zarapkin method consists of a comparison of the relative values of standard deviation. Any population can be taken as the standard: in the present researches, the White Sea population has been taken as the standard:

$$\left(\frac{\sigma \text{ White Sea}}{\sigma \text{ Yan-Maien Region}} \text{ and } \frac{\sigma \text{ White Sea}}{\sigma \text{ Newfoundland Region}} \right)$$

No specific regularity for either males or females is observed when comparing the standard deviation of absolute values, nor during the comparison of relative values of sigma obtained from the initial perusal of the curves (Figures 13 and 14). In such cases, one main factor is outstanding and that is a great common character in all populations. It is clearly seen that the majority of the ratios are above one; this reveals the comparatively greater magnitude of sigmas for the White Sea population than for similar populations.

The relative values of sigma can be arranged in a different way. This method helps to compare sigmas not only of the organs within a system but even organs of any measurements, because the values with which we are dealing now are concrete.

So it is possible to propose one additional step in the formalization which would lead to better future comparisons. While comparing relative as well as absolute values of the standard deviation, a leveling of all traits takes place[1]; hence it is possible that it just does not matter whether

---

[1] Dissenting voices (among morphologists) are generally raised against mathematical analysis of data, especially since the biological value of a trait is removed. Of course, normal functioning of the nervous system or even only the brain, is more important for an animal than completeness of dental system or having the full number of phalanges in fingers, etc.; secondly, selection in nature proceeds on "important" as well as "unimportant" organs and structures and the main process in effective selection will probably be the same in all instances. It has again to be understood that the concept of importance of organ is to a great extent relative and, as a rule, the majority of "unimportant" organs become vitally important at a particular moment of life.

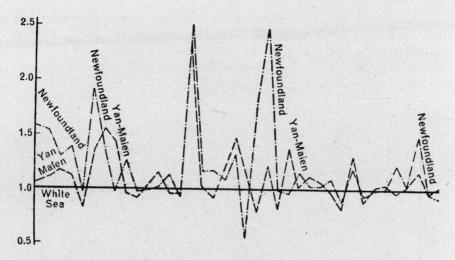

Figure 13. A comparison of relative values of the standard deviation for traits in
females of the Greenland seal for three populations (Sigma values of the
White Sea population have been taken as standard).

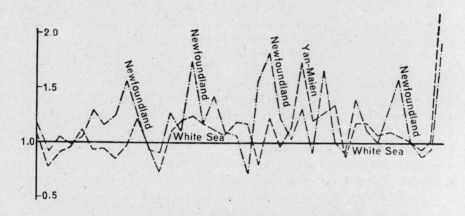

Figure 14. A comparison of relative values of the standard deviation for traits in
males of the Greenland seal for three populations (Sigma values of the
White Sea population have been taken as standard).

sigma of the Newfoundland region coincides on the graph with the position
of sigma for the same trait from the region of Yan-Maien. And if this is
so, there is a possibility of formulating two independent courses, gradually
declining in a sigma value, in relation to the White Sea population whose
sigma is taken as a unit.

An analysis of such curves as seen in Figure 15 is not difficult and the conclusions are very specific. The population in the Yan-Maien region (II) is much nearer to the White Sea population, and the New-foundland population (I) is significantly farther away in respect to standard deviation values for the traits studied.

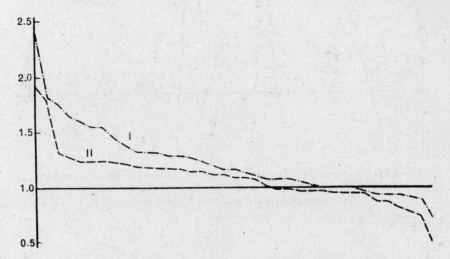

Figure 15.   A comparison of relative values of the standard deviation
in three populations of the Greenland seal.
(Explanation given in the text).

An analysis of the distribution of the standard deviation values, unlike the analysis of absolute indices characterizing this or that organ or structure, does not lead to any ecological conclusions, but makes the conclusions about the degree of closeness of populations in respect to the traits studied, more understandable and sound.   This conclusion is based not on the variability value of one trait or of a small group of functionally homogeneous traits, but of all the characteristics of morphological structures.

Comparison of coefficients of variation.   The second stage of the analysis is to analyze the variability of different populations expressed in coeffi-cients of variation.

As a start, let us see how the magnitude of the coefficient of variation is distributed for different groups of the traits studied (Figures 16 and 17).   In a number of cases, the values of the coefficient of variation may differ significantly, but in fact they are determined by very accidental reasons, as, for example, during the comparison of variability in the last (eighth and ninth) lines of vibrissae on the lip region.   When the arith-metic means for the traits are very small, an increase of a tenth or even a hundredth changes the value of the coefficient of variation.   Naturally, a great biological importance could not be attached to such deviations.[2] It is more important to take into consideration any general tendency for increase or decrease of variability in the given trait.

When approaching the data on variability of adult males and females

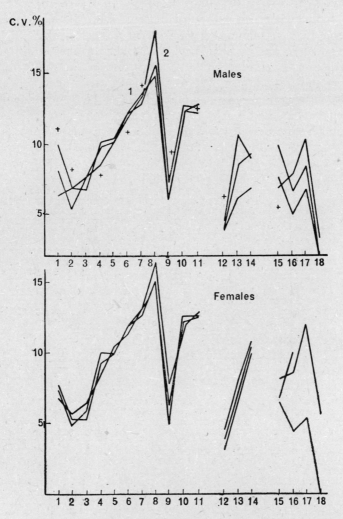

Figure 16. Coefficient of variation for number of vibrissae (1-11), body measurements (12-14), number of tracheal rings (15), caudal vertebrae (16), and ribs (17-18) for three populations of the Greenland seal (*Pagophilus groenlandicus*) and ("+" symbols) the ribbon seal (*Histriophoca fasciata*).

[2] In the given example, it happens because the nature of the distribution of number of vibrissae in the last lines does not coincide with the formula of the normal distribution.

in the previously studied populations of the Greenland seal with such criteria, it becomes necessary first of all to note the great homogeneity in the behavior of the coefficient of variation in a comparison of the variability of vibrissae, body, and skull measurements, and other traits.

Some traits, whose variability deviates from the common tendencies, come to light at once on the above background. In males these traits are low variability of number of vibrissae in the first lip line of the New-foundland population, reduction of variability in the measurements of "anal orifice to opening of urethra," reduction of variability in number of rings of the trachea from White Sea males, and the interrelations of variability for length and width of nasal bone in the Newfoundland region (measurements 18-19). In females, the deviations are expressed by a sharply increased variability in the number of caudal vertebrae for the populations of the White Sea and Yan-Maien regions, and similarly, by increased variability of mastoid width and braincase width of the skull (measurements 7-8) in the White Sea population.

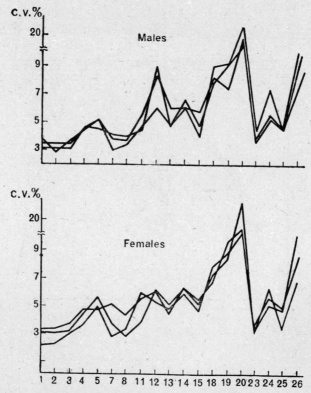

Figure 17.   Coefficients of variation for skull measurements of three populations of the Greenland seal. For measurement legend, see Figure 11.

An analysis of the factual data shows that the majority of the deviations noted can be explained. The differences regarding the variability of vibrissae need not be considered because the sampling error of the coefficients of variation generally masks the discrepancies. The fact that during the collection of White Sea data, observations of adult males were totally lacking, and only a mixed catch (consisting mainly of new-borns) was available for comparison, could have caused the lower variability observed for the number of tracheal rings. The reported tendency in arrangement of traits for other populations with regard to variability (Figure 16) allows one to assume that in an adequate sample, the variability in number of vibrissae for the White Sea population would be about 10%. The difference in the magnitude of skull measurements, determining the deviation of those coefficients of variation which affect the general trends, also seems to be quite insignificant when expressed in qualitative terms. As a result, the sharp decline in variability for only one trait in the body of males in the White Sea remains as real. This difference cannot be explained on the basis of insufficiently representative sampling and small differences in the variability, and thus it attains a special importance if it is compared with less detectable similar situations arising during the comparison of variability of these very traits in females (Figure 15).

A comparatively sharp increase in variability of number of caudal vertebrae over the variability of rings in the trachea, is observed in the White Sea females. This is unlike the situation for females from the Newfoundland region and, to a lesser extent, from the Yan-Maien region. Data on females are sufficiently large and are trustworthy. In other words, during the analysis of variability of males, instead of a comparatively increased variability of number of tracheal rings, now a large variability of number of caudal vertebrae in comparison with the variability of number of tracheal rings draws attention. Whatever the case may be, the difference in variability for these traits in the populations studied is evident, and the coincidence in behavior of coefficients of variation in the samples of males and females makes this difference more convincing.

The next step in the analysis of variability is to analyze the factual results obtained in conformity with the appearance of simple relationships among parameters (Chapter V). This method offers a possibility of posing questions about the specific effect of evolutionary factors on the structure under study in the event of an occurrence of sharp deviations from the usual relationships.

A good correlation between the number of vibrissae and the coefficient of variation was observed in all the groups where lip vibrissae were studied. Minimum variability is characteristic for the first four lines of lip vibrissae, when the number of vibrissae is maximum. Maximum variability is characteristic of the vibrissae in the last lines, where the number of vibrissae is minimum (Table 29). The maximum number of vibrissae is in the lip group, from 45 to 49 (in different samples, Table 3, Appendix). Variability in number of vibrissae in this group is quite low, from 5 to 8%, in different groups according to growth and sex for all populations. The eye group averages three vibrissae and variability ranges from 26 to 37%; compared to the variability of number of vibrissae in the lip group, it is sharply increased (which corresponds with the already determined elementary regularity—Chapter V). In the last group—nasal vibrissae—there are generally two vibrissae and the coefficient of variation ranges from 14 to 35%; this is, in six cases out of nine, less than for the eye group. On the whole, it seems that the group of nasal vibrissae is controlled by factors of different intensity than the group of eye vibrissae.

In all the female samples, the distribution of magnitude of variability for body measurements corresponds well with the elementary regularity :

Table 29. Variability in number of vibrissae of new-born males of the Greenland seal from the Newfoundland region (1963)

$\bar{x}$	Row			$\bar{x} \pm s_{\bar{x}}$	σ	$c.\ v. \pm s_{c.v.}$	n
				Lip vibrissae			
1st	From the right	..	..	7.16±0.07	0.37	5.1± 0.66	30
	From the left	..	..	7.30±0.09	0.47	6.4± 0.85	29
2nd	From the right	..	..	9.7 ±0.12	0.64	6.6± 0.85	30
	From the left	..	..	9.9 ±0.07	0.37	3.7± 0.49	29
3rd	From the right	..	..	9.5 ±0.09	0.50	5.3± 0.68	30
	From the left	..	..	9.4 ±0.09	0.50	5.3± 0.69	30
4th	From the right	..	..	8.5 ±0.12	0.67	7.9± 1.02	30
	From the left	..	..	8.8 ±0.11	0.60	6.8± 0.88	30
5th	From the right	..	..	6.3 ±0.10	0.54	8.6± 1.11	30
	From the left	..	..	6.5 ±0.11	0.62	9.5± 1.23	30
6th	From the right	..	..	3.7 ±0.15	0.82	22.2± 2.86	30
	From the left	..	..	4.1 ±0.10	0.54	13.2± 1.70	30
7th	From the right	..	..	2.0 ±0.12	0.63	31.5± 4.07	30
	From the left	..	..	1.9 ±0.14	0.79	41.6± 5.37	30
8th	From the right	..	..	0.40±0.09	0.52	130.0±16.78	30
	From the left	..	..	0.30±0.08	0.46	153.3±19.79	30
	All rows : right	..	..	47.6 ±0.51	2.81	5.9± 0.76	30
	From the left	..	..	48.2 ±0.51	2.73	5.7± 0.74	30
				Eye vibrissae			
Right and left		..	..	2.60±0.10	0.77	29.6± 2.80	56
				Nose vibrissae			
Right and left		..	..	1.39±0.07	0.49	35.3 ±3.33	56

the greater the magnitude of all measurements, the less the variability. This situation is true for the sample of males from the Newfoundland and Yan-Maien regions but not for the sample from the White Sea region (see Figure 16).

In all the samples, the variability of the number of asternal ribs (mean number of ribs, 4-5 on eash side) is considerably higher than the variability of the number of sternal ribs (mean number, ten pairs) without exception; this corresponds well with the elementary regularity.

The interrelations of magnitude of variability for different skull measurements have been examined in detail in Figure 18, where all the measurements have been arranged on the abscissa in decreasing order of absolute value. If there is conformity with the elementary regularity, the coefficients of variation for these measurements must increase monotically from left to right. It may be said that overall, in both males and females, such a tendency appears sufficiently clear though many deviations make the picture more complex. As seen from Figure 18a, the first nine measurements of the skull in males quite exactly follow the general regularity; the coefficient of variation for these measurements increases from 3 to 5% in all the three populations (the deviations in the curves are insignificant and may be attributed to errors of measurements). Measurement 24 (height of lower jaw) sharply increases the variability in the population of the White Sea and measurement 25 (length of tooth row of the lower jaw) has decreased variability in all the three populations. In the first instance, the differences between the White Sea population and the other two populations have been expressed markedly; this is confirmed by the fact that data for right and left measurements of the White Sea population give exactly the same picture. Similarly, the decline of variability in the length of the tooth row of the lower jaw in all groups of males undoubtedly exists. It can be proposed with confidence that this phenomenon is dependent on the adaptive value of the given trait, i.e., length of tooth row is a very important trait, which can determine the possibility of catching, holding, and killing the prey (Yablokov, 1958). It is significant that the variability of the length of the tooth row of the lower jaw practically coincides with the variability of the length of the tooth row of the upper jaw measurement 5).

For a further analysis of variability of skull traits, let us use the concept of "variability drift", which is discussed in Chapter V.

A sharp rise in variability as a result of such analysis is seen for measurement 18 in all populations (length of nasal bone), measurement 9 (width of jugal bone) for the White Sea sample, and to a lesser degree for measurement 26 (height of lower jaw near the base of canines) for the Newfoundland sample. A considerably reduced variability seems to be characteristic of width of palate (measurement 11), length and width of

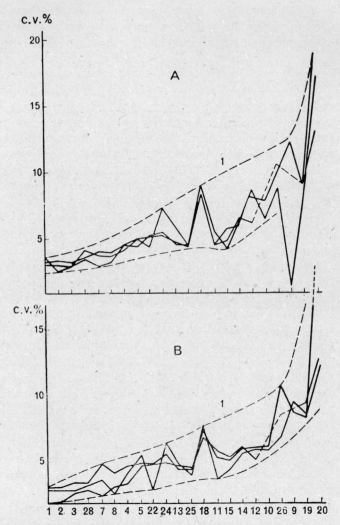

Figure 18. Magnitude of coefficients of variation for skull measurements of different populations of the Greenland seal, arranged in order of decreasing absolute values of the measurements. For the identity of the measurements, see Figure 11: *A—males; B—females; 1—limit of the variability "drift".*

right auditory bulla (measurements 14-15) for all populations, width of nares (measurement 10), and width of jugal bone (measurement 9) for the Yan-Maien sample. Although, in the absence of detailed functional analysis, it is difficult to say anything about the functional significance of the palate (though it is undoubtedly true that this trait must have a specific relation to the feeding habits), for measurements of the auditory bulla such analysis directly shows that the growth of this structure is directly relevant to hearing. The obvious decline in variability of measurements of the bulla in all populations cannot be compared with the absence of sexual dimorphism, especially in regard to the same trait noted during the investigations of absolute values characterizing the skull of Greenland seals (Yablokov and Serzhent, 1963). The decrease in variability of the width of the nostrils is more characteristic of the populations in the Yan-Maien region than of the other populations, though there is a tendency in the White Sea population also (Figure 15a). Finally, the sharp decline in variability values for the width of the jugal bone in the Yan-Maien sample cannot be explained yet, but it is suspicious that conflicting tendencies in the appearance of this trait arise in different populations. Does this situation represent the genuinely different vectors of selection in different groups ?

The last measurement to exhibit deviation in variability from the mean values is the width of the nasal bones (19); it behaves similarly in all the comparable populations. It seems impossible to correlate the low variability of this trait with a great functional importance; it is known that the nasal bone is a sufficiently variable trait—in respect of form and of asymmetry—and these variations can be examined adequately by the methods of study of epigenetic polymorphism. But a comparison of the variability of the width of the nasal bones with the variability of their length allows one to put forward another explanation of the low variability of the first trait. The variability of the width of the nasal bones is controlled by factors similar in scope to those which are active during the regulation of the character of primary importance. Other instances of similarity in variability for two quantitatively different but functionally homogeneous traits (length of upper and lower tooth rows in the skull of males), have already been cited in this chapter and Chapter I.

While commencing the analysis of variability of traits in the skull of females (Figure 18b), the common tendencies of variability for the sample of both sexes may be noted in the beginning: the general dependence of variability on regulation of characters of primary importance, resulting in an increase in variability with a reduction in size of the trait. On this background, a number of deviations fall in the framework of "variability drift" on one side; they correspond to those that have already been indicated in the variability of traits for the skull of males, and on the other hand, there are some traits specific for females.

In the first eight measurements (1, 2, 3, 23, 7, 8, 4, 5) some differences in the values of variability for different populations could be observed; the variability of all these traits in the White Sea population is somewhat higher while the variability of the same traits in the population in the Newfoundland region is lower. The variability values of the Yan-Maien region are between those of the other two populations in the sample of males, which confirms the above conclusion to a certain extent (Figure 18a). A somewhat higher level of variability for all traits is observed in the White Sea samples; it continues almost up to the midpoint of the curve (up to measurement 24 inclusive). In this case, if we consider the absolute values, the White Sea population is quite close to the rest of the populations; any individual instance does not matter, but the general trend is important.

In females, a sharp decline in variability of the length of the tooth row of the lower jaw (measurement 25) in all populations is observed exactly as in males. The variability is surprisingly similar for all the populations under investigation. As increase in the variability for length of the nasal bones (measurement 18) and a decrease in the variability of width of the nasal bones (measurement 19), which brings the variability values of these traits quite close (despite the large difference in their absolute measurements), is observed here in the same way as in males. The variability of the auditory bulla is reduced in females just as it is in males. In the sample of females, the variability of width of the nostrils (measurement 10) also seems to be decreased; this tendency was likewise observed in males (Figure 18a). Among the differences noticed in the variability of females are the homogeneous behavior of the coefficient of variation for jugal bones (measurement 9) and (from the traits specific for individual populations) the increase in variability of width of the lower jaw behind the canines (measurement 26) for the sample made in the White Sea region, and generally scattered coefficients of variation for different traits of the Yan-Maien population.

Thus, as a result of analyzing the coefficient of variation, data characterizing the unity of the general characteristics of variability for all three populations emerge on the one hand, while the existence of specific differences among all three of the population groups studied is revealed on the other. This has already been confirmed by the observations made during the analysis of concrete traits and standard deviations. However, the most significant result of the study of variability of structures in this case is the possibility of an analysis of micro-evolution. The study of variability allows one to investigate comparable populations not only from a static but also from a dynamic point of view, while making an effort to understand the peculiarities in the development of their morphological nature.

A separation in this way of the most and of the least variable traits may seem to be the key to understanding recondite ecological characteristics of animals with regard to specific relations with the environment. This is a factor overlooked in other methods of investigation.

Variability of traits for three groups of ringed seals from the Okhotsk sea

Comparison of standard deviation values.[3] With the experience obtained from a comparison of the absolute values of standard deviation for various traits in different populations of the Greenland seal, let us examine the interrelationship of sigma values for skull measurements of male ringed seals (*Pusa hispida*) from three regions where they are hunted. As seen from Figure 19, the values of the standard deviation for all three populations are very close to each other. For a visual appraisal, this figure can be compared with Figure 12, in which the interrelationships of absolute values of sigma for three populations of Greenland seal in the North Atlantic have been depicted through the same methods. There is no doubt that all the three samples of Okhotsk seals are considerably closer to each other than the samples from different populations of the Greenland seal.

But further analysis of the data on the Okhotsk seal indicates that there is a greater similarity between samples from the Gizhigin Inlet and the region of Shantar Islands, than between these samples and the sample from the region of the Taui Inlet. This similarity is especially evident

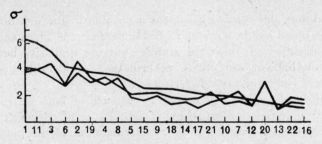

Figure 19. A comparison of absolute values of the standard deviation for skull measurements of males of the ringed seal (*Pusa hispida*) from three regions of the Okhotsk Sea. Measured traits are arranged in order of decreasing value of sigma for the Tauisk sample.

in the beginning of the curve (traits 1, 11, and 6) and at the end of the curve (traits 12, 20, 13, 22, and 16). In these traits not only the mode of behavior but also the absolute values of sigma coincide. In addition, it can be seen that the values of sigma in the Taui sample are as a rule somewhat higher than the corresponding values of sigma for other samples (with the exception of four traits for the Shantar sample and five traits for the Gizhigin sample).

---

[3] The works of G. A. Fedoseev and A. V. Yablokov (1965) and G. A. Fedoseev (1964, 1965) have been devoted to a characterization of the ringed seals of the Okhotsk Sea and of other Far East seas.

A comparison of the samples regarding relative values of sigma allows one to confirm the already derived conclusions about the relatively great closeness between the Shantar and Gizhigin samples (Figure 20).

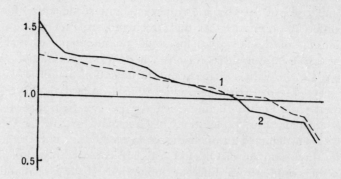

Figure 20.   A comparison of relative values of the standard deviation for skull measurements of males of the ringed seal from three regions of the Okhotsk Sea (The sigma value of the Taui sample has been taken as standard):
1—*Gizhigin sample;* 2—*Shantar sample.*

In addition, this comparison opens a possibility (through determining the area occupied by the curves) to conclude that the Shantar sample is somewhat dissimilar to the Taui sample (but the similarity between the Shantar and Gizhigin samples is, nevertheless, considerably higher than that between Taui and any other sample).

Comparison of coefficients of variation. Absence of data on traits other than the skull makes a comparison of coefficients of variation for these samples rather easy, reducing it to a determination of the magnitude of variability in accordance with absolute size. Let us analyze the variability drift by arranging the skull traits in decreasing order of their absolute values (Figure 21). Our samples are small in number (9, 12, and 30 individuals) and hence, despite some corrections made through a special formula in the calculations of statistics for such small samples (Rokitskii, 1961), it is not worth relying upon some of the values of the coefficients of variation thus obtained. During analysis, attention should be given mainly to the places where the curves coincide; in other words, it is more promising to carry out an ecological analysis of the data than to show the degree of similarity or difference in the magnitude of variability among samples.

The increase in the variability of measurement 11 (length of nasal bones) in all three samples is immediately noticeable. It is interesting that, as in the Greenland seal, the variability for length of the nasal bones corresponds well with the variability for the width of these bones

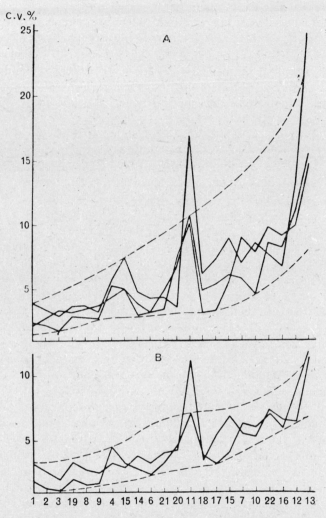

Figures 21-22. Variability of skull measurements for (*A*) males, and (*B*) females of the ringed seal from different regions of the Okhotsk Sea. Traits have been arranged in decreasing order of the absolute value of the measurements:

1—*Condylobasal length;* 2—*Occiput-to-nose length;* 3—*Snout-basicranium length;* 4—*Length of palate;* 5—*Width of palate;* 6—*Length of upper tooth row;* 7—*Width of snout;* 8—*Mastoid width;* 9—*Width of braincase;* 10—*Width of nasals;* 11—*Length of nasal bones;* 12—*Width of nasal bones;* 13—*Width between orbits;* 14—*Condyle width;* 15—*Height of skull;* 16—*Width of jugal bone;* 17—*Length of auditory bulla;* 18—*Width of auditory bulla;* 19—*Length of lower jaw;* 20—*Height of lower jaw;* 21—*Length of lower tooth row;* 22—*Height of lower jaw at the end of the tooth row.*

(measurement 12); this provides a basis for concluding that this pair of traits is not dominated by other characters of primary importance.

In the Okhotsk seal, the variability of measurements of the auditory bulla and length of the lower tooth row (measurements 17, 18, and 21 respectively), condyle width (14), and height of skull (15), seem to be low in all three samples. A tendency toward low variability of brain width (9) is also observed. It is interesting that the low variability for parameters of the auditory bullae and the length of tooth rows was likewise observed in the Greenland seal.

On the whole, the variability of the sample from the Taui region seems to be higher and characterized by sharper fluctuation between the upper and lower boundaries of the drift.[4]

If the values of variability characteristic of females are transferred to a graph, then it will be observed that all the basic peaks of variability correspond in males and females (Figure 22). Some other tendencies not noticed before appear, i.e., an increase in the variability of measurement 22 (height of lower jaw at the end of the tooth row); increases in variability of length of palate (measurement 4) and length of lower jaw (19); and similarly, a decrease in variability of occiput-to-nose length (2). Such coincidence in basic tendencies in the variability of traits in males and females and between males of different groups is quite significant. It confirms the correctness of concluding that there is a relatively fixed amount of variability, from an evolutionary point of view, and allows one to use this material for a functional analysis of structure.

An analysis of population morphology for three different groups of ringed seals from the Okhotsk Sea (Fedoseev and Yablokov, 1965) showed a similarity among populations in absolute measurements for almost all the traits studied, as well as in the standard deviations and in coefficients of variation. If the results obtained are compared, then a specific conclusion about the similar underlying morphological processes between these three groups of Okhotsk seals and three populations of Greenland seals can be drawn.

At the same time, the results obtained throw light on the presence of specific differences between comparable samples. These differences give, in general, a basis for recognizing a similarity between samples from the Gizhigin Inlet and the region of the Shantarsk Islands, and the relative independence of the Taui sample.

---

[4] Such sharp fluctuations in the magnitude of variability correspond well with a few characteristics observed especially in the Taui region, and show on the other hand that the general characteristics in variability of traits can be determined even on very small samples.

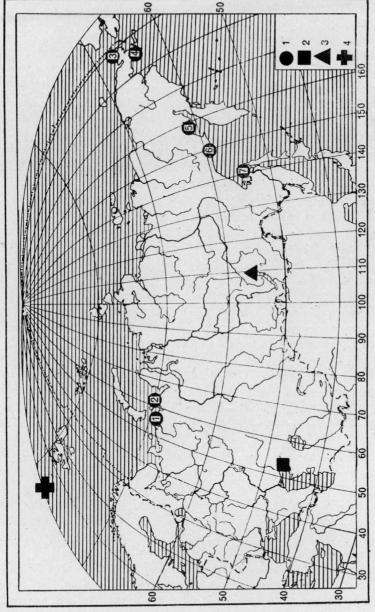

Figure 23. Places of collection of data on (*1*) ringed seal, (*2*) Caspian seal, (*3*) Baikal seal, and (*4*) Greenland seal.

Variability of ringed seals of the northern and far-east seas of the USSR

A comparison of different groups of ringed seals from the Okhotsk Sea revealed the heterogeneity of the morphological characters of the major populations of seals in that region. But some large populations of ringed seals, isolated to a greater extent than the ones studied in the Okhotsk Sea, live in almost all the northern and far-east seas of the USSR. It is interesting to compare these populations, geographically separated from each other by thousands of kilometers, existing in quite different climatic conditions, and characterized by ecological differences (Fedoseev, 1965). Using data on the ringed seal from Okhotsk (three groups), Bering, Chukchi,[5] Kara, and Pechora Seas (Figure 23), let us examine first the characters of the territorially close populations in the Kara, Pechora, Chukchi, and Bering Seas, and then carry out a comparison of all populations.

Unfortunately, there are not sufficient comparable data from the region of the Kara Sea in our collection; all that we have is a good group of skulls, whereas data from the Pechora Sea have been specially collected for the purpose.

The standard deviation.   First of all, let us compare the absolute values of the standard deviation for skull-size measurements in the ringed seal from different populations (Figure 24) by arranging all the values in descending order for one population. The population from the Pechora Sea has been taken as the standard in Figure 24.

It is clear from the figure that there are many general tendencies in the distribution of standard deviations for skull measurements of females from different populations. If the concept of "variability drift" is applied to these curves, then it seems that the data on the Pechora seal give the mean line of this drift, especially in the second part of the whole figure beginning from measurements 4 and 15. It may also be noticed that the absolute value of sigma for the Taui, Chukchi, and Kara samples is considerably less than for the Pechora sample. A considerable similarity can also be noticed in the relative and absolute values for measurements 6, 11, 4, 19, 3, 18, and 22 in the samples from the Bering and Chukchi Seas and in the two samples from the Okhotsk Sea. The distribution of standard deviations in the majority of cases for the Kara sample similarly coincide with the rest of the samples.

The next step is an analysis of the relative values of the standard deviations. The Chukchi population has been taken as a standard for this analysis because it has a central geographical situation (see Figure 23).

The distribution of the relative values of sigma for traits in the order

---

[5] The values of standard deviations are given by G. A. Fedoseev for the Chukchi and Bering Seas.

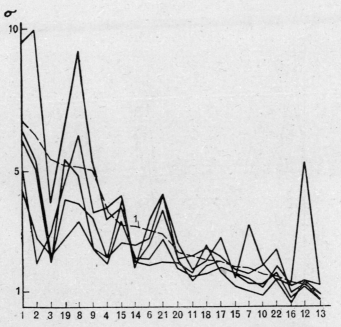

Figure 24. A comparison of the standard deviations for skull measurements of females of the ringed seal from different populations:
1—*Pechora population.* Explanation in the text.

arranged in the table of skull measurements, does not allow one to analyze the picture obtained because of its complexity (Figure 25). Hence, let us analyze the standard deviation values by the method proposed above, using the proper order.

It is seen from Figure 26 that the relative values of sigma for two populations, namely the Bering Sea (minimum) and the Taui region (maximum), differ clearly from the others. However, the sigma values for the Taui population are closest to those of the Chukchi population, which has been taken as a standard in the graph. If the degree of deviation for different populations from the Chukchi sample is determined simply by measuring the area which is occupied by the sigma values of the populations studied, it seems that our samples arrange themselves in the following order: Chukchi, Taui, Shantarsk, Pechora, Kara, and Bering Seas.

For further analysis, it should be noted that not all the natural populations of seals on the shores of Europe and Asia have been investigated. There are no data on the East Siberian, Laptev, or Kamchatka seals. Because of this, it is not possible to draw any final conclusions, but the data obtained allow one to review the interrelationship of neighboring populations.

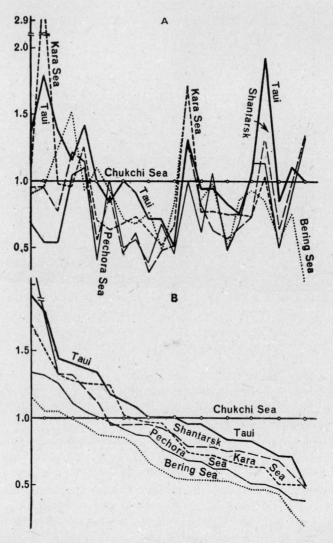

Figures 25-26. A comparison of relative values of the standard deviation for skull measurements for females of the ringed seal from different populations [Sigma value of the Chukchi population has been taken as a basis in the (*A*) usual and (*B*) regulated manner.   See text]:

1—*Chukchi Sea;* 2—*Taui;* 3—*Shantarsk;* 4—*Pechora Sea;* 5—*Kara Sea;* 6—*Bering Sea.*

An analysis of the relative values of sigma (using the graph) points to the similarity of the characters in the Taui Inlet and Shantar populations, to the similarity of the characters in the Kara and Pechora populations, and to the sharp differences between the Bering Sea and Chukchi populations.

A comparison of the arithmetic means calculated for all the relative values of sigma for the skull gives similar results $\left(\frac{\bar{x}\sigma_a}{\sigma_b} \pm \frac{s\bar{x}\sigma_a}{\sigma_b} \right)$:

Bering Sea	.. ..	0.69 ± 0.17
Pechora Sea	.. ..	0.79 ± 0.07
Shantar region	.. ..	0.95 ± 0.06
Kara Sea	.. ..	0.98 ± 0.11
Taui region	.. ..	1.07 ± 0.21

$$t_{\text{Bering Sea}-\text{Taui region}} = 1.44$$

It is not difficult to notice that with regard to the mean values of relative sigma our samples could be arranged in an order close to the one in the graph : Bering Sea, Pechora Sea, Shantar/Kara, Chukchi, and Taui.

The coefficient of variation. A comparison of variability of traits for different populations of the ringed seal is depicted graphically in Figure 27, where dependence of the magnitude of coefficients of variation on the

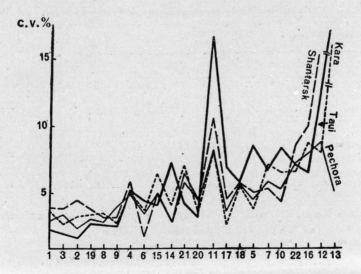

Figure 27. A comparison of values of coefficients of variation for skull measurements for males of Shantar, Kara, Taui, Pechora populations of the ringed seal. For identification of measurements, see Figure 22.

absolute value of the trait has been examined. Some specific tendencies are brought out more clearly in the usual "variability drift" than during the analysis of only Okhotsk seals; these are as follows :

A very high variability of length of the nasal bones(11), a high variability of length of the palate (4) and length of the lower tooth row (21);

A low variability in measurements of the auditory bulla (17), width of palate (5), height of skull (14), and mastoid width (6).

There are some local characteristics in the variability of measurements for certain samples : increased variability for large measurements of the skull in the Kara sample, sharp fluctuations in the magnitude of variability in the Taui sample, and a low variability for traits having small absolute values in the Pechora sample.

The variability of body measurements coincides well with the elementary regularities in three populations, but it is not so in the Pechora sample. This may be "chance," because the sample of females shows a sharp increase in variability with a decrease in the value of the measurement (Table 30).

The Pechora sample stands out because of the strange reduction in the magnitude of variability in the number of caudal vertebrae (which can be explained, perhaps, by an insufficiently exact analysis of material due to the difficult conditions of winter trade in seals).

The ecological significance of many of the above-mentioned deviations from the mean values of variability, has already been discussed.

Table 30. Variability of body measurements of Pechora ringed seal, 1962

Measurement	$\bar{x} \pm s_{\bar{x}}$	σ	$c.\,v. \pm s_{c.v.}$	n	$t\male\female$
Adult males					
Body length ..	118.5 ± 1.44	10.8	9.1 ± 0.86	56	$+2.92$
Measurement : Anus to navel ..	33.1 ± 0.38	2.92	8.8 ± 0.84	55	$+3.12$
Measurement : Anus to penis ..	18.2 ± 0.22	1.61	8.8 ± 1.55	54	—
Adult females					
Body length ..	112.1 ± 1.65	9.5	8.5 ± 1.04	33	—
Measurement : Anus to navel ..	30.7 ± 0.66	3.81	12.3 ± 1.51	33	—
Measurement between nipples ..	8.0 ± 0.36	2.13	26.6 ± 3	—	—

Certain Results from the Study of Variability of Characters for Different Populations of One Species

The comparison of morphological statistics for different samples (of different age and sex) allowed us not only to establish differences for specific traits between individual samples (for which the usual methods of comparative anatomy would also do), but also to determine the degree of these differences. This method made it possible to determine that sexual dimorphism is expressed in different degrees among young and adult animals and in a characteristic manner in each population of the species [Yablokov, 1963; Yablokov and Serzhent (Sergeant), 1963; Fedoseev, 1965; and others].

While studying the characters themselves of traits in different samples and determining the general characteristics of the groups of different sexes and ages, as well as for the individual populations as a whole, it was possible on the basis of knowing the quantitative characters of traits to make hypotheses also on differences in the ecology of the groups under study or to determine prospective lines of ecological research.

It seemed possible to draw conclusions from the magnitudes of differences about the similarities or dissimilarities of populations as a whole, though this conclusion is based only on the absolute values of traits and can only be made in a most general form (Fedoseev and Yablokov, 1965).

The second method of study especially examined above—the study of regularities in the distribution of standard deviations of traits—permitted us to obtain data directly characterizing the degree of similarity between the populations under study and the sub-samples according to age and sex. It is important to emphasize that the use of the relative value of sigma allowed us to compare populations not by individual traits but by a complex of quite heterogeneous traits, which is close to the question raised by R. Sokal and P. Sneath (1963). The third way of studying population morphology examined in this work—the study of variability expressed in coefficients of variation—opens up a new possibility of obtaining the ecological significance of a trait, by briefly characterizing the degree of dependence and the relationship of the trait to effective evolutionary (ecological and genetical) factors. The study of coefficients of variation confirms the existence of a well-developed sexual dimorphism in various structures, and shows varying degrees of dimorphism in various populations; here is a similarity with the study of the absolute magnitudes of traits. However, this similarity is superficial because variability expressed in coefficients of variation seems to be an index of rather common peculiarities, regularities, and interrelations among various age-sex groups within a population, and also an index of the relations by which the whole population is situated in the biogeocenose.

Finally, on the basis of analyzing variability of traits expressed in coefficients of variation, and also analyzing standard deviations, it seems possible to say a little (based on a comparison of a number of traits) about the degree of difference and similarity of different populations where age and sex have been considered.

All the three methods used, while characterizing a population from different points of view, allow its consideration as a dynamic unit consisting of complex and at times conflicting parameters (in different age and sex groups) and differing, on the whole, from other populations of the species.

It is important to emphasize the possibility of conflicting tendencies arising in the degree of differences among populations for individual traits. For example, the greatest differences in color are observed between the White Sea and the Yan-Maien populations of the Greenland seal, and for many other traits, maximum differences are found between the New-foundland and White Sea populations. Such divergence in the degree of dissimilarity for different traits may indicate their evolutionary indepen-dence and the presence of specific differential methods for the effectiveness of evolutionary factors. This conclusion is confirmed by a comparative analysis of variability for certain traits in different populations of the ringed seal.

In reviewing the study of population morphology for different popula-tions within a species, the following statements can be advanced:

Different populations within a species exhibit a high degree of similarity with regard to absolute values for traits as well as in the nature of variability for individual structures and groups of traits;

On the background of the similarities noted, it can be seen that real differences in variability exist between individual age-sex groups on the one hand and between individual populations on the other;

The range of characters for the morphological structures of the populations studied seems to be always insufficiently wide and differen-tiated to reliably distinguish populations on the basis of the absolute magnitude of individual morphological traits. For this, it is better to consider the general trends in the variability of the traits (by the method of comparing the values of standard deviation and coefficients of variation).

Comparison of Variability of Population within a Genus

While studying the variability of a single population, attention has to be given (to a greater degree than during the study of variability of different populations within a species), not to the absolute values charac-terizing the various traits of each of the species, but to indices of variability (like standard deviation and coefficient of variation).

A comparison of variability of traits within a genus has been carried out below, taking a genus of seals (*Pusa*) as an example, including the Caspian (*P. caspica*), Baikal (*P. sibirica*), and ringed (*P. hispida*) seals.

Comparison of the standard deviations. As observed from the comparison of standard deviation (Figure 28), a great similarity was noticed for the respective values of different species, and it is difficult to determine the degree of their divergence. The comparison of relative values of standard

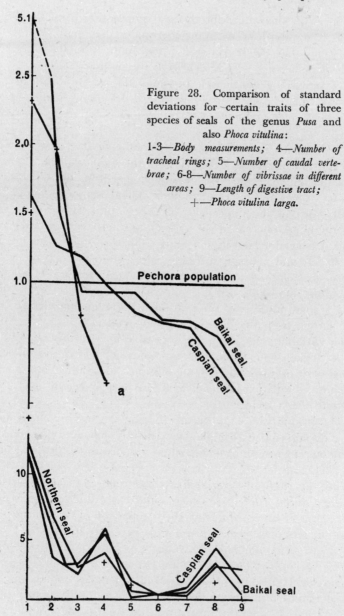

Figure 28. Comparison of standard deviations for certain traits of three species of seals of the genus *Pusa* and also *Phoca vitulina*:
1-3—*Body measurements;* 4—*Number of tracheal rings;* 5—*Number of caudal vertebrae;* 6-8—*Number of vibrissae in different areas;* 9—*Length of digestive tract;*
+—*Phoca vitulina larga.*

Figure 29. Comparison of relative values of standard deviations for certain traits of three species of seals of the genus *Pusa* and (a) *Phoca vitulina.* For identification of measurements, see Figure 20.

deviations with the values for the seal population from the Pechora Sea taken as a standard, seems somewhat more divergent (Figure 29).

It seems that the Baikal seal differs more from the ringed seal than from the Caspian seal. It is seen from the figure that a sharply deviating value of sigma for gut length provides the greatest difference. Other comparisons of relative values of standard deviations, comprising 30 traits (mainly skull measurements) for three species of seals, are depicted in Figure 30.

It is well seen in the figure (30) that the sigma values of the Pechora seal (taken as a unit) are rather close to the sigma values of other populations of the same species, i.e., the ringed seal from the Okhotsk Sea, and the sigma values of the Caspian and Baikal seals are more different—especially seen in the upper half of the graph. However, it is difficult to say anything concrete about the relative degree of difference between the Baikal, ringed, and Caspian seals from this figure because the curves of the Baikal and Caspian seals pass very close to each other.

Comparison of coefficients of variation. A comparison of coefficients of variation for non-skull traits is shown in Figure 31. Notwithstanding the rather small number of traits studied, the following specific conclusions can be drawn from the data already available :

The variability for all traits is similar in all samples;

The Baikal and Caspian seals seem to be similar in variability, differing only in variability of the number of caudal vertebrae, whereas the Pechora population of the ringed seal has a usually lower variability (in six out of ten traits);

The variability in number of vibrissae is the only single measurable trait which corresponds completely with the elementary regularities. For body measurements, these regularities are disrupted (rather considerably in the ringed seal);

With regard to the variability for number of caudal vertebrae, all the species differ from each other, but these differences do not exceed those which were observed during the comparison of variability for different populations within a species (See Figures 16 and 26).

The last situation appears to be very important in determining the place of variability analysis in the general framework of population morphology. If the range of variability among populations within a species does not differ from the range of variability among populations of different species, then this means that the analysis of variability expressed in coefficients of variation with an aim to determining the degree of differences among populations seems to be considerably less valuable for comparisons among species. Let us add a conclusion from the analysis of standard deviations: while comparing the standard deviations of different species, the results obtained seem to be less

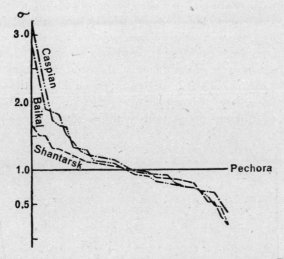

Figure 30. Comparison of relative values of standard deviations for certain traits of the seal *Pusa*. Explanation in the text.

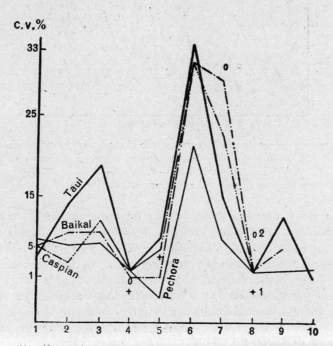

Figure 31. Comparison of variation coefficients of non-skull measurements within the genera of (*Pusa*), *Phoca* (*1*) and *Histriophoca* (*2*): Legend to measurements as in Figure 28. 10—*asternal ribs*.

significant than when populations are compared within a species.

However, this conclusion holds good only with regard to an analysis of variability done with the aim of determining the degree of differences among populations and species. In studying biological characteristics of populations, the analysis of coefficients of variation seems to be useful even while comparing different species. For an illustration of this situation, let us analyze the magnitude of coefficients of variation for skull measurements of different populations within a genus of seals (Figure 32).

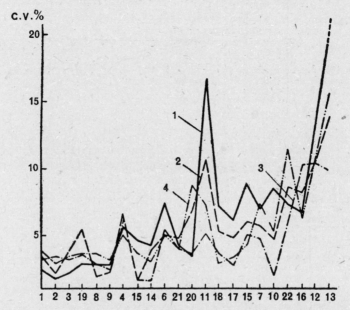

Figure 32.   A comparison of the magnitude of coefficients of variation for skull measurements in females within the seal genus *Pusa*:
1—*Taui;* 2—*Shantar;* 3—*Baikal;* 4—*Caspian.*
For identification of measurements, see Figure 22.

During the comparison of variability for these measurements, it must be remembered that the samples from the Caspian and Baikal are very small and the probability of obtaining insufficiently characteristic values is great. Hence, in the analysis, attention must be paid to the general character of the curves and not to the sharp fluctuations in the variability value of one or the other trait. The following features come to light:

1. An increase in variability for length of palate (measurement 4) is correlated in a surprisingly homogeneous manner with regard to coefficients of variation for all the samples compared;

2. A reduction in the variability of the length of the auditory bulla (measurement 17);

3. A reduction in the variability of the width of the nostrils (measurement 10), except for the Taui sample of the ringed seal.

The several agreements in the variability of traits provide a basis for a conclusion about the magnitude of the variation.

A study of the coefficients of variation with regard to differences among groups seems to be rather ineffective for a comparison of different species within a genus because the coefficients of variation for different species may not differ more than those of different populations of the same species. The species as a whole, perhaps, does not possess characteristic values of coefficients of variation; these appear to be very mobile traits, easily changed depending upon the conditions of existence for a population in the biogeocenose.

On the other hand, an analysis of coefficients of variation in a study of different species, carried out not to determine their degree of systemic differences but to understand the regulation of their development in definite conditions of existence, seems not only promising but also the only effective means of analysis at present. An analysis of coefficients of variation for three species of seals showed their rather great similarity in all the habitats of the genus. Such a situation is perhaps determined mainly by a sufficiently similar relationship of each species to evolutionary factors. In all instances where coefficients of variation of similar value are observed, the evolutionary control acts with approximately similar force on homologous traits.

An analysis of variability for traits seems to be even more important than the direct analysis of morphological characters for the study of tendencies in the evolution of each species. By knowing that the number of vibrissae in one species of seal is a little more than in another, we can only make an assumption about the role of specific conditions existing in the past which may have brought out such differences. But the fact of similar variability in these structures for various species shows that at present these structures have an identical relationship to evolutionary factors.

Comparison of Variability of Populations of Closely Related Genera

The characteristics of variability of species belonging to different but closely related genera, could be seen while comparing representatives of the seal genus *Pusa* and of the common seal (*Phoca vitulina*), which is systemically close to it; for a long time both groups of seals were placed in one genus. Interest in such a comparison is greater because the morphological characteristics of the Okhotsk seal, common seal, and other species and populations of seals living in the same body of water (Okhotsk Sea), as well as those living in the very different conditions of other waters like the Arctic and Pacific Oceans, can be compared from available data.

The standard deviations for a number of traits of the common seal (*Phoca vitulina*) with homologous traits of *Pusa* are shown in Figure 28. In accordance with the differences in absolute value of traits, the values of the standard deviation show considerable differences for the various traits. The ordering of standard deviations in this case is close to that for the mean values of the traits.

In the comparison of relative values of the standard deviation and coefficients of variation, the matter is different. The relative value of sigmas for the traits of the common seal (*Phoca vitulina*) has been given in Figure 29. If the degree of deviation is expressed in the form of area under the curve obtained (the one from the data on the Pechora population of the ringed seal being taken as a straight base line), it is observed that the Caspian seal deviates (with regard to four traits, taken from the beginning of the curve) by approximately 14 to 15 cm^2, the Baikal seal by 27 to 28 cm^2, and the common seal by 39 to 40 cm^2; in other words, the sample from a population belonging to another genus differs sharply from the samples from the populations of species within one genus.

The comparison of values of coefficients of variation for traits of *Pusa* and the *Phoca* (Figure 31) leads to some interesting conclusions. As seen from the coefficient of variation for the common seal (*Phoca vitulina*), there are no differences (with the exception of a somewhat lower variability for lip vibrissae). An interesting trend becomes apparent. The values of coefficients of variation for the ringed seal of the Okhotsk Sea are closer to the coefficients of variation for the common seal (*P. vitulina*) of Okhotsk than to the coefficients of variation for other species and populations of seals. It seems possible that the variability of traits for the common seal and the ringed seal are close to each other because of the similar demands made by natural selection in the same body of water.

Such an hypothesis is appealing, but it must be noted that a number of other factors are needed for its confirmation. The fact that a small number of traits have been studied does not speak in favor of this assumption. A detailed additional examination of such a proposal and a comparison of the variability of organs of the common and ringed seals of the Okhotsk Sea with the variability of other species of pinnipeds living in the Okhotsk Sea is needed.

The species *Pagophilus groenlandicus* and *Histriophoca fasciata* can be examined as representatives of closely related genera (Chapskii, 1955a; Scheffer, 1958; Shustov and Yablokov, 1967). The results of analyzing the morphological material obtained are presented in a table of the Appendix. A comparison of the morphological characteristics of the Greenland seal and *Histriophoca fasciata* as related genera (genera in the family of true seals) shows that there is a considerable morphological difference in many traits between the two (Table 31).

Table 31. Degree of difference (t) of morphological traits of the banded seal (*Histriophoca fasciata*) **and Greenland seal** (*Pagophilus groenlandicus*) **(From data of Shustov and Yablokov, 1967)**

Traits			t_1	t_2	t_3
Body length	..	..	−11.50	− 8.12	− 6.37
Number of tracheal rings	..	..	+ 2.72	+ 1.67	+ 1.90
Eye vibrissae	..	..	− 4.94	− 6.15	− 5.41
Lip vibrissae	..	..	+37.0	+26.7	+34.5

NOTE : t_1—banded seal, White Sea population of Greenland seal; t_2—banded seal, Yan-Maien population of Greenland seal; t_3—banded seal, Newfoundland population of Greenland seal.

A comparison of absolute values of standard deviations shows a great similarity in the disposition of all values for three populations of the Greenland seal and noticeable differences in the corresponding values for *Histriophoca fasciata* (Figure 33). A comparison of relative values of sigma (with the population of the Greenland seal from the White Sea taken as a standard), leads us to conclude that the degree of differences in comparable traits is lowest in the population from Newfoundland. The population of the Yan-Maien region differs considerably and the curve corresponding to the sigma values of *Histriophoca fasciata* shows these differences (Figure 34).

A comparison of the coefficients of variation for the traits studied in the Greenland seal and *Histriophoca fasciata* leads us to conclude that there are no significant differences in the magnitude of variability in the latter (Figure 16). The variability of number of vibrissae in various lines is almost identical in the Greenland seal. The variability of the last line, for which there are always a larger number of vibrissae in *Histriophoca fasciata* than in the Greenland seal, appears to be reduced. The variability of the total number of vibrissae in the lip group of *H. fasciata* appears to be somewhat increased, which corresponds with the reduced number of vibrissae in this group. The variability in number of eye vibrissae is similar, which is rather strange since the number of these vibrissae in *H. fasciata* is twice as large.[6] The variability of body length appears to be somewhat higher; yet, on the other hand, the variability of number of tracheal rings appears to be lower. But all these deviations and situations observed from different populations of the Greenland seal are not fundamentally characteristic.

[6] This may be explained as due to a similar action of the controlling factors of this trait.

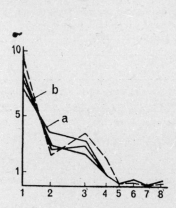

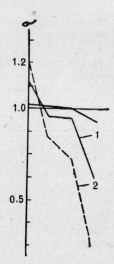

Figure 33. A comparison of absolute values of standard deviations for certain traits of two seal genera: (*a*) *Pagophilus* and (*b*) *Histriophoca*:
1—*Body length; 2—Number of tracheal rings; 3-4—Number of lip and eye vibrissae ; 5-8—Weight of heart, liver, kidneys and spleen.*

Figure 34. A comparison of relative values of standard deviations for a number of traits (see Figure 33) of two seals: (1) *Pagophilus* and (2) *Histriophoca.* Sigma of the White Sea population of the Greenland seal has been taken as a base.

On the whole, it may be said that the variability for the traits studied in *H. fasciata* is close to that of the Greenland seal.

Now let us compare the characters of these and other genera of the subfamily Phocinae which are more distant taxonomically (Figure 35). For the comparison, we shall first take the Greenland seal on one side and two populations of the ringed seal (Okhotsk and Pechora Seas), the Baikal seal, and the Caspian seal on the other side. After that all these seals will be compared with *H. fasciata,* and finally the common seal with the Greenland seal. The comparison of values of the standard deviation has been intentionally left out because it has been specifically shown above that such a comparison of relative values of sigma above the generic level reveals just a formal significance, and a comparison of absolute values of the standard deviation does not add significantly new information in the analysis of morphological differences.

The comparison of coefficients of variation for traits in the species of different genera shows (Table 32) a picture opposite to the one that is observed during the comparison of absolute values of the traits (Table 33). A considerable number of comparable pairs of traits do not show significant differences in their coefficients of variation. During the comparison of absolute values, out of 145 comparisons only 21 were indistinguishable,

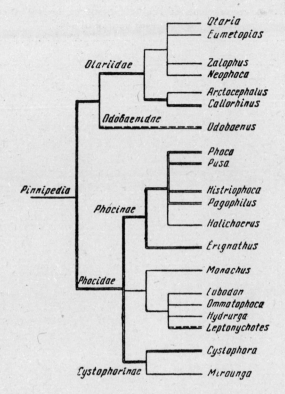

Figure 35. Taxonomy of Pinnipedia (Scheffer, 1958). The comparison
carried out in the present work has been shown by a double line.

but in the comparison of coefficients of variation, there are 74 indistinguishable pairs. The distribution of differences in coefficients of variation exhibits certain features :

The variability of *H. fasciata* is more similar to that of the other seals
than is that of the Greenland seal;

The greatest similarity in variability is observed between *H. fasciata*
and the Okhotsk seal and between *H. fasciata* and the Baikal seal. The
variability of the Pechora seal and the Caspian seal is not much more
different than is that of the Okhotsk seal or the Baikal seal;

During the comparisons of *Pusa* with the Greenland seal, the pair of
the Greenland seal and the Okhotsk seal showed the fewest differences,
followed by the Baikal seal (and here the Pechora and Caspian seals differ
from the first two representatives of this genus).

It is clearly seen that a tendency for a greater variability of body
length is observed in comparison with the same trait in the Greenland seal,
but traits like number of tracheal rings, number of ribs, and the total number

Table 32. A comparison of coefficients of variation of certain traits for different genera of seal*

Trait	t_1**	t_2	t_3	t_4	t_5	t_6	t_7	t_8	t_9	t_{10}
Body length	+	+	+	Nil	+	Nil	Nil	Nil	Nil	++
Anus-navel measurement	Nil	Nil	++	,,						
Anus-penis measurement	,,	++	Nil	,,						
Number of :										
Tracheal rings	++	++	++	++		Nil	Nil	Nil	Nil	+
Caudal vertebrae	+	Nil	Nil	++						Nil
Sternal ribs	++	++		++						+
Asternal ribs	++			++						Nil
Nasal vibrissae	++	Nil	Nil	Nil						
Eye vibrissae	++	,,	++		++	Nil	++	Nil		
All the lip vibrissae	Nil	,,	Nil	++	++	,,	++	++	+	+
1st line	++	,,	++	++	++	++	++	++	+	+
2nd line	Nil	,,	++	Nil	Nil	Nil	++	Nil	+	|
3rd line	,,	,,	Nil	,,	,,	,,	Nil	,,	Nil	Nil
4th line	+	++	++	++	,,	,,	,,	,,	+	+
5th line	++	Nil	Nil	Nil	,,	,,	,,	,,	+	+
6th line	Nil	++	++	++	,,	,,	,,	,,	+	+
7th line	,,	Nil	++	++	++	,,	++	++	+	+
8th line	,,	,,	++	++	+	+	+	Nil	+	Nil
9th line			+	+			+	+		

* For ease of reading, the following abbreviations have been used in the table : $t > 1.96$; difference exists (+ + when $t = +1.96$ or + when $t = -1.96$); when t is less, there are no detectable difference (Nil).

** For abbreviations t_1 to t_{10}, see Table 33.

of vibrissae, show a tendency towards a lower variability in all the species of *Pusa*.

If these trends with regard to body length, number of tracheal rings, and number of vibrissae could be well understood in the language of elementary regularities, then the increased variability for number of sternal and asternal ribs could not have another explanation, such as changes in certain biological relations in the populations of these genera.

In the majority of traits in the Greenland seal and *H. fasciata*, the variability is greater than in the common seal (Tables 32 and 33) and this attracts attention; moreover, in the first comparison, the lower variability of all vibrissae in the common seal (*Phoca vitulina*) is remarkable because their number is less.   Similarly, a somewhat lower variability in number of vibrissae of the lip group for the Caspian seal, whose absolute number

Table 33. A comparison of absolute values of traits for species of the genera
Pagophilus, Pusa, Histriophoca, **and** *Phoca**

Trait	t_1	t_2	t_3	t_4	t_5	t_6	t_7	t_8	t_9	t_{10}
Body length	++	++	++	++	++	++	++	++	Nil	+
Anus-navel measurement	++	++	++	++						
Anus-penis measurement	++	++	++	++						
Number of :										
Tracheal rings	++	++	++	++	+	+	+	+	++	++
Caudal vertebrae	++	Nil	++	Nil						+
Sternal ribs	++	,,		++						Nil
Asternal ribs	+	+		+						++
Nasal vibrissae	++	++	++	++						
Eye vibrissae	++	Nil	+	+	++	++	Nil	Nil		
All the lip vibrissae	+	+	+	+	+	+	+	+	Nil	+
1st line	+	+	+	+	+	+	+	+	++	Nil
2nd line	+	+	+	+	+	+	+	+	Nil	+
3rd line	+	+	+	+	+	+	+	+	++	+
4th line	Nil	Nil	+	+	+	+	+	+	Nil	+
5th line	+	+	+	+	+	+	+	+	,,	+
6th line	+	+	+	+	+	+	+	+	,,	+
7th line	+	Nil	+	+	+	+	+	+	,,	+
8th line	Nil	,,	+	+	+	+	+	+	+	Nil
9th line			+	+			+	+		

* For ease of reading, the following abbreviations have been used in the table: $t \geqslant 1.96$; difference exists (++ or +); when t is less, there are no detectable differences between comparable traits (Nil):

t_1—*Greenland seal, Pechora seal;* t_2—*Greenland seal, Okhotsk seal;* t_3—*Greenland seal, Caspian seal;* t_4—*Greenland seal, Baikal seal;* t_5—*H. fasciata, Pechora seal;* t_6—*H. fasciata, Okhotsk seal;* t_7—*H. fasciata, Caspian seal;* t_8—*H. fasciata, Baikal seal;* t_9—*Common seal, H. fasciata;* t_{10}—*Common seal, Greenland seal.*

of vibrissae is the greatest of all the species studied, cannot be explained on the basis of elementary regularities. Apparently, the controlling factors acting naturally on this trait in the Caspian Sea differ considerably from those in the biogeocenose in which other pinnipeds are included.

One of the conclusions which can be derived from the above comparisons of variability among species belonging to different close and distant genera, coincides with the conclusion arrived at earlier from the comparison of variability between individual species within a genus : the value of a direct quantitative comparison of morphological traits appeared to be of little significance for comparing different species, because such species usually differ clearly and specifically not by quantitative peculiarities (brought to light only through refined methods of population morphology) but by qualitative differences (brought to light by the usual methods of comparative anatomy).

Although it is necessary to have a large sample and an exact statistical analysis of quantitative data for a comparative characterization of some population with another population of the same species, there is no necessity for using methods of population morphology for comparative characterization of different genera. There is no sense in using quantitative analysis of refined peculiarities where qualitative differences exist. Of course, some special problems may show up in the analysis of individual homologous structures in a number of cases, but as a rule there is no need for wide usage of quantitative methods to find differences between species of different genera.

Thus, a quantitative analysis of traits becomes less important during the analysis of differences between species of different genera. But this analysis happens to be the basis for a further, a more detailed, and deeper study of the processes taking place in a population and in the biogeocenose, and the analysis of quantitative features of morphological structures of different species begins to play a leading role in the study of evolutionary processes.

In this analysis at the level of closely related genera, analysis and inference with regard to variability is of primary importance, because it can relate structures to the process of evolution in populations. Methods of comparing the variability of ecologically different structures in different species provide the possibility of discovering the trend of evolution in one population as compared with another population belonging to a different species and sex. A comparison of values of a trait in different species gives the possibility of detecting larger or smaller differences, but the comparison of variability of the traits allows one to judge the very first drifts in the mode of morphological changes in a population.

The analysis of variability of structures in different species within closely related genera is not less important in presenting specific problems for ecological research (by drawing attention to structures existing in specific relationships to evolutionary factors).

One general conclusion can be drawn from the data of this chapter : Any trait can change independently in different populations. This conclusion was drawn up in principle by H. F. Osborn (1915), A. N. Severtsov (1939), and R. Goldschmidt (1935); it is now widely used in the "new systematics" (Mayr, 1947, 1962; Beregovoi, 1963; Krivosheev and Rossolimo, 1964; Schwartz, 1965; and many others). But it has significance in principle for population morphology by asserting the importance of studying many individual traits of an organism even in cases where we do not know their adaptive significan te as yet.

Characteristics of Variability in Populations
of Different Subfamilies

Two subfamilies (Figure 35) can be distinguished in the family of true seals (Phocidae) : the true seals themselves (Phocinae) and the sea elephants (Cystophorinae).

There are a number of references in this work to the morphological features of *Cystophora cristata*, which is the only northern representative of the subfamily of sea elephants (Cystophorinae).

While comparing the absolute values of traits typical of pinnipeds, only one very general conclusion can be drawn : All the species differ from each other and the sea elephant differs quite considerably from others (Table 34). The situation when comparing the coefficients of variation (Table 35) is altogether different : for absolute values of morphological traits, the sea elephant differs from others by 83%, whereas in the coefficients of variation it differs only by 50% (in 73 comparisons out of 145).

No specific trends in the distribution of variability of the traits are observed when other pinnipeds are compared with *Cystophora cristata* and *Erignathus barbatus*. It is possible that the incompleteness of the data presented leads to such a conclusion as might accrue from the complexity of the phenomenon itself along with the various factors which determine the coefficient of variation in each specific case. That is why the tendency toward no difference in the coefficients of variation in the total number of lip vibrissae is significantly expressed during the comparison of almost all types (with the exception of the comparisons of *Cystophora cristata* with *Phoca vitulina* and *Erignathus barbatus* with all the rest of the seals). On the other hand, in every case (except when comparing *C. cristata* with the Pechora seal), the variability in number of nasal vibrissae appears to be different.

To examine the variability of *C. cristata* with a view to evaluating general environmental factors, is inevitably to compare the variability of traits of *C. cristata* and the Greenland seal living in the same region. Hence, a comparison of *C. cristata* with the Greenland seal has been carried out in detail by presenting data in Table 35 on all the three populations of this seal studied thus far. The results obtained deserve a special discussion.

There are clear differences in the variability of body length between *C. cristata* and the Greenland seal. It is interesting to observe that *C. cristata* does not differ from other types in the variability of body length (except *Histriophoca fasciata*, which is the nearest relative of the Greenland seal). On the other hand, none of the three populations of the Greenland seal differ from the population of *C. cristata* in variability of number of tracheal rings, though the rest of the seals differ with regard to this trait. *C. cristata* and the Greenland seal are also close in variability of number of asternal

Table 34.   A Comparison of absolute values of traits within the family Phocidae*

Trait	t_1	t_2	t_3	t_4	t_5	t_6	t_7	t_8	t_9	t_{10}	t_{11}	t_{12}	t_{13}
Body length	++	++	++	++	++	++							
Anus-navel measurement	++	++	++	++									
Anus-penis measurement	++	++	++	++									
Number of :													
Tracheal rings	+	+	+	+	+	+	+	++	+	+	Nil	++	++
Caudal vertebrae	++	++	++	++	++	++	++	++	++	++	++	++	++
Sternal ribs	Nil	Nil	Nil	Nil		Nil	+	Nil	Nil	Nil	Nil		Nil
Asternal ribs	??	+		+		??	Nil	??	??		??		??
Eye vibrissae	++	Nil	+	Nil	+		+	+	??	+	+	+	
Nasal vibrissae	+	??	Nil	??									
All the lip vibrissae	+	+	+	+	+	+	+	++	++	++	++	++	++
1st line	+	+	+	+	Nil								
2nd line	+	+	+	+	+	+							
3rd line	+	+	+	+	Nil	+							
4th line	+	+	+	+	+	+							
5th line	+	+	+	+	Nil	+							
6th line	+	++	+	+	+	Nil							
7th line	+	+	+	+	+	+							

*See Table 32 for symbols; t_1—Sea elephant, Greenland seal; t_2—Sea elephant, Pechora seal; t_3—Sea elephant, Caspian seal; t_4—Sea elephant, Baikal seal; t_5—Sea elephant, *Histriophoca fasciata*; t_6—Sea elephant, *Phoca vitulina*; t_7—*Erignathus barbatus*, Sea elephant; t_8—*E. barbatus*, Greenland seal (Yan-Maien region); t_9—*E. barbatus*, Okhotsk seal; t_{10}—*E. barbatus*, Caspian seal; t_{11}—*E. barbatus*, Baikal seal; t_{12}—*E. barbatus*, *Histriophoca*; t_{13}—*E. barbatus*, *Phoca vitulina*.

Table 35.   A comparison of coefficients of variation within the family Phocidae*

Trait	t_1	t_2	t_3	t_4	t_5	t_6	t_7	t_8	t_9	t_{10}	t_{11}	t_{12}	t_{13}	t_{14}	t_{15}	t_{16}
Body length	++	++	++	Nil	Nil	Nil	Nil	++	Nil							Nil
Anus-navel measurement	++	Nil	++	"	+	"	"	++								
Anus-penis measurement	++	++	Nil	"	++	++	++									
Number of :																
Tracheal rings	Nil	Nil	"	++	++	++	++	++	++	++	+	Nil	Nil	Nil	++	Nil
Caudal vertebrae	"	"	"	++	Nil	++	+	Nil	Nil	Nil	Nil	"	"	++	Nil	
Sternal ribs	+	"	+	++	++	++	++	+	++	+	+	+	+	Nil	+	
Asternal ribs	Nil	++	++	++	++	++	++	Nil	+	+	+	++	++	+	++	
Eye vibrissae	"	+	Nil	Nil	Nil	Nil	Nil	Nil	+	+	++	++	++	++	++	Nil
Nasal vibrissae	++	+	++	"	++	+	+	"	++	+						
All the lip vibrissae	++	Nil	++	++	Nil	++	Nil	+		++	++	Nil	++	++	"	"
1st line	Nil	"	Nil	Nil	"	++	Nil	+	++							
2nd line	++	"	Nil	Nil	"	++	Nil	Nil	++							
3rd line	Nil	"	"	"	"	Nil	"	"	Nil							
4th line	+	+	+	+	"	"	"	"	++							
5th line	+	+	Nil	Nil	"	"	"	"	++							
6th line	Nil	Nil	"	"	"	"	"	"	++							
7th line	++	++	++	"	++	++	++	++	++							

*See Table 32 for symbols; t_1—*Cystophora cristata*, Greenland seal (Yan-Maien region); t_2—Sea elephant (*C. cristata*), Greenland seal (White Sea); t—Sea elephant, Greenland seal (Newfoundland region); t_4—Sea elephant, Pechora seal; t_5—Sea elephant, Okhotsk seal; t_6—Sea elephant, Caspian seal; t_7—Sea elephant, Baikal seal; t_8—Sea elephant, *Histriophoca fasciata*; t_9—Sea elephant, *Phoca vitulina*; t_{10}—Sea elephant, *Erignathus barbatus*; t_{11}—*E. barbatus*, Greenland seal (Yan-Maien region); t_{12}—*E. barbatus*, Okhotsk seal; t_{13}—*E. barbatus*, Caspian seal; t_{15}—*E. barbatus*, Baikal seal; t_{16}—*E. barbatus*, *Histriophoca fasciata*.

ribs and caudal vertebrae. All this taken together gives a basis for saying that the Greenland seal shows a specific similarity with *C. cristata* in the variability of the traits mentioned above, a rather closer relation than with any of the other seals studied.

It is interesting that in comparing *E. barbatus* with other seals the greatest similarity in variability was observed between it and the Okhotsk ringed seal, which is geographically rather close to it. The data are meager for deriving a specific conclusion, but one cannot rule out the possibility that here lies a chance to decipher the effect of natural selection on variability, through a comparison (using a sufficiently large number of traits) of species inhabiting the same regions. It is quite possible that such a comparison may in the future open the possibility of differentiating variability (brought about by general environmental factors with non-specific relation to each species) and that resulting from a specific interrelation of a given population in its own biogeocenose.

The last stage in the analysis of variability for *C. cristata* is a comparison of variability with absolute values of traits in order to seek out deviations from the elementary regularities of variability. Such a comparison can be done, for example, by comparing variability values of skull traits. In Figure 36 the coefficients of variation for different traits have been depicted

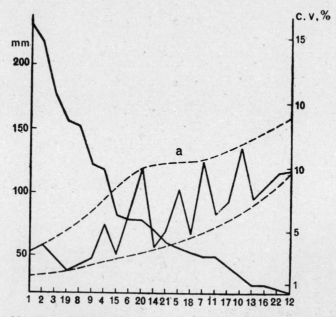

Figure 36. The variability (coefficients of variation) of skull measurements for females of *Cystophora cristata* as compared to the absolute values of the trait: *a—Border of variability drift*. For identification of the traits, see Figure 22.

as usual by placing them on the abscissa in order of declining absolute values of the trait.

A comparison of the curves and variability drift in the male and female *C. cristata* shows that, as with all seals, the variability of skull traits generally increases with decreasing absolute values. But a number of values considerably deviate from the mean drift in both males and females. Moreover, the trends coincide in both samples in certain instances : the variability for both males and females is low in relation to the mean for the following traits : braincase width, height of skull, condyle width, width of auditory bulla, length of auditory bulla, width of zygomatic arch. The width of palate and width of nostrils for both male and female *C. cristata* are characterized by relatively high variability.

Variability of the following traits differs most sharply in males and females: length and height of lower jaw, length of nasal bones, and width of nasal bones. The differences in variability of major measurements of the lower jaw, like its length and height, are inexplicable as yet. It must be noted that the height of the lower jaw is the only trait for which the variability is higher in females than in males; the variability of all the rest of the traits, except for the auditory bullae, is greater in males than in females. But the remaining two traits for which a considerable difference in variability exists between males and females, can be explained specifically. The variability of length and breadth of nasal bones in males of *C. cristata* is higher because the nasal bones carry a hypertrophied cartilaginous partition serving as a base for the large (up to one meter or more in expanded form) nasal pouch, which is a secondary sex characteristic of the animal and which gives it its name; the pouch does not grow in females.

The increased variability of the measurement "width of palate" might have been influenced by the fact that in *C. cristata*, because of its feeding on cephalopods (which invariably leads to a reduction in number of teeth : Tomilin, 1954; Yablokov, 1958), a process leading to an early and frequent loss of the last cheek teeth takes place. But according to the standard method the width of the palate is measured between the borders of the alveoli of the last cheek teeth. In some instances a full set of cheek teeth exists in the upper jaw, but in others the last cheek teeth may be absent, which brings about a sharp reduction in the measurement (although the skull width in this region may have no reduction).

It is not clear how to explain the rather high variability of width of nostrils, a trait which usually has low variability in other pinnipeds. The relatively high or low variability of certain traits of *C. cristata* coincides with analogical deviations for *Pusa* and *Pagophilus* (Figure 37). This is apparent in the greater variability of the palate, lower variability of braincase width, greater variability of the width of the snout, and especially in the lower variability of length and width of the auditory bullae.   The characteristics of variability noted must be dependent on some factors which are common to the whole family of true seals.   Further ecological research would show what these factors are.

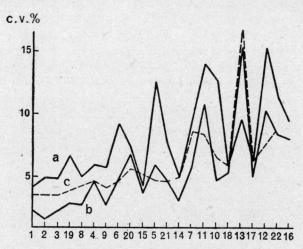

Figure 37.   The coefficients of variation for skull traits of (*a*) male *Cystophora*, (*b*) *Pagophilue*, and (*c*) *Pusa hispida*.   For identification of the traits, see Figure 22. A comparison of variability for other traits is given in Figure 38.

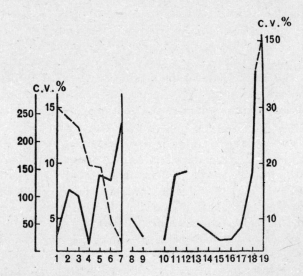

Figure 38.   Coefficients of variation for some traits of *Cystophora* :
1-7—*Body measurements (dotted line—absolute magnitude of measurements)* ;   8—*Number of caudal vertebrae;   9—Number of tracheal rings;   10-12—Total number of vibrissae in different regions;   13-19—Number of lip vibrissae by rows.*

The variability of number of rings in the trachea is lower than the variability of caudal vertebrae, as in many other seals. The behavior of the coefficients of variation is somewhat unusual in the case of body measurements. The least variability is not of the body length with fins but of the girth. There is a disproportion also in the variability of other values like body length measured along projections and curves, the distance from nose to navel, and the distance from anal orifice to navel.

The comparison of variability for morphological traits of different genera within one large and varied family of seals (the earless) does not contradict the general conclusions derived from the comparison of species within a genus, close genera among themselves, and different genera within one subfamily. Morphological traits expressed in absolute values can yield little information on the processes of micro-evolution. It is reasonable to think that the features once formed under the influence of those micro-evolutionary processes which still change the face of a population, are now largely beyond the control of these processes. For example, ecological divergence in feeding habits leads to a restricted diet in *Condylophora* (deep-water cephalopods), in *Erignathus* (benthonic invertebrates), and in *Pagophilus* (fish). And the adaptations to these diets (a reduction of teeth, an improvement of eyesight, a capacity for deep submersion under water, etc., in *Condylophora;* a growth of large numbers of lip vibrissae in *Erignathus;* a development of dental specializations together with a uniform development of the vibrissae in *Pagophilus,* etc.), at the present moment of evolution, partly determined the variability of such traits in each species. Thus a delicate and soft trachea with many tracheal rings does not occur in *Condylophora* as in *Erignathus;* and in the latter, all the results of a low number of vibrissae, which are incapable of getting food from the ocean floor, will necessarily be eliminated. A more general conclusion seems possible : Without a considerable change in the external environment, all the individual features of the pinnipeds now alive should develop in the direction of further specialization, the general trend of which was determined long before the present-day occurrence of the group.

Therefore knowledge of specific morphological features is essential only for orientation within the boundaries of that variability which is characteristic of a given population as an evolutionary unit in its present development. The variability itself, expressed rather exactly and significantly by the coefficient of variation, is capable of answering quite concrete questions on relatively recent micro-evolutionary processes and on effects of general and partial controlling factors.

By comparing certain populations within a species, some species within a genus and some close genera, it was not possible to find those traits controlled by common environmental factors and those traits controlled by specific conditions; a broad comparison of species within the boundary of the whole family, and perhaps such a comparison of specific traits, permits one to do such an analysis. In all the seals studied in the family, the variability in skull measurements appeared to have a similar trend: relatively large variability of length of palate, relatively low variability of braincase width, relatively high variability of width of snout, relatively low variability of parameters of the auditory bullae, etc. There can be only one conclusion on this level: that specific factors present in all instances, influence all species and all populations. Even one such conclusion helps in separating the "doubtful factors" out of thousands of factors which might have an influence on the variability of these traits. But the analysis only begins at this point. The possibility arises of selecting different organisms ecologically and geographically and, as it were, *"asking" nature in each specific instance to sort out the analogically influencing factors by selecting traits which are comparable to a maximum extent with regard to variability.*

One of the possible ways of making such investigations is to compare the variability of species which are considerably separated taxonomically from each other but living in one biogeocenose. In the pinnipeds, these will be *Erignathus barbatus, Phoca vitulina, Pusa hispida,* and *Histriophoca fasciata* in the Okhotsk Sea, the Bering Sea, etc.; I am confident that the results of such an analysis will let us arrive at conclusions of ecological as well as of evolutionary importance. Even now, the comparison of variability in a number of genera looks promising in spite of the limited data, for *Erignathus barbatus* and *Pusa hispida* in the Okhotsk Sea and for *Pagophilus groenlandicus* and *Cystophora cristata* in the North Atlantic. Naturally, such an approach should prove itself to be very fruitful in studying other animals also. But for the time being, while continuing the study of variability within the boundaries of an order, it is essential to investigate the general trends which appear at the level of a family.

The Nature of Variability in Populations of Different Families within an Order

The amount of data available for a comparison of the three living families of pinnipeds is not as much as was available for a comparison of species within genera, or genera within the family of earless seals. But I think that it would be improper not to attempt the comparison, though in a most general way, with the limited data already available.

The three living families of pinnipeds are represented by different numbers of species. We have studied the family of earless seals, which constitutes about 60% of the living species of pinnipeds.[7] The other two

[7]According to V. B. Scheffer (1958), the earless seal family (Phocidae) has 18 species; the family of eared seal (Otariidae) 12 species; and in the family of the walrus (Odobenidae) there is one species.

families of pinnipeds—eared seals (Otariidae) and walruses (Odobenidae)—have a smaller number of species. The walrus family is represented by a single genus and species (*Odobenus rosmarus*), and the family of eared seals has a comparatively large number of species of fur seals, and sea lions (Scheffer, 1958).

In the investigations carried out to date, there are practically no data on population variability of walruses and few on the variability of fur seals (*Callorhinus ursinus*) (Scheffer, 1958; Bychkov, 1965). It is possible to compare variability for skull traits of earless seals with that of the northern fur seals (*Callorhinus ursinus*) of the commercially exploited group, because V. F. Muzhchinkin has kindly made the analysis possible by providing unpublished data. These measurements, taken for earless seals, are presented in Figure 39.

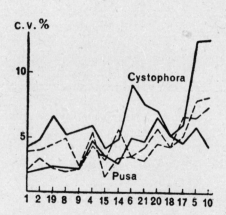

Figure 39. A comparison of coefficients of variation for some skull measurements in a fur seal (*Callorhinus ursinus*), from the data of V. F. Muzhchinkin, in dotted lines; *Cystophora* and *Pusa* are in solid lines. For identification of traits, see Figure 22.

As seen from this figure (where the variability of 15 skull traits of two different age and sex groups of fur seals is given), a common trend is observed in a number of traits. They appear to be interesting and significant in the given comparison, thus allowing one to bring forth some traits typical not only for the species but, perhaps, for the whole family Otariidae. These traits are as follows: braincase width (very similar in all groups with a rather low variability); length of palate (showing rather high variability for all groups); height of skull (variability is low); width of occipital condyles (variability is high); height of lower jaw (variability similarly high); and width of bullae (variability low).

The coefficients of variation for the same traits of the ringed seal (*Pusa hispida*) and the hooded seal (*Cystophora cristata*) have been put on the same graph (Figure 39). A comparison of these data with the data for the fur seal shows that a high variability of length of palate and a low variability in height of skull and of width of bullae is characteristic of pinnipeds. Of these three traits, only the low variability of the auditory bullae can be explained on a functional basis. (They undoubtedly play a major role in auditory reception in the case of aquatic mammals.)

Considering the data of V. A. Bychkov (1965), a gentle slope of the ceiling of variability appears to be the general character for the sample of northern fur seals. The coefficients of variation of measurements for traits of the smallest absolute size, do not differ considerably from the coefficients of variation for traits of the largest absolute size (condylobasal length, etc.). It is difficult to say now to what extent this peculiarity is inherent in the eared seals, though such a possibility is not ruled out.

In finishing the discussion of features of the population morphology for different families of pinnipeds, let us note that the data on the variability of the walrus are poor; only general information on the number of teeth in the upper and lower jaws is available (Table 36).

Table 36. **Variability of number of teeth in adult male walrus from the Chukchi Sea (From data of Bel'kovich and Yablokov, 1960)**

		$\bar{x}\pm s_{\bar{x}}$	σ	$c.v.\pm s_{c.v.}$	n
Lower jaw, right	..	4.1 ± 0.32	0.47	11.5 ± 0.63	165
Lower jaw, left	..	4.2 ± 0.33	0.53	12.6 ± 0.69	165
Upper jaw, right	..	6.2 ± 0.43	1.08	17.4 ± 0.35	212
Upper jaw, left	..	6.2 ± 0.42	1.00	16.1 ± 0.77	216

This trait (number of teeth in the walrus) is very specific and for the time being cannot be compared with any other single trait among those already studied.

It will be interesting in the future to compare the variability in the number of teeth in the walrus with that for certain other species of pinnipeds in the following order: walrus, hooded seal, crab-eater seal, bearded seal, ringed seal. It can be assumed that the variability of number of teeth will be highest in the walrus among all seals (as determined by its special trophic relationships). The usual mode of feeding by the walrus leads to the fact that it has completely reduced eye vibrissae, unlike the rest of the pinnipeds (Figure 40), but the lip vibrissae are the best developed. Yablokov and Klevezal' (1964) found for this species a somewhat unusual function. Direct observations in nature and in captivity showed that walruses always contact the substrate with their vibrissae, perhaps detecting small vibrations of sediment which are caused by travelling snails. The lip vibrissae form a perfect net at the same time (Figure 41).

We see that the comparison of skull traits carried out among the families of the order Pinnipedia show that among the families studied there are common features in the variability of traits. This may mean that such features are controlled by some environmental factors common to the whole order. In the absence of large field investigations, it is difficult to say what these factors may be.

Figure 40.   A young walrus resting on Ruder Beach (Anadir Bay).
Notice the absence of vibrissae near the eyes.   Author's photograph.

But, it seems, a wider comparison of the variability of traits of pinnipeds with the variability of the same traits for other mammals could answer
this question, particulary a comparison of pinnipeds with Carnivora (near
relatives of pinnipeds) having representatives accustomed to an aquatic
(Kamchatka beaver) as well as a semi-aquatic (otter and polar bear) mode
of life.   In such a comparison, traits specially conditioned to an aquatic
life would come to light.

Figure 41.   Muzzle of an adult male walrus; the clear disposition of different
rows of vibrissae and an evenly assembled surface of the "brush" is seen.
Ruder Beach, 1960.   Author's photograph.

A determination of such general regularities in the development of traits, or of the nature of the variability of those traits (increased or decreased as compared to the expectations of the elementary regularities) would give an opportunity to analyze the mode of variability of a species and of individual populations. This would be by comparing the observed deviations in variability, and by knowing the magnitude and direction of deviation, depending on the conditions of existence for the whole group. No doubt during this analysis deviations from the general trends of the whole group would be found in concrete populations, and these very differences should be the object of further thorough studies of population morphology, which is the study of the micro-evolutionary processes going on in such "hot points."

Certain Characteristics of Population Variability on Different Taxonomical Levels

The experiment of making a systematic study of population morphology for different species within one order at various taxonomical levels (for the first time carried out in this work) gives an opportunity for establishing certain general relationships.

The comparison of variability among populations within one species, among closely related genera within a family, and among the representatives of closely related families can be carried out in three main directions: by comparing the means of quantitative characters for structures in different samples, by comparing absolute and relative values of the standard deviation and by comparing the variability as expressed in coefficients of variation.

The first method—the comparison of the means of quantitative characters of the samples—is the first step on the way to an analysis of population morphology and gives factual material for conducting all further investigations. However, this direction has an important independent significance in lower levels of comparison (the comparisons approximately up to the limits of a subfamily), indicating the existence of morphological differences between different groups within a population as well as between populations of different species. By such an analysis it seems possible to derive a conclusion even about the degree of such differences (which is not possible to do with the usual methods of comparative anatomy).

This way leads to conclusions having direct ecological significance because it seems possible to presume the existence of fine adaptive peculiarities in the groups under study, on the basis of differences in morphological characteristics which can be gauged by methods of quantitative morphology.

The second method of studying variability—investigating the

distribution of standard deviation values—allows one to obtain data directly characterizing the degree of similarity between the populations being studied. Attention must be given to an unjustifiably forgotten method— the method of comparing not the absolute but the relative values of the standard deviations, which was proposed by S. R. Zarapkin (1934-1939). The foregoing modification of this method allows a comparison of populations having most heterogeneous traits. This method of studying population morphology occupies an intermediate position between the study of absolute quantitative characters of traits and the study of variability itself.

The most important at all levels—from the comparison of intra-population samples to the comparison of populations, genera, families and maybe even of orders—is the third method of studying population morphology : the study of variability expressed in dimensionless (without any particular unit of measurement) figures of coefficients of variation. The significance of this method in the investigation of a population consists mainly in the fact that it characterizes the degree of interdependence and relation of the trait to the effective evolutionary factors (of genetical and ecological kinds). The variability, expressed in coefficients of variation, should be looked at as the expression of the most general relations and interdependence established between the age-sex groups within a population as well as among those relations by which the whole population is held in the biogeocenose.

In a comparison of populations belonging to species of different genera, the methods of comparing direct and absolute quantitative values of traits assume secondary importance, since the differences between the traits of different genera are so clear-cut that sensitive quantitative methods of analysis are not required for characterizing and finding out these differences. The usual methods of comparative and descriptive anatomy quite satisfactorily solve the problems of similarities and differences between various samples. The methods of analysis of variability assume the foremost place during such analysis. The comparison of different species in absolute quantitative expression of specific traits is useful only for ascertaining the presence of larger or smaller differences, but the comparison of these species with regard to degree of variability in the traits under investigation, allows one to evaluate the earliest steps in the appearance of morphological differentiation of the species, which are the very first steps in the evolutionary process.

It can be said on the whole that the knowledge of absolute values of variability in traits during the analysis of different genera and families is useful only for determining the limits of variability for the groups in the present stage of their development. The variability itself, expressed in terms of coefficients of variation, seems capable of answering related questions on the present micro-evolutionary processes.

While studying the characteristics of the variability of different species, it seems important to pay attention to comparing as large a number as possible of both taxonomically close and distant species. Such a wide comparison provides an opportunity to infer which of the characteristics of variability in one trait or another are determined by general environmental conditions for populations of species, and which ones are determined by specific conditions in the direction of natural selection for a given biotic community (biogeocenose). The comparison of variability of species placed even widely apart in the taxonomy, but inhabiting one biotic community, seems to be important in biogeocenosal relations. With such species there could be a number of common features in the variability of structures which again could be interpreted as the effect of general biogeocenosal factors. Such analysis gives an opportunity for recognizing a developing species and the formation of its peculiarities, and also a system of regularities acting at the level of populations.

The data considered in this chapter allow one to draw an important conclusion having great importance for the problem of studying variability as a whole: Population variability does not depend on the taxonomic position of a species. In the populations of very close species and in different populations within one species, the coefficients of variation may differ more significantly than the coefficients of variation for populations of taxonomically distant species, genera, and families. This differentiation in coefficients of variation perhaps reflects differences in the force of evolutionary factors.

Chapter IV

CLASSIFICATION OF THE PHENOMENA OF VARIABILITY

A Short Survey of Certain Classifications of Variability

Terminology

Researchers usually attempt to classify the phenomena of variability as phenotypic and genotypic; of the two, phenotypic variability is studied to a lesser extent. At the same time, it is clear that any phenotypic variability has a genetic basis. Though the relationship between phenotypic and genotypic variability is far from clear, it is evident that a separate classification of the phenomena of phenotypic variability is necessary in the development of research in the field of population biology.

One of the first investigators, H. F. Osborn (1915) divided characters into numerical (number of teeth, number of vertebrae, etc.) and proportional (magnitude, form, intensity of color, etc.) characters, and observed that there is a major and qualitative difference between these two categories.

One of the best known attempts at classification of the phenomenon of variability was done by Robson and Richards (1936), who differentiated variability according to structure, function, and activity, and separated individual, group, and species variability. They attributed such phenomena as polymorphism, dimorphism, mimetic, and seasonal forms, presence of different stages of growth, etc., to species variability. While analyzing this classification, I concluded that the author did not differentiate very clearly between variability and variation in the wider meaning of the word (see Introduction).

When considering the causes of variability, they separate the non-hereditary somatic variation (phenotypic variability), the effect of recombining existing genes, and mutational variability (genotypical). This classification, although with merits on the whole, must now be seen only from an historical point of view.

In the work of Mayr, Linsley, and Usinger (1956) on the principles of zoological taxonomy, another classification of variability is presented, based mainly on the requirements of taxonomists. The phenotypic variability of mammals is divided by the authors into individual variability over time (growth and seasonal), ecological (biotopical, determined by the host, depending upon the density of the population, climatic, alternation of generations, and variability of colors), and traumatical (brought about by parasites, by accidents, and teratologically). The hereditary variability (genotypical) is divided into variability related and not related to sex, continuous and discontinuous (genetical polymorphism).

In this classification, there are some disputable questions probably of concern even to taxonomists. First, there is no clear difference between variability and variation; when the authors talk about growth variability, they mean growth variation, and when the discussion is on seasonal variability, they mean seasonal variation, etc.

Moreover, it seems unjustified to combine so many different biological concepts like variability from growth and variability from season (the first is irreversible and the second is reversible) in one type (variability over time). The variability of growth cannot be seen only from the point of view of time variability. This phenomenon is complex and deeper and is not related directly to the concept of generally understood "physical" time but is also related to the concept of "biological" time.

Certain other subtypes of variability included in the ecological type of variability[1] do not, in my opinion, deserve a special separation; at the same time, other variabilities should have been separated into individual types. The variability "depending upon the density of the population" (1B3, according to the terminology of Mayr *et al.*, 1956 translation), variability from alternation of generations (1B5), and variability of color (1B6) fall into the first category. Biotopical variability falls into the second category; it deserves placement in a separate type because each individual population exists only in a specific climatic and geographical environment.

An attempt to classify the phenomena of variability within a population was done by P. V. Terent'ev. He considers it possible to distinguish topographical (or geographical) variability, the variability of "form," (which consists of variation in different stages of growth and ecological

---

[1] Here it will be proper to cite the opinion of E. I. Lukin, who wrote that the terms "local" or "ecological" variability have to be used with caution, because the local or ecological forms are usually not the categories of variability, but the systematic units formed through natural selection on the basis of hereditary variability, traits of which have been adapted to the places of life for these forms (Lukin, 1940; p. 14).

conditions), and finally, the "undetermined" variability, which serves as a normal curve of variability; to determine its properties it is sufficient to give its mean value, standard deviation, and their errors of measurement (Terent'ev, 1957; p. 79).

This classification also has some points. It appears that all variability of any type, and not only the so-called "undetermined" variability, may have a distribution in the form of a normal curve. The variability of "form" distinguished by P. V. Terent'ev is very wide (encompassing all ecological and growth variability) which hardly makes this classification useful. This observation applies also to geographical variability, a concept of very wide scope, in which the concepts of biotopical and climatic variability should also be included.

S. S. Schwartz (1963), while observing the complexity and extent of variability within a species and the inevitable one-sidedness in forming any classification of it, proposes to divide variability into individual, biotopical, growth, seasonal (chronological), and geographical categories. This classification is far more constructive than previous ones and reflects well the differences in expression of variability with regard to the effect of evolutionary factors in a population in one area. It does not look proper to separate only "individual" variability from other variability. Any variability within a population occurs through an individual and only through an individual; hence all the variability encountered by a researcher during a population study is individual variability (which can also be called intra-population or, to be more exact, population variability).

The other observation which must be made with regard to Schwartz' classification of variability is concerned with the concept of "chronological" variability. It is doubtful whether this concept could be confined only to seasonal variability as has been proposed. It seems that all the forms of variability of time should be included in the concept of chronological variability instead of only seasonal variability.

The last and most detailed classification of variability has been done by E. Mayr (1963), in which he proposes to divide all phenotypic variation into four large groups : (1) individual over time, (2) social (insects), (3) ecological, (4) traumatical. Notwithstanding here the further fractional differentiation of these main groups (which have specific points of interest as, for example, fractional classification of time variations in growth, seasonal, and generational variation, etc.), the basic shortcoming of such an approach should be noticed. Here there happens to be a mixing of different types of variability and uncomparable phenomena are compared. Any individual variations in time could be at the same time ecological; therefore dividing variability into variability of time and ecology is not correct.

Finally, in the same work of Mayr (1963) there is a very complete attempt to classify the phenomena of morphological variability. All the kinds of morphological variability have been examined by Mayr from two basic positions. First, the variability could be quantitative (measurable) and qualitative (present-absent)[2]. Secondly, continuous (greater, smaller, brighter, darker) and discontinuous (blue, grey, with white, without white, and the like) variations can be separated among the morphological variations. The last type, discontinuous variation, is called the phenomenon of polymorphism. In this classification a clear-cut distinction of morphological variability can be made into quantitative and qualitative variability, though the position of meristic variability remains undecided. The separation of the phenomenon of polymorphism or discontinuous variation is fundamentally important in the proposed classification.

While evaluating all the above-mentioned classifications of variability, it can be noted that they have a common deficiency, i.e., the mixing up of various approaches in the classification of the phenomenon; it appears that this has not yet allowed the construction of a logical system of variability. There is no doubt that one of the reasons for such mixing of different approaches in the study of variability is the "narrowness" of the question posed, either from a taxonomic point of view or genetical or ecological point of view.

Taking into consideration the previous experience of researchers, and analyzing the data obtained on mammalian variability, it is considered necessary and proper to group all the phenomena of individual or population variability into three large categories, which should be pursued independently.

1. Division of all the kinds of variability in nature into types (morphological or structural, biochemical, functional or physiological, psychological or behavioral).[3]

2. Classification of variability according to measurements (manifestation of variability) by weight, volume, meristic, colorimetric, etc.

3. Classification of the phenomena of variability with regard to factors influencing the development of the population (form of variability: growth, sex, chronological, etc.).

However, before writing in detail about the identified types, manifestation and forms of variability, it is necessary to stop and consider the peculiarities in the usage of certain terminologies. It was said above

[2] E. Mayr observes here that non-metrical characters of morphological variability are characteristic of mammals, birds and molluscs. This assertion of his indicates perhaps that he had insufficient material on variability of mammals. As shown in various parts of this work, the non-metrical variability of mammalian traits can be studied quite broadly.

[3] E. Mayr (1963) divides all phenotypic variability into two large groups: variability of behavior and variability of development. The phenomenon of development of different phenotypes under different conditions of life falls into the last category.

that all the variability studied in a population appears in a population only through an individual and hence can be fittingly termed individual variability.

Understanding two aspects of the problem of variability, i.e., within-population and between-population, originating from the work of Yr. A. Filipchenko (1916, 1926) which has spread appreciably of late (Simpson, 1948; and many others) does not, in my opinion, result in a "mixing up of the phenomena of variability and evolution" as indicated by E. E. Lukin (1940). In the given case, the use or interpretation of the concept of "group" or "between-population" variability need not be declared wrong, but the exact place of the phenomenon, which is expressed in this concept as a general theory of variability, should be found out. Further, it is difficult to take objection to the claim that the phenomenon of "group" variability really exists in nature. This between-population variability should also be clearly classified and should be widely studied; the forms and methods of such study are examined in this work in passing, and of course should form an independent object of research although they are closely related to the study of intra-population variability and are based on such study.

It is clear from the above that the term "intra-specific" or only "specific" variability, which has been widely used in the recent past, seems to combine phenomena of different types such as within-population (individual) variability and the between-population (group) variability; moreover, the latter category of variability seems to be wider than the concept of "species" variability and "within-species" variability. To be exact, perhaps it would have been better if the concept of "intra-specific" variability had been rejected and more specific terms like "within-population" variability and "between-population" variability had been used. In the present work, the term "variability" always and everywhere means individual within-population variability.

E. Mayr (1963, p. 139) writes: "Non-genetic variation adapts the individual, while genetic variation adapts the population." (Non-genetic variation is considered by Mayr as variation arising with a single genotype.) On the other hand, it may be thought that in the framework of variability in each trait controlled by natural selection, sometimes a situation arises resulting in the appearance of variability which is not dependent on factors of selection acting at that moment. There is no doubt that at the root of any type and form of appearance of variability, there are genetical factors. E. Mayr (1963, p. 150) correctly says that "much of this genetic variation contributes to the variations of the phenotype." All types of variability in natural populations are genetically constituted, larger in some situations (or with regard to one trait) and smaller in other situations (with regard to other traits).

Among many difficulties in evaluating genetic and non-genetic variability of a population, the most serious is the separation of the evolutionary factors acting on that variability at the present moment and those that acted in the past. For example: a short tail is an adaptive and advantageous trait in a cold climate but, at the same time, without any sort of selection for it in a population developing at colder temperatures, the tail is shorter than in the control (Sumner, 1909; Mayr, 1963). In the evolution of a species this feature of adaptive reaction is fixed in the normal way by selection, but in the given generation and in the given population there cannot be a straight correlation of this trait with the selection. It is possible that the study of the interrelations of genotypic and phenotypic variability in a population will be one of the basic approaches in investigating population morphology, but its relation to phenotypic variability is too complex to be examined in detail in such a cursory account. It seems important to show the presence of genetical variability in populations through specific examples. This class of variability can become manifest only during experimental studies of different populations.

It has been shown through special methods of study (Wright, 1952) that genetic factors accounted for 43% of all the observable variability in one experiment, while the remaining 57% (even under experimental conditions) are controlled by environmental factors. This dependence on environmental factors increases considerably in inbreeding and decreases while maintaining the experimental population under conditions approaching normal (Falconer and Latyszewski, 1952).

The data given by Castle (1941) have been used to calculate variability (Table 15, Appendix) of four lines of white rats. Since in the present example we can exclude the effect of variability due to age (only individuals of similar age were studied), and the conditions of existence of these four populations were identical, it has to be suggested that the differences observed in the variability depend on genetic factors. It is interesting to note that the data on females show a considerably higher constancy than the data on males.

The analysis of data from the work of Castle, Gates, Reed, and Law (1936) on the important independent value of variability as a genotypic character of a trait, shows that in a number of instances the considerable differences with regard to the absolute value of a trait among the experimental populations are not related to the presence of differences in the variability of the trait. The reverse is also true. Differences in the magnitude of variability are specific between groups which do not differ in the absolute values of a trait.

An analysis of variability of wild and inbred populations could be important for understanding the role and value of "genetic" and "nongenetic" factors affecting variability. It must be noted that there are characteristic differences in different populations within a species with regard to genotypic variability (Timofeev-Ressovskii, 1927; Zarapkin, 1934, 1937; Demerec, 1937; Olenov and Khrmats, 1939; and many others). The last work shows that the spontaneous mutability in different populations in nature differs more than ten times in insects. This has a great significance in creating a heterogeneity among populations in the magnitude of variability for many morphological and other traits.

On the whole, it is clear that the part of phenotypic variability which is dependent on genetical factors, makes the analysis of variability observed in nature somewhat difficult (Romashov and Il'ina, 1943; Mayr, 1963), but this situation shows how important is the study and calculation of all phenotypic and also non-genetic variability (Schwartz, 1963, 1965).

Types of Variability

Structural variability

Structural variability is the variability of parameters in systems of organs, individual organs, and their parts.

This type of variability is usually investigated by morphologists in the class Mammalia. Such attention to structural (morphological) variability is not accidental, because the care in detecting it and performing exact calculations of structural variations make the study of mammalian populations considerably easier by giving a chance to carry out the analysis at a high level with sufficiently specific and exact data.

Information on variability of this type comes from works of quite different kinds—from some works on ecology to some on physiology, morphology, and zoogeography. Data on structural variability of various orders of mammals (mainly, works in the last decade) are given below.[4]

Order Marsupialia. The data are as yet scanty (Tribe and Peel, 1963; Hughes, 1964; Sharman *et al.*, 1964).

Order Insectivora. A number of researchers in different countries have studied the morphological variability of small Insectivora and this information is often published in the current literature (Markov, 1957; Fateev, 1962; Schwartz, 1962; Dolgov, 1961, 1963; Kogteva, 1963; Mezhzherin, 1964a, 1964b, 1965; Lavrova and Zazhigin, 1965; Bazan, 1953; Borowski and Dehnel, 1953; Puček, 1956-1963; Stein, 1963; Osborn, 1964; and others).

Order Chiroptera. Special works on variability of Chiroptera are very few, but among those available there are some interesting data comparing fossil and recent Chiroptera (Bader and Hall, 1960; Lawrence,

---

[4] In addition to the references cited here, many references to variability of mammals are given in Chapters II and III and in subsequent sections of the present chapter.

1960; Jegla and Hall, 1962; Jegla 1963; Sigmund, 1964; Troyer, 1965).

Order Primates. Comparatively few works are found on Primates in the zoological literature, but some quite interesting data are found on variability of the most unexpected traits and structures in some special anthropological and medical literature (Roginskii, 1954, 1959, 1960; Derums, 1964; Zhdanov and Nikityuk, 1964; Swindler *et al.*, 1963; Hromada and Strnad, 1962; Freedman, 1963; Schultz, 1917, 1926; James, 1960; Lowrance and Latimer, 1957; Basu and Hasary, 1960; Banerjee, 1963; Decaban and Lieberman, 1964; Cave and Steel, 1964; Nissen and Riesen, 1964; Matsui, Takayasu, 1964; Pšenička and Jurin, 1964; Ashton and Oxnard, 1964, 1965; Broadhurst and Jinks, 1965; and others).

Order Lagomorpha. Some works have appeared in the recent past (mainly of Polish researchers) on the structural variability of European hare. They form a good basis along with the works previously done, for obtaining a full picture of variability for the representatives of this order (Filipchenko, 1916; Fateev, 1961; Labedkina, 1957; Bronson, 1958; Latimer and Sawin, 1955; Sawin, 1937, 1945; Bujalska, 1964; Cabon-Raczynska, 1964a; Lyne *et al.*, 1964; and others).

Order Rodentia. The largest number of researchers have studied variability for representatives of this order. It is not possible to give a complete list of works, but the references made here create a common understanding about the basic approaches in the study of structural variability for these mammals (Argiropula, 1946; Artem'ev, 1946; Astanin, 1960, 1962; Bashenina, 1962; Bol'shakov, 1962-1965; Bol'shakov and Schwartz, 1962, 1965; Vorontsov, 1961, 1963; Gershenzon, 1946; Gladkina *et al.*, 1963; Zubchaninova, 1962; Kogteva, 1963; Korotova, 1962; Rossolimo, 1962; Krivosheev and Rossolimo, 1964; Kryl'tsov'a, 1957; Larina, 1958, 1962, 1964; Meier, 1957; Ovchinikova, 1962, 1964; Petrov, 1961; Pokrovskii, 1962; Popov, 1960; Razorenova, 1952; Straka, 1963; Fadeev, 1958; Schwartz, 1959-1964; Sumner, 1909-1932; Clark, 1940; Hoffmeister, 1951; Hoffmeister and Lee, 1963; Newson and Chitty, 1962; Packard, 1960, 1964; Ursin, 1956; Spitz, 1963; Hinze, 1950; Pelt von and Bree, 1962; Puček, 1956; Kubik, 1953a; Wasilewski, 1952-1956; Haitlinger, 1962; Zejda, 1960, 1965; Guthrie, 1965; Schumacher *et al.*, 1965, Nord, 1963; Klemnt, 1960; Jackson, 1913; Gentile, 1952; and others).

Order Cetacea.[5] Because of the mass of material obtained from the whale industry, data on structural variability of cetaceans is abundant (Tomilin, 1957; Kleinenberg, 1956; Barabash-Nikiforov, 1940; Tryuber, 1937; Ivanova, 1961a, 1961b, 1961c; Slentsov, 1961; Kleinenberg, Yablokov, Bel'kovich and Tarasevich, 1964; Yablokov, 1958-1964;

---

[5] The order Cetacea perhaps consists of two independently originating orders, the toothed and baleen whales (Kleinenberg, 1958; Yablokov, 1964).

Ichihara, 1963; Omura, 1964; Brownell, 1964; Nishiwaki *et al.*, 1965; Kasuya and Ichihara, 1965; Paulus, 1964; Brown, 1965; and others).

Order Carnivora. This order stands in the third place in the number of works devoted to structural variability (after rodents and primates). As in other orders, it is not possible to quote all the works related to the study of morphological variability for the representatives of this order, but the list given introduces one to the scale and various approaches of such studies (Kuznetsov, 1941a, 1941b; Popov, 1959, 1960; Fateev, 1961; Belyaev, 1962; Bogolyubskii, 1941; Gerasimova, 1958; Krushinskii, 1946; Ognev, 1935; Pavlinin, 1962-65; Romashov and Il'ina, 1943; Smirnov, 1962; Kurtén and Rausch, 1959; Kurtén, 1964, 1965a, 1965b, Rausch, 1963; Harlow, 1962; Hysing-Dahl, 1954, 1959; Schmid, 1940; Bader, 1955; Crusafont-Pairó and Truyols-Santonja, 1956; Latimer, 1936, 1944; 1944a, 1961; Sauer and Ruble, 1946; Voipio, 1962; Wood, McCowan and Daniel, 1965; and others).

Order Pinnipedia. Works on the structural variability of pinnipeds have begun to appear mainly within recent years (Popov, 1959, 1961; Bel'kovich and Yablokov, 1960; Yablokov and Serzhent, 1963; Fedoseev and Yablokov, 1965; Fedoseev, 1965; Khuzin, 1963, 1964; Bychkov, 1965; Yablokov, 1963a, 1963b, 1964a; Scheffer, 1962, 1964). Detailed references to the works on variability of pinnipeds are given in Chapter III.

Order Perissodactyla, Artiodactyla (even- and odd-toed ungulates). Data on the structural variability of ungulates in comparatively small (Tsalkin, 1956, 1960; Sokolov, 1960; Demidova, 1941; Paaver, 1964; Tumurzhav, 1964; Segal', 1962; Mezhzherin, 1965; Bader, 1955; Tribe and Peel, 1963; Bergerud, 1964; Anderson *et al.*, 1965; McMeekan, 1940; Shaw, 1929; Klein, 1964; and others).

Data on the structural variability of other mammalian orders are very scanty, or I do not know them (Newman, 1913 on Edentata; Bothma, 1966 on Hyracoidea and none for Monotremata, Dermoptera, Pholidota, Tubulidentata, Proboscidea, and Sirenia).

While concluding this short survey of works on the structural variability of mammals, mention must be made of the ever-increasing stream of publications concerned with discontinuous variability of the type called epigenetic polymorphism, for quite diverse kinds of mammals (Berry, 1963; Berry and Searle, 1963; Dunn, *et al.*, 1937; Dunn *et al.*, 1960; Stein, 1963; Puček, 1962; Brownell, 1964; and many others). This approach is examined in greater detail below in a special section of this chapter.

Many examples and many factual data on structural variability of mammals are presented further in this chapter as well as in other chapters of this work and also in the Appendix. On the whole, it may be concluded that structural variability is the type which provides the basic material in the current study of population morphology of mammals.

Physiological and biochemical variability

Functional variability. Functional variability is the variability of the characteristic functions of different systems of organs, individual organs, and the organism as a whole.

There is an appreciable literature on the physiology of mammals in which the question of variation in the physiological functions of organisms in different conditions has been studied. But in the majority of these works, the variability has not been examined by the method we want. This can be explained not only, and not very much, by the complex and troublesome work this approach requires, but rather by the neglect of physiologists to study the population as a whole. In this regard, the work of B. P. Ushakov (1959a, 1959b) is very interesting; it shows what important theoretical conclusions can be drawn from functional researches in population variability.

It is natural that the works of functional morphology and physiology be very close to each other. Likewise, all the works on variability in weight of organs are definitely very close to the phenomenon of functional variability because they offer conclusions directly related to the study of physiological features and the intensity of metabolism in animals. That is why these traits are called "morpho-physiological" traits in current works (Schwartz, 1959, 1962; a summary of data on physiological variability of mammals is also given there).

An example of functional variability in mammals is a work which studies the prolongation of periods of apnea in the seal *Leptonichotes wedelli* under natural conditions (Littlepage, 1963). A. V. Pokrovskii (1962) analyzed variability of the rate of attaining sexual maturity in females of *Lagurus lagurus* during the major part of a year. The experiments of Ponomarev (1944) and Kalkowski (1966) in determining temperatures proffered by martens are interesting and exact from a methodological point of view. Analogical work on mice has been conducted in experimental ecology (partial summary by N. V. Bashenina, 1962).

The data of Korotova (1962) on ascorbic acid and glycogen content in the liver and sugar in the blood, and of Sidorkin and Mikhalev (1964), Denisova (1966), House *et al.* (1961), and Groulage (1961) on protein fractions of blood plasma, should also be grouped under functional or physiological variability, though these works are more concerned with biochemical variability, which undoubtedly has an independent importance in the life of a population. The data of Newson and Chitty (1962) on variability of the quantity of blood hemoglobin is in the same category.

Recently, it has become known that it is necessary and possible to investigate biochemical aspects of purely chemical variability (Vinogradov, 1964). These investigations show that different populations of organisms have different chemical compositions and give the variability of these indices.

An analysis of the data presented above allows one to conclude that for ascertaining the finer details of each population, the study of functional (physiological) and biochemical variability is quite possible and useful.

Ethological variability. This is the variability of characteristic behavior. Very little study of this type of variability has been carried out by zoologists. However, it is necessary to draw attention to the fact that broadly speaking variability of behavior is shown by the immediate reaction of an organism to environmental changes. It is very clear that before physiological or biochemical changes take place, or still further, before the appearance of morphological changes in the structure of a trait takes place, an active change in the behavior of the animal occurs under the effect of the changed conditions (Bei-Bienko, 1959). In this way, the study of variability of behavior takes the researcher very close to those first steps of micro-evolution which are the first reactions of all populations of higher animals to changed conditions in their lives.

Because of the complexities involved in studying this type of variability and similarly, because of an insufficient appreciation of the importance of obtaining information on the character of a population, our knowledge in this field is very meager.

The work of M. P. Kol'tsova-Sadovnikova (1931) on the psychological peculiarities of rats of different genetical lines may be cited as an example of a detailed work in this line known to me. The animals were let out in a maze with closed doors; the problem was to find food by the shortest route and then to remember this route (which was calculated in terms of time taken for passing through the maze). Our analysis of the factual data in this work showed that there were no differences in the value of variability of time taken by laboratory-bred versus wild rats (Table 36).

Table 36. Variability of behavior of wild and laboratory rats (Absolute values have been taken from the data of Kol'tsova-Sadovnikova, 1931)

	Line "Abrashka"		"Wild" rats		$t_{\bar{x}}$	$t_{c.v.}$
	$\bar{x} \pm s_{\bar{x}}$	$c.v. \pm s_{c.v.}$	$\bar{x} \pm s_{\bar{x}}$	$c.v. \pm s_{c.v.}$		
Log of number of minutes taken to traverse the maze	1.675 ± 0.016	20.3 ± 0.66	2.642 ± 0.043	22.0 ± 1.15	-2.1	-1.2
Mean errors for 10 experiments	58.33 ± 11.79	135.4 ± 14.3	55.00 ± 2.91	54.5 ± 3.74	$+0.3$	$+5.4$

At the same time these populations vary significantly $(t=2.1)$ in the absolute value of the logarithm of the number of minutes taken to traverse the maze.   While the number of errors committed when conducting the experiment between the wild and the laboratory lines are non-significant $(t=1.2)$, for variability of this trait, the differences are highly significant $(t=5.4)$.   In this way the study of variability showed that wild rats are psychologically homogeneous. This can be understood from an ecological point of view.   In the laboratory, selection on "sharpness" or "quick wits" was absent for many generations, whereas among the wild rats the inferior animals died soon. A number of works on genetics devoted to analyzing behavioral peculiarities of different genetically pure lines have appeared recently. In these works (for example, R. Anthony, 1966; P. L. Broadhurst and J. L. Jinks, 1966), interesting data are given for mice and rats on activity in open space, crossing obstacles, frequency of defecation, running away from water, and other such parameters of behavior.

In the work of St. Skoczeń (1962) there are data which show that the composition of samples changes, depending on the method of catching and the time of day. (The mole *Talpa europaea* was studied.)   In the morning, considerably more males are caught, while more females are caught in the evening. The data of T. V. Koshkina (1964) show a significant difference between the frequency with which males and females fell into various types of traps—spiral or grooved. Bank voles (*Clethrionomys glareolus*) were investigated.

There are data on the variability of parameters (like measurements, volume, weight) of tree nests built by golden mice (*Peromyscus nuttalli*) in Texas (Packard and Garner, 1964), which again can be taken as a typical variability of behavior.

All these studies point to the fact that there is a specific sexual dimorphism in the behavior of animals (see also Krushinskii, 1946), the variability of which should be investigated in different populations. At present such fine ecological investigations are not a great necessity, but it may be remembered that only 20 to 25 years ago investigations were carried out on samples of animals obtained at different times, at different places, and of different sexes; now taxonomy requires samples of each population having one sex and the same stage of growth. There is no doubt that ethologists will also have to pass to the next step, i.e., the within-population level of investigation, by using morphological and other methods of study.

Manifestation of Variability

We have now data for differentiating the following manifestations of variability: time, weight, linear, and volume measurements; colorimetry; variability of surface area, of angles, and of temperature. All these manifestations of variability are examined below in detail because such a classification is being done for the first time.

Variability of time. Variability of time is the variability in duration of some life process.

A good example of such variability is the data presented by Hall and Schaller (1964) on the variability of time spent by *Enhydra lutris* while obtaining different types of food: molluscs, sea urchins, and fish. Another example of time variability is the data on the time spent out of water and in water by the Antarctic seal *Leptonichotes wedelli* (Littlepage, 1963). Finally, the above-mentioned data by M. P. Kol'tsova-Sadovnikova (1931) on the variability of time taken by rats of different populations to traverse a maze, can be cited as an example.

There are further examples of variability of time. Data on the variability of lifetime in rats maintained on food with or without vitamins are presented by John Gowen (1936), and A. V. Pokrovskii (1962) have studied the variability of time taken to attain maturity in females of *Lagurus lagurus* depending upon the season of birth (Table 37).

Table 37. **Variability of time taken to attain sexual maturity in** *Lagurus lagurus* (**Absolute values, according to the data of Pokrovskii, 1962**)

Month of birth	Time taken to sexual maturity (days)	
	$\bar{x} \pm s_{\bar{x}}$	$c.\,v. \pm s_{c.v.}$
January	84.5 ± 5.05	28.6 ± 4.22
May	21.6 ± 0.75	14.4 ± 2.47
June	55.9 ± 10.55	65.5 ± 13.1
October	140.9 ± 14.9	35.7 ± 7.77

It is seen from this table that there is no direct relationship between variability and the time taken for sexual maturity. This means that in this case the coefficient of variation may be an important independent character revealing specific biological facets of the animal under study.

Interesting data on the variability of time taken for passing different types of food through the intestinal tract and the time taken for its excretion in various types of mice are presented in the work of A. Kostelecka-Myrcha and Myrcha (1964).

As seen above, the study of time variability is usually associated with the study of physiological (functional) and psychological (ethological) variability.

Variability of weight. This is the variability of the weight of an organism, a system of organs, an organ, or their parts.

Variability of weight is one of the most usual manifestations of variability with which researchers have to deal during the analysis of data concerning population morphology.

The dependence of weight variability on seasonal factors, sex, growth, and the general condition of the animal makes it an interesting index— one which should be given foremost ecological and physiological importance (Schwartz, 1960, 1964). This fact is at once illustrated by the comparative data on variability of weight and variability of other traits obtained from an analysis of the data of W. E. Castle *et al.* (1938). In this work the effect of reciprocal crosses in various combinations was studied where the separate phenotypes of male and female mice were compared (black, brown, dark or light colors, etc.). It was observed that the variability of weight was correlated with the linear variability.

In another series of experiments (Castle, 1938), the increase and decrease in variability of body weight exactly coincides with the trends of variability of body and tail length. Moreover, it is important to note that in this case the variability in each individual phenotype seemed to be higher than the variability of all the males and females in the population. Finally, in a third series of experiments with different phenotypes of one population, an average situation is met when the coefficient of variation for weight (and also for other traits) for the whole population appears about average as compared to its values for the seven individual phenotypes. These features were not noticed by the authors, either in the first or the second case, because Castle and his colleagues failed to calculate the coefficients of variation.

The study of variability of weight as a method of genetical research is promising not only in experimental populations. There are a number of examples where variability of weight has been used for the study of ecological aspects of a population in nature. Data from the work of S. S. Schwartz (1960) on variability of the relative[6] weight of organs in various populations of hamsters can be presented (Table 38).

Unfortunately, the errors of the coefficients of variation have not been given in that work, which makes it difficult to carry out an exact comparison of the magnitude of variability of different populations; but even from the data presented, it can be concluded that the populations investigated have, perhaps, rather different relations with environmental factors.

In the case cited, the differences between populations were clearly manifested only between the groups of animals having similar age and

---

[6] The question of variability of relative and absolute indices has been specially discussed in Chapter V.

Table 38. Variability of weights of certain traits of *Citellus pygmaeus* **from different populations (Schwartz, 1960)**

Group	Population	Coefficient of variation of relative weight for			
		Heart	Liver	Pancreas	Kidneys
Adult males	I	6.7	21.4	46.8	—
	II	19.7	9.0	21.0	14.9
Immature females	I	22.2	16.4	21.6	—
	II	15.4	12.0	13.7	—

sex (adult males in one case and immature females in the other). It is clear that all these differences would have been nullified if the variability of the population had been calculated without forming any groups. For an exact comparison of populations in such a case, it is necessary to compare them not only for one season but during the same year. This rule is especially important in the study of the variability of mammalian populations having short life spans.

The situation given in the foregoing paragraph is well illustrated from the data calculated on the basis of variability of body weight of the common shrew (*Sorex araneus*) caught in consecutive years in a single population; the data are presented in Table 39.

Table 39. Variability of body weight of the common shrew (*Sorex araneus*) in different months and years in the same population (Calculated from data of Borowski and Dehnel, 1953)

Month	1949 $c.\,v.\pm s_{c.v.}$	1950 $c.\,v.\pm s_{c.v.}$	t_{49-50}
June	14.8±1.46	23.7±3.84	—2.19
July	10.0±0.94	28.0±4.54	—3.89
August	11.7±0.95	10.0±1.17	+1.15
September	12.2±1.10	13.1±1.97	—0.39

As seen from the data presented in Table 40, the variability of the body weight of shrews of the same population in different years and in different months of the year differs significantly, and these differences are comparable to the differences in variability for different populations within a species.

There are many more works on the variability of weight. Some of them, with data calculated by myself, have been presented in other parts of this book. Different research workers have investigated this variability

Table 40. Variability of body weight of the common shrew (*Sorex araneus*) **in different populations** ($c.\ v. \pm s_{c.v.}$) **(All calculations are ours)**

Animal reserve of Ok. (Dolgov, 1963)	Belovezh-1 (Puček, 1956)	Belovezh-2 (Borowski and Dehnel, 1953)
June-August	June-September	June-August
9.7±0.68 (males) 9.7±1.82 (females)	8.7±1.14—13.9±1.79	10.0±1.17—28.0±4.45

of weight in unexpected ways, in an attempt to ferret out some exact and significant traits. For example, data are presented on variability of hair weight in relation to the square of body length in the work of F. B. Sumner (1903). The variability of hide weight of wild animals of different ages is presented in the investigations of V. Scheffer (1962) on fur seals. The weight of the skull and its individual parts, the total musculature and separate functional muscle groups, weight of intestines and stomach, weight of eyeball and eye lens, in fact the weight of practically all the internal organs has been studied (see Chapter II and the Appendix).

On the whole, it may be said that all those research workers are right who discern in the weights of organisms of a population an important tool for knowing the characteristics of populations. One can only add to this that the study of variability of weights deepens the investigations of populations and permits conclusions to be drawn which otherwise would have slipped from the observation of researchers had they calculated only the absolute parameters.

Linear variability. This is the variability of linear parameters for an organism, a system of organs, individual organs and their parts.

The study of variability of linear measurements appears to be the kind most widely used in mammals. Body measurements for individual parts of the skeleton, intestinal tract, and hair, and linear measurements of organs and individual cells are studied. It was linear variability which until now served as a foundation in works on the taxonomy of vertebrates. Linear variability has great significance in the study of population morphology because it presents methodological advantages such as simplicity and accuracy of measurements.

Linear variability, like variability of weight, is related to the sex and age composition of a sample and also to the seasonal availability in obtaining samples. This fact regarding seasonal (and in that way, chronological) variability is still used very little today in investigations on morphology of animals. Because of this, data from many investigations cannot be utilized for an exact comparison.

This situation compels us to examine in detail certain examples of the relationship of variability of linear values to the influence of chronological factors (Table 41).

Table 41. Variability (*c. v.*±*s*c.v.) **of a number of traits in small mammals by months (Calculated from data on variability presented in the works of Adamczewska, 1959 and Borowski and Dehnel, 1953)**

Month	*Apodemus flavicollis*			*Sorex araneus*
	Foot length	Ear length	Tail length	Body length
June	7.1±0.60	10.5±0.87	—	4.9±0.79
July	5.2±0.23	8.0±0.36	—	8.4±1.37
August	5.2±0.36	7.6±0.52	31.5±2.25	4.8±0.82
September	4.1±0.17	5.0±0.21	22.1±0.97	4.4±0.66
October	5.8±0.62	5.7±0.60	12.3±1.45	2.0±0.38
November	4.0±0.31	5.0±0.38	11.4±0.91	—

It can be seen from the data in Table 41 how significantly (in some instances by more than a factor of two) the variability of a single trait changes during half an year.

The difference in the variability of linear traits for a single population of mammals from year to year is not less significant. From the results obtained by me as a result of calculations made on data of body length of the common shrew in Belovezh (Tables 42 and 43), one specific conclusion can be drawn : The variability of the same trait in a population can sharply deviate from year to year. It is interesting to note that though the absolute values of these deviations are not always significant, the trend toward increase or decrease of variability can be detected quite clearly. For example, during a comparison of data on variability of shrews born in the 1946-47 season, with similar data for shrews born in the seasons of 1947-48 and 1949-50, for the majority of those months in which the data were collected, the variability in the season 1946-47 was low (in seven instances out of nine). Further, during the comparison of variability in the seasons of 1947-48 and 1949-50, the variability in the latter season appeared to be higher in all eight cases. The variability of the traits studied was also higher in the 1949-50 season when compared with the 1950-51 season. The same trend was likewise observed during the comparison of mean yearly values of variability.

Another example is taken from the work of V. N. Pavlinin (1962) (Table 44). From the data presented in this table it is seen that the variability of linear traits of the skull varies absolutely and characteristically in different years. Of the four traits investigated in both males and females,

Table 42. **Chronological variability** $(c.v. \pm s_{c.v.})$ **of body length of the common shrew** (*Sorex araneus*) **(Calculated on the basis of data on variability presented in the work of Borowski and Dehnel, 1953)**

Month	1946/47	1947/48	1949/50	1950/51
June ..	—	3.8 ±0.30	4.0±0.21	3.6±0.38
July ..	—	3.8 ±0.18	4.6±0.15	4.5±0.28
August ..	—	4.1 ±0.21	4.7±0.14	4.1±0.38
September ..	—	3.6 ±0.29	4.9±0.33	4.1±0.42
October ..	—	4.5 ±0.65	5.7±0.70	—
April ..	4.3±0.43	6.8 ±0.53	—	—
May ..	3.6±0.63	5.10±0.60	—	—
June ..	4.9±0.65	3.8 ±0.28	8.4±1.37	—
July ..	3.6±0.48	4.4 ±0.41	4.9±0.79	—
August ..	4.3±0.54	4.6 ±0.36	4.8±0.82	—
September ..	5.0±0.52	—	4.4±0.66	—
October ..	—	—	2.0±0.38	—
Average ..	4.3	4.5	4.8	4.1

Table 43. **Comparison of difference** (t) **in the variability of body length in the common shrew born in different years (From the data of Table 42)**

Month	1946/47— 1947/48	1946/47— 1949/50	1947/48— 1949/50	1947/48 — 1950/51	1949/50— 1950/51
June ..	—	—	−0.58	+0.40	+1.15
July ..	—	—	−3.38	−2.06	+0.03
August ..	—	—	−2.36	0.0	+1.46
September ..	—	—	−2.89	−1.00	+1.49
October ..	—	—	−1.25	—	—
April ..	−3.59	—	—	—	—
May ..	−1.76	−1.97	−1.85	—	—
June ..	+1.59	—	—	—	—
July ..	−1.29	−1.39	−0.56	—	—
August ..	−0.49	−0.54	−0.33	—	—
September ..	—	+0.69	—	—	—

Table 44. Chronological variability of skull traits of a population of American mink (*Mustela vison*) in Bashkir (Calculated on the basis of data presented in the work of Pavlinin, 1962)

Trait	1957/58 $c.\,v.\pm s_{c.v.}$	1958/59 $c.\,v.\pm s_{c.v.}$	t_{1-2}
Condylobasal length :			
Males	4.4±0.6	2.8±0.4	+2.22
Females	2.3±0.3	2.9±0.4	−1.20
Width of zygomatic arch:			
Males	12.0±1.7	5.6±0.8	+3.35
Females	6.4±0.9	5.0±0.7	+1.23
Width between orbits :			
Males	6.6±0.9	7.2±1.0	−0.44
Females	7.9±1.1	6.5±0.9	+0.42
Width of snout :			
Males	8.5±1.2	5.1±0.7	+2.43
Females	6.3±0.9	4.5±0.7	+1.64

in the season of 1958-59, the variability was higher for three traits.

The linear variability is clearly related to the variability of age and sex. The relation of linear variability to sex variability in morphology and ecology of animals has been examined also in Table 44. The fact that the degree of difference among females is somewhat lower than among males, immediately attracts attention.

On the whole it can be said that the phenomenon of linear variability, perhaps better called the variability of linear traits, which appears to be very simple and clear at first sight, seems to be related to a whole complex of other factors in natural populations. This shows the desirability of studying linear variability in relation to other phenomena.

Variability of volume. This refers to the variability of volume of an organism, a system of organs, individual organs and their parts.

Theoretically, it could be imagined that the variability of volume is not less important or significant than weight and linear variabilities. However, the works on variability of volume are not many. These few references confirm the possibility of using volume traits for characterizing a population as a whole and also individual groups within a population. The data on variability of volume of stomach and intestines for minks show that the males are quite different from the females in this respect (Table 46).

Specific differences in the variability of the volume of skull have been observed in the work of J. Hromada and L. Strnad (1962), who studied the craniology of *Macaca* (Table 46).

It is seen from the data in this table that the variability of volume appears to differ among age groups : for example, between infants and adults of *M. rhesus* and between Young I and Young II in *M. cynomolgus;* and between animals of different sexes (between males and females of Young I and Young II groups in *M. cynomolgus*).

Table 45.　Variability of volume of stomach and intestines in (*Mustela vison*) **and fox** (*Vulpes vulpes*) **(Calculated from the data of Sokolov, 1941)**

		Males $c.\,v. \pm s_{c.v.}$	Females $c.\,v. \pm s_{c.v.}$	$t\mathord{\raise1pt\hbox{$\circlearrowleft$}}\mathord{\raise1pt\hbox{$\circ$}}$
		Minks		
Stomach	..	6.1±0.82	12.9±1.86	−3.79
Intestine	..	9.7±1.27	10.5±1.55	−0.38
		Foxes		
Stomach	..	9.1±1.37	16.6±2.04	−2.20
Intestine	..	12.5±1.97	12.6±1.71	−0.01

Table 46.　Variability $(c.\,v. \pm s_{c.v.})$ **of volume of skull in two species of** *Macaca* **(According to Hromada and Strnad, 1962, with addition of calculated error of coefficient of variation)**

Age group		M. rhesus		M. cynomolgus	
		Males	Females	Males	Females
Infants	..	8.8±0.72	8.0±0.75	—	—
Young I	..	10.1±0.83	9.3±0.69	7.3±0.96	13.3±2.35
Young II	..	13.0±1.96	9.3±1.60	13.7±1.37	8.9±0.95
Adult	..	13.0±2.11		11.5±1.46	11.8±0.77

Variability of volume is very closely related to variability of weight and possibly should be taken as a part of the latter. However, the behavior of the coefficient of variation[7] of volume traits does not always coincide with the behavior of weight traits (see Chapter V).

As can be concluded from the above examples of variability of volume, this manifestation of variability can be compared with any other

---

[7] Some expressions usually used in mathematics but not in biological works, are found herein, for example : "behavior of coefficient of variation," "behavior of curve," etc. These expressions represent exactly the phenomenon under consideration and so I think they may be used in some cases.

manifestation with regard to the coefficients of variation, and so there is no reason why the variability of volume should not be studied during investigations of a population.

Meristic variability. Meristic or countable variability is the variability in number of discrete elements in an individual system of organs or in life processes.

The study of the variability of meristic traits is quite tempting from several viewpoints: First, the arresting exactness and objectivity of the data obtained; and second, as will be shown below, the meristic traits are among the most stable because they are little affected by chronological and age variabilities. Nevertheless, the last statement is not always correct and traits like number of hair on a unit area of body surface are affected by age and seasonal variability. Similarly, the number of small glands of different types in the digestive tract of animals is affected by the sharp differences in the food of various seasons. The number of such examples can be increased. They show that somewhere here lies the line of demarcation between qualitative and quantitative variability.

Some of the known meristic traits being used in morphological investigations of a population, should undoubtedly be attributed to qualitative variability (number of vertebrae or ribs; number of individual elements in hands and feet; number of embryos, etc.); but another part of the meristic traits, with the same specificity, should be attributed to quantitative variability (number of hair; number of sensory endings in the skin and other organs; number of glands in the surface of the digestive tract; number of cells in histological structures, etc.).

Because of the need for a precise demarcation of the phenomenon of quantitative and qualitative variability of meristic traits, an approach proposed by N. A. Bernshtein (1962) appears to be interesting : "That subclass of the arguments which we considered as 'insignificant' (in the sense of Gel'fand-Tsetlin), mainly determines the continuous traits (measurements, angles, amplitudes of movements, etc.) and forms the corresponding variable populations. In other cases, where the changes are discrete and related to phenomena of comparatively large numbers like, for example, numbers of hair on the head, cells or the synaptic contacts in the cerebral cortex, etc., instead of a discontinuous variability, there appears a variability having all the characters of randomization. The determination of one or another large number obtained in each individual case (number of cones of the fovea centralis of the retina, Purkinje cells, cilia of chorion cells, etc.) has all the characters of accidental processes which do not in any manner separate it from the laws of causality. However, this situation places an important biological question before us : Where lies the line of demarcation between the area of the numbers which can be exactly determined and which are not changed by heredity, and the area where the accidental and random processes and numbers dominate the species ?" (pp. 62-63).

While answering the question, N. A. Bernshtein concludes : "...The numerical investigations carried out on those frontiers of study where deterministic exactness yields to variation and chance, are interesting from the point of view of answering this question. In morphogenesis, the determined quantities do not exceed two-figure numbers (number of vertebrae or teeth in animals of one species; number of legs, fingers, eyes, cyto-architectural fields in the brain; etc.). After this, in my opinion, in a parallel and corresponding action, comes the jump from the determinable to the accidental...." (p. 63).

In the light of the data presented in this work, it is seen that the demarcation between random aud determined quantities carried out by Bernshtein (1962) is not exact. Many examples of wide variations in the number of teeth in different mammals are known. Moreover, it is important to note that only in the toothed whales are there all the gradations from truly randomized distribution of number of teeth in some species of dolphins to an exactly determined number of teeth in others (more than in Carnivora, Rodentia, and Ungulata) (Yablokov, 1958). The common dolphin (*Delphinus delphis*) can be cited as an example of the first type; it has the highest number of teeth among all mammals (reaching 240 in number). The beaked whale (*Ziphius*) and narwhale (*Monodon monoceros*), which have only one to four teeth, can be cited as examples of the second type. It is important to note that there are all types of transitions between these extreme situations. Unfortunately, data on exact quantitative variability of organs of this system in cetaceans are very scanty. But those few that have been obtained are of interest (Table 47).

To analyze these data in the desired manner, it has to be noted that the white whale has the fewest teeth of the three species being compared (seven

Table 47. Variability ($c. v. \pm s_{c.v.}$) **of number of teeth in certain toothed whales (According to the data of Kleinenberg, 1956, and the author)**

	Bottlenosed dolphin (*Tursiops truncatus*)		Common dolphin (*Delphinus delphis*)		White whale (*Delphinapterus leucas*)	
	Females	Males	Females	Males	Females	Males
			Lower Jaw			
Left ..	5.4 0.82	6.7 ± 1.44	5.2 ± 1.05	5.1 ± 0.82	13.8 ± 3.69	9.1 ± 1.01
Right ..	4.8 0.74	7.3 ± 1.72	5.2 ± 1.06	5.6 ± 0.98		
			Upper Jaw			
Left ..	4.1 ± 0.59	3.9 ± 0.77	5.2 ± 1.05	6.2 ± 0.95	11.4 ± 3.05	8.0 ± 0.88
Right ..	5.5 ± 0.79	6.5 ± 1.23	4.5 ± 0.95	5.7 ± 0.88		

to nine teeth on each side of the jaw); the bottlenosed dolphin has 19 to 21 teeth in each half of the upper and lower jaws; and finally, the common dolphin has 41 to 44 teeth in each half of the upper and lower jaws. We then see that the variability in number of teeth is inversely proportional to their numbers, i.e., the more teeth, the lower the variability. Such an exact corresponding relationship (Chapter V), to the elementary regularities of variability, at once makes investigations difficult "where deterministic exactness yields to variation and chance" (Bernshtein, 1962) and makes the solution of the question more interesting.

On the basis of the available data on population morphology, it may be said that the jump—from deterministic to random, which N. A. Bernshtein writes about—lies somewhere within the limits of such traits as number of extremities, eyes, vertebrae, fingers, and teeth. All these traits are susceptible to a rather noticeable variability in mammals, even within an order of mammals, i.e., cetaceans. The number of eyes in toothed whales varies from two to none (eye being understood here as an organ functioning for sight, and in this sense it is absent in certain river dolphins (Platanistidae); the number of extremities varies from two to four. Well-developed hind extremities have been recorded in *Physeter catodon* (Zemskii and Berzin, 1961). The number of fingers in cetaceans varies from five to three. The variability in number of teeth has already been discussed above. The data reveal the variability of vertebrae in practically all regions, even the neck (Beddard, 1900).

Significant data on variability of number of caudal vertebrae in other aquatic mammals, certain species of Pinnipedia, have been obtained by us (Table 48).

Table 48. Variability of number of caudal vertebrae in certain pinnipeds (Adult males)

Species	$\bar{x} \pm s_{\bar{x}}$	$c.\,v. \pm s_{c.v.}$	Remarks
Hooded seal (*Cystophora cristata*)	14.0 ± 0.17	6.6 ± 0.84	Yan-Maien region, 1962
Greenland seal (*Pagophilus groenlandicus*)	13.4 ± 0.12	7.8 ± 0.62	White Sea region, 1961
	12.6 ± 0.11	4.5 ± 0.61	Newfoundland region, 1963
Common seal (*Phoca vitulina*)	12.8 ± 0.14	6.5 ± 0.81	Okhotsk Sea, 1963
Bearded seal (*Erignathus barbatus*)	11.9 ± 0.25	8.0 ± 1.51	Okhotsk Sea, 1963
Baikal seal (*Pusa sibirica*)	13.0 ± 0.09	4.4 ± 0.53	
Caspian seal (*Pusa caspica*)	12.1 ± 0.28	9.3 ± 0.58	
Ringed seal (*Pusa hispida*)	13.4 ± 0.29	8.1 ± 1.91	Okhotsk Sea, Taui, 1963
	12.9 ± 0.03	1.5 ± 0.14	Pechora Sea, 1962

Even these limited data show that the number of vertebrae varies considerably not only among different species but within each species; coefficients of variation reach up to 8 or 9%. It may be remembered here that pinnipeds have a very short tail and in animals with long tails, for example in whales, the number of vertebrae may vary more significantly. The difference in the variability of such an insignificant trait as the number of caudal vertebrae among different species of pinnipeds would appear to be significant.   In the Pechora seal the coefficient of variation is only 1.5% and in the Caspian seal it is six times more ! Such large differences could hardly be explained on the basis of randomness. As shown in our investigations on the ice of the White Sea, the tail of the Greenland seal plays an important role in coital behavior in the breeding season, indicating the degree to which the female is ready to copulate with the given male, and the degree to which the male is ready to fight for her and follow her. Thus it would appear that a less significant trait takes on an important biological significance.

Coming back to the problem of classification of variability in mammalian populations, one must observe what phenomena the meristic variability of traits is associated with and to what extent this variability can characterize the population as a whole and also the groups within a population. From the data already presented, it can be concluded that the variability of the same trait may be different in different species. Interesting data on the variability in number of phalanges for the second and third fingers of cetaceans have been obtained from the work of I. I. Barabash-Nikiforov (1940) (Table 48a).

Table 48a. Variability in number of phalanges for 2nd and 3rd fingers in different populations of the common dolphin (*Delphinus delphis*) **(Absolute indices have been taken from the data of Barabash-Nikiforov, 1940)**

Region	$\bar{x} \pm s_{\bar{x}}$	$c.\,v. \pm s_{v.c.}$	Region	$\bar{x} \pm s_{\bar{x}}$	$c.\,v. \pm s_{c.v.}$
Yalta ..	7.83 ± 0.05	4.7 ± 0.48	Batumy ..	7.60 ± 0.08	6.7 ± 0.71
	5.94 ± 0.05	6.2 ± 0.63		5.78 ± 0.06	7.1 ± 0.79
				l_{y-n}	l_{y-b}
Novorossiisk ..	7.82 ± 0.05	5.0 ± 0.42	2nd finger ..	-0.47	-2.32
	5.96 ± 0.06	8.6 ± 0.71	3rd finger ..	-2.51	-0.90

The next example of the use of meristic variability is also concerned with the variability of certain structures of cetaceans, this time on baleen whales (Mystacoceti) (Table 49).

It is seen that the variability of the number of vibrissae on the upper jaw is greater than for the lower jaw; moreover, the difference in variability in this case is not governed by elementary regularities (Chapter V),

Table 49. Variability of number of vibrissae on different parts of head of the finwhale (*Balaenoptera physalus*) (**Kuril Island, 1959**)

Portion of head		$\bar{x} \pm s_{\bar{x}}$	$c.\ v. \pm s_{c.v.}$	n
Lower jaw, anterior	..	34.8±1.46	23.7±2.97	32
The same, sides	..	8.5±0.38	27.3±3.21	36
The same, total	..	52.8±2.01	20.6±2.70	29
Total on upper jaw	..	21.1±1.45	32.4±4.88	22
Total on the head	..	73.4±2.80	16.4±2.70	19

so there is a basis for postulating the presence of specific functional and ecological reasons which create the given situation. Such reasons have been worked out in previous studies (Bel'kovich and Yablokov, 1963; Yablokov, 1963b; Yablokov and Klevezal', 1964), and they are discussed in detail in Chapter VI of the present work. Here it should be emphasized that the meristic variability in this case appears to be strongly related to the functional characteristic of the organ.

In this connection, other data on the variability of another trait—the number of individual fringes in 1 cm of whalebone sheets—in baleen whales are interesting (Table 50).

Table 50. Variability of number of fringes on 1 cm of the edge of a plate in certain baleen whales* (Adult animals)

Species	$\bar{x} \pm s_{\bar{x}}$	$c.\ v. \pm s_{c.v.}$	n	Remarks
Blue whale (*Balaenoptera musculus*)	30.1±1.77	26.2±4.15	21	
Finwhale (*B. physalus*)	24.6±1.18	21.4±3.39	20	Male of 18.9 meter length
Lesser rorqual (*B. acutorostrata*)	20.0±1.05	18.1±3.69	12	
Humpback whale (*Megaptera nodosa*)	18.4±0.82	19.8±3.14	20	

* The calculations of different baleen plates, taken from the same animal, were carried out by a Diploma student of the Vertebrate Zoology section of Moscow State University, T. V. Andreeva.

It is known that the sheets of whalebone with fringed edges represent a portion of the filtering apparatus for baleen whales. Details are insufficient about the function of this structure. The data presented on variability in number of fringes show that in *Balaenoptera musculus,* which eats plankton and crustaceans, the variability of fringes is greatest, and in the humpback whale and lesser rorqual, which feed more on fishes than the others, the variability is least.   Such an interrelationship cannot be accidental and needs further careful ecological investigation.

From the scanty data in the literature on the meristic variability of mammals, interesting results have been obtained by us from an analysis of data of F. Sumner (1909) on the number of hair per unit of body surface in mice depending upon their living conditions ($c. v. \pm s_{c.v.}$ and t) :

Males		Females	
Hot	Cold	Hot	Cold
11.7 ± 2.49	$12.9 \pm 2,52$	15.2 ± 3.80	17.7 ± 4.43
t♂♂ hot-cold	t♀♀ hot-cold	t♂♀ cold	t♂♀ hot
-0.34	-0.43	-0.76	-1.13

A comparison of the coefficients of variation shows that, although the differences are not significant statistically in even a single case, some specific trends exhibit themselves uniformly :

1.   Variability in the cold room is greater than in the hot room;

2.   Variability of this trait in males is less than in females, both in the cold and hot rooms.

The material presented is sufficient to show not only the possibility but even the desirability for wide use of meristic traits in the study of mammalian populations.

Colorimetric variability.   This is the color intensity of an organism and of different systems of organs.

Variability of colorimetric traits and the nature of mammalian structure is many-sided in expression.   First, it is possible to determine variability of intensity in some color with the help of a densitometer or photometer; secondly, it is possible to measure variability of area occupied by the colored field.   The last method actually belongs to another type of variability—variability of field area—but in addition to changes in the field area, in many instances the variability of color can be expressed simply by linear measurements of the length of white patches on the tail or individual hair, number of hair of a particular color, by number of homogeneous patches on the surface, etc.

But the variability of colorimetric traits must be taken as most typical (more or less intense color with regard to some shade).

Let us examine some examples of colorimetric variability.   Hemoglobin content of blood measured with the help of a hemoglobinometer is widely used in the studies of mammals.   In the work of John Newson and D. Chitty (1962) it is shown that the hemoglobin content of the blood of field voles (*Microtus agrestis*) is not directly correlated with the size of the spleen. An examination of the coefficients of variation for this trait (Table 51) permits one to draw a more exact and specific conclusion: The greater the weight of the spleen, the lesser the variability in quantity of hemoglobin.

A determination of the variability of hemoglobin content in the blood of white-footed mice (*Peromyscus*) depending on whether they are infected with botflies allows one to notice characters of comparable groups that escaped the attention of the author of the paper (Table 52).

Only some higher values of hemoglobin and hematocrit in non-infected animals are given in the paper, but on the basis of data presented in Table 52 we can see a greater stability of these traits in healthy animals and a greater variability in infected animals.

Table 51. Variability of hemoglobin quantity in the blood of field voles (Absolute data taken from Newson and Chitty, 1962)

Weight of spleen (mg)	Females		Males	
	$\bar{x} \pm s_{\bar{x}}$	$c.\,v. \pm s_{c.v.}$	$\bar{x} \pm s_{\bar{x}}$	$c.\,v. \pm s_{c.v.}$
Less than 100	111.6±2.85	8.8±1.80	—	—
100—250	101.5±2.53	8.6±1.76	—	—
251—630	102.7±2.19	6.7±1.51	108.6±1.65	5.9±1.07

Table 52. Variability of blood indices in infected and non-infected
Peromyscus **(Absolute data taken from Sealander, 1961)**

	Infected		Non-infected		
Quantity of hemoglobin, in g/100 ml	12.2±0.2	14.9±0.1	14.9±0.1	14.9±0.1	$\bar{x} \pm s_{\bar{x}}$
	7.5±1.16	5.2±0.47	4.5±0.47		$c.v. \pm s_{c.v.}$
Hematocrit, in percentages	39.8±0.8	46.3±0.4	46.3±0.3		$\bar{x} \pm s_{\bar{x}}$
	9.2±1.42	6.7±0.61	4.3±0.46		$c.v. \pm s_{v.c.}$

Good examples of the study of colorimetric variability are the works of A. V. Pokrovskii, V. S. Smirnov, and S. S. Schwartz (1962) and V. N. Bol'shakov (1962), which have been devoted to the study of narrow-skulled (*Microtus gregalis*), red-backed and bank voles (*Clethrionomys rutilus* and *Clethrionomys glareolus*). Two indices were studied in these works : "whiteness" (coefficient of reflection in white light), and "shade index" (reflection of red light in percent of whiteness); stable values in the variability for one or the other trait have been obtained for each of the species. Data presented in the work of R. A. Boolootian (1954) on variability of percent of red coloration in the color of three subspecies of kangaroo rats (*Dipodomys nitratoides*) also allow one to draw the same conclusion:

	D. n. nitratoides	D. n. exilis	D. n. brevinasus	t_{1-2}	t_{1-3}	t_{2-3}
$\bar{x} \pm s_{\bar{x}}$	15.8 ± 1.37	16.2 ± 1.87	17.7 ± 1.69	−1.25	−6.33	−4.28
c. v. ± $s_{c.v.}$	8.7 ± 0.82	11.5 ± 1.10	9.6 ± 0.91	−2.03	−0.73	−1.28

Data on colorimetric variability in different species of mammals can be found in many other works (Dice, 1938; Sumner, 1923, 1924; Huestis, 1925; Hayne, 1950).

From the limited data presented, it is seen that the study of variability of coloration should be widely used during the study of the population morphology of mammals.

Variability of temperature. This refers to the variability of traits of mammals expressed in units of temperature; for example, preferred temperature. Calculations of data on temperatures preferred by laboratory mice show comparatively high coefficients of variability—42 to 112% (Kalkowski, 1966).

Variability of surface area. This is the variability of parameters of area characterizing an individual system or portions of organs.

In the review of colorimetric variability it was noted that in many instances color variability is taken as the variability characterizing the size of the area of an organ or structure.

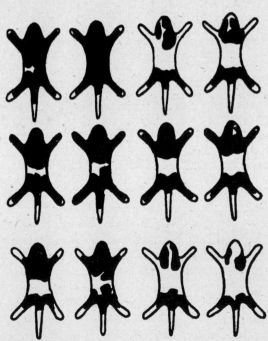

Figure 42.   Genetic types of mice differing in color (Charles, 1938).

It can easily be shown that mice of different genetic lines (Figure 42; Charles, 1938) can be clearly defined in quantitative expressions of light and dark areas on the hide. A second way is to divide all the variants into more or less homogeneous groups with regard to size of white area and then calculate the statistical parameters for each homogeneous group for sex and age.

An example of such an approach to the analysis of data on variability of colored area can be found in the work of Dice (1938) in which conventional parameters of color of area around the ears of *Peromyscus maniculatus* from nine populations in Arizona were studied (Table 53). As seen from these data, the variability of size of area of colored spots corresponds well with the absolute area of colored spots.

Table 53. Variability in the size of patches in the area around the ears in *Peromyscus maniculatus* (**Absolute data taken from Dice, 1938**)*

Population	$\bar{x} \pm s_{\bar{x}}$	$c.\,v. \pm s_{c.v.}$	Population	$\bar{x} \pm s_{\bar{x}}$	$c.\,v. \pm s_{c.v.}$
I	1.36±0.06	46.3±3.10	VI	0.75±0.12	72.0±11.4
II	1.52±0.08	37.5±3.75	VII	1.82±0.06	28.6±2.35
III	1.36±0.06	43.4±3.13	VIII	2.08±0.09	14.9±3.04
IV	1.66±0.09	46.4±3.80	IX	1.86±0.09	18.3±3.45
V	1.95+0.05	20.0±1.81			

* The animals were divided into four classes with regard to color area—from 0 to 3. Data on males and females, aged one year.

It should not be thought that the variability of area is concerned only with the manifestation of variability of color. Size of glandular surfaces in the intestinal tube, the size of respiratory surfaces in the lungs, the size of the body surface as a whole or of its parts, are a few of the many traits which can be expressed in variability of surface area. N. I. Larina (1966) gives data on the variability of nuclear surface in the cells of the mesentry in two closely related species of forest mice, which ranges in two populations of *Apodemus tauricus* from 24.3 to 25.3% and in *A. sylvaticus* from 20.8 to 24.1%.

Angular variability. The variability of angles is the variability of the angle of attachment or detachment of individual elements of organs for different systems.

In view of the importance of obtaining the greatest number of different characters for the organs and structures under study, it is not proper to leave unattended the variability of a number of traits in angular values, even though it is not yet widely used.

In the work of E. Ashton and C. Oxnard (1964) an attempt was made to obtain exact statistical parameters for the angles of disposition of muscles and bones in 26 families of higher and lower primates.   The primates were divided into two large functional groups—quadrupeds and those standing erect.   Some characters of angular variability calculated from these data are given in Table 54.

Table 54.   Variability of angular traits of the shoulder girdle in primates*
(**Absolute data taken from Ashton and Oxnard, 1964**)

Trait		Quadrupedal $(n=39)$	Standing erect $(n=31)$	P
Angle of attachment	..	8.1 ± 1.66	22.7 ± 0.71	<0.01
m. trapezius	..	128.6 ± 16.7	17.5 ± 2.2	<0.01
Angle of attachment of caudal part	..	66.9 ± 3.09	62.0 ± 1.07	$0.2—0.1$
m. serratus magnus	..	28.6 ± 3.2	96.6 ± 12.1	<0.01
Angle of orientation	..	80.2 ± 0.90	57.9 ± 2.32	<0.01
m. serratus, m. trapezius	..	69.7 ± 7.9	22.4 ± 1.80	<0.01
Orientation of glenoid cavity	..	125.5 ± 0.93	115.7 ± 0.66	<0.01
		4.6 ± 0.52	3.2 ± 0.40	<0.01
Bend of clavicle	..	3.4 ± 1.99	34.1 ± 2.2	<0.01
		39.4 ± 4.4	36.2 ± 4.0	0.43

* For each pair of lines, the upper represents the mean and the lower represents the coefficient of variation.

Strictly speaking, the data in Table 54 are from a study of inter-population variability and not for an individual population (intra-population). But it can still be noted from the data how angular variability can be used in morphological investigations.   It is interesting to note that with regard to the absolute value of the angle of attachment of the caudal part of the *serratus magnus*, there are no appreciable differences between the erect primates and the quadrupedal ones; but with regard to the variability of these traits, the differences are specific.

The variability of the angle of deviation of the upper edge of the ischial tuberosity from the axis of the ilium was investigated by V. A. Dolgov (1961) on two species of the genus *Sorex*, and by M. Pawlik (1967) on other species of the same genus.

These few examples of the use of variability of angular characters in the study of mammals, confirm the correctness of separating this phenomenon of variability as an independent group.   It is possible that with the development of exact and simple methods of investigation, the study of variability of angles will attain a great significance in population morphology of mammals.

Polymorphic variability.   Epigenetic polymorphism is the presence of certain quite different, discontinuous characters of an organ or its parts (of any measurements) within a population.

This category of variability first attracted the attention of researchers many years ago. It is enough to remember the work by Charles Darwin (1868, 1877) and an interesting and unforgettable monograph by W. Bateson (1894), which contained impressive factual data on epigenetic polymorphism of mammals, birds, reptiles, amphibians, and many invertebrates. Since this variability has been studied for the last ten to fifteen years intensively, at present the number of works is increasing tremendously. This is a part of the study of population variability where long stagnating facts, viewpoints, and different approaches suddenly broke through the barrier of obscurity and are now capturing still more fields of investigation in a wide and forceful current. The success of the new approach perhaps depends on the fact that this is the place where a profound intermixing of two sciences—population genetics and morphology—takes lace; previously these fields were considered separate.

The study of populations by morphological methods allows the researcher to see that differences in the form of skull bones and in other parts of the skeleton, differences in the variation of growth of individual bones, etc., are met with in all the species, populations, lines, and groups studied. Works on polymorphism of other organs, for example the circulatory system, internal organs, and skin, are close to the works on epigenetic polymorphism of the skeleton. We will look into the basic manifestations of epigenetic polymorphism in the same order below. It is considered that both genetic and environmental factors are at the root of epigenetic polymorphism and that this phenomenon is brought about by "threshold mechanisms acting on the background of continuous variation" (Berry, 1963; Berry and Searle, 1963; Berry, 1964; etc.). In this way, epigenetic polymorphism appears to be a type of continuous variability (first type—genetic polymorphism) and its study is directly related to the study of mechanisms in micro-evolution (Timofeev-Ressovskii and Svirezhev, 1966).

With the help of enzymatic maceration, R. Berry (1963-1964) obtained preparations of the skeleton for many series of the grey squirrel (*Sciurus carolinensis*), guinea pig (*Cavia porcellus*), lemming (*Lemmus lemmus*), field vole (*Microtus agrestis*), house mice (*Mus musculus*), black rats (*Rattus rattus*), Malayan rats (*Rattus exulans*), etc. The skeleton (including skull) showed 55 different deviations from the normal[8]; moreover, not a single skeleton was found without any deviations. (Some tens of thousands of animals have been examined in this respect by different authors.) The number of such deviating traits varies in each individual case from 12 to 39. Some

---

[8] In the present case, the meaning of "normal" loses its meaning because there are no "normals" as such in nature. There is only a more or less usual group of different deviations from some mean values.

of the traits are as follows : curved nasal cavity; presence of interfrontal bones; additional foramen in the frontal bones; fusion of certain bones of the skull (nasal, frontal, and others); presence of a number of additional foramina in the skull, scapula, and limbs; presence of pterygoid processes and palatal processes on certain skull bones; absence of certain molar teeth; fusion of specific vertebrae; presence or absence of individual protuberances and processes on the body of vertebrae; fusion of pelvic bones and posterior extremities; and so forth.

It has been determined (Cave, 1930; Deol, 1955; Searle, 1954, 1954a; Grüneberg, 1950, 1955, 1963; Berry, 1963, 1964; Manville, 1961; Stecher, 1961; Freye, 1964) that epigenetic polymorphism in the skeleton normally is not affected by age variations and that clear differences in the frequency of occurrence of different variants are observed between individual populations and lines. All this makes the study of the phenomenon of epigenetic polymorphism a useful method of differentiating populations (see also Chapter IV).

Some examples of epigenetic polymorphism are given below. J. Hromada and L. Strnad (1962) observed different frequencies of occurrence of unfused parietal bones and the presence of bregmatic bones and foramina in the parietal bone in certain species of *Macaca*. In the work of R. Manville (1959), the phenomenon of epigenetic polymorphism with regard to an individual structure (bregmatic bone) in different populations of lynx (*Lynx lynx*) has been shown. On the basis of a study of 1,790 skulls of lynx it was possible to characterize the occurrence of the bregmatic bone of different populations in the following manner (expressed in percentages) :

Alabama	0	Texas		7.0
Georgia	0	Nevada		14.6
South Dakota	0	Oregon		16.8
New Brunswick	0	West Virginia		37.5
Nova Scota	0	Missouri		44.0
British Columbia	0	Mexico		100.0

Puček (1962) drew attention to the same phenomenon for a number of other mammals. R. Haitlinger (1962) records a rare instance of an occurrence of these bones in a population of field voles (*Microtus agrestis*).

E. L. Green (1941) showed that variations in the vertebral column, including additional ribs on the border of the thorax and abdomen, and similarly in the lumbo-sacral region, are met with in "so many species of mammals that it seems probable that no species of mammals is free of such variability" (p. 221).

During a morphological study of the white whale (*Delphinapterus leucas*), the structure of its manus appeared to be variable. The constant

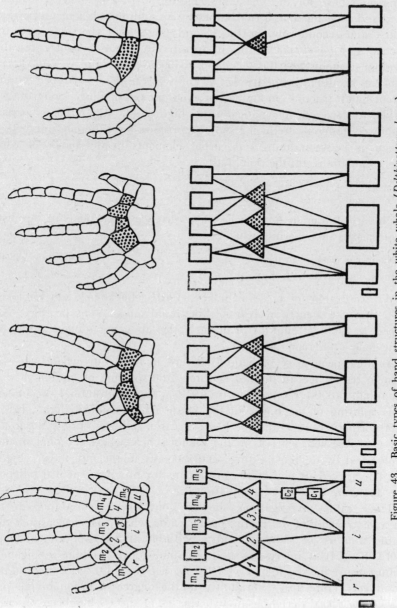

Figure 43. Basic types of hand structures in the white whale (*Delphinapterus leucas*). Identification of individual elements is given in the text.

elements found were as follows : *ulnare, radiale, intermedia, pisiforme* (first line) 1 to 4, *carpalia distalia* (second line), and finally, *metacarpalia* 1 to 5 serving as a basis for the phalanges (Figure 43). This general structure of the hand is changed, as a rule, either by an addition of elements between the first and second row, or the second finger and the additional five elements—*carpalia distalia*. Still, it appears in a number of cases that individual elements like the *centralia* 1 to 3, *pisiforme*, and certain *carpalia distalia* can be absent in the hand. All this leads to the appearance of quite different hand structures in animals of even one population. Some of these have been depicted schematically in Figure 43. Calculations carried out showed different frequencies of occurrence for different numbers of connections between limbs and carpal elements in the hands of white whale populations in the Far East :

Number of connections		1	2	3	4	5
In % to occurrence	..	1.6	31.1	57.5	1.6	8.2

and similarly, different frequencies of occurrence of elements in the distal row of carpals in the white whale :

Number of elements in the line		1	2	2	4
In % of occurrence	..	3.3	27.8	57.4	11.5

We were able to show (Yablokov, 1961b; Bel'kovich and Yablokov, 1965), that the structural type of the hand appears to be very close between the mother and her calf, i.e., the above-mentioned variability is of a genetic character.

Another peculiarity of hand structure in the white whale was even known to researchers in the last century—the splitting of the fourth digit (Kükenthal, 1890, 1909; Kunze, 1912). One substantial peculiarity in this splitting of the finger in the white whale came to light: In the seas of northern Europe and the Kara Sea, the splitting of only the fourth finger was observed, whereas in the Okhotsk Sea, where the phenomenon was observed by us, the splitting occurred only in the fifth finger (Figure 44). This served as one of the arguments for proving genetical independence between these large populations.

These same investigations showed considerable variability in the form and structure of the thorax of the white whale, which consisted of a variable number of elements and a variable number of attached ribs (Figure 45). It is interesting that an analogous variability (epigenetic polymorphism) has been observed by A. Schultz (1917) for a group of orangutans (Figure 46). Variability in the degree of fusion in the processes of the sacral vertebrae in two species of shrews has been observed by V. A. Dolgov (1961). The number of such examples could be considerably increased, but I will cite only three which I think show satisfactorily that the study of variability of the epigenetic polymorphism

Figure 44. Different instances of splitting in fingers of hands found in the white whale (*Delphinapterus*), North (lower line) and Far East (upper line).

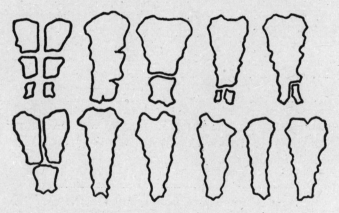

Figure 45. Epigenetic polymorphism in the structure of the sternum of the white whale (*Delphinapterus*).

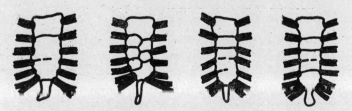

Figure 46. Epigenetic polymorphism in the structure of the orangutan sternum (A. Schultz, 1917).

type reveals the specific biological relations which could be lost sight of if other approaches are used.

In the work of S. Wright (1926) it is shown that the number of abnormal individuals in guinea pigs with additional fingers on the extremities (polydactyls), appears to be related to the age of parents (Table 54a). It is interesting that the decrease in the number of polydactyl individuals in the offspring of older animals is observed not only in the whole population, but also in the four different inbred lines (A, B, C, D) having different frequencies of polydactyls.

Table 54a. Number of polydactyl individuals (in %) in four lines of guinea pigs depending on the age of parents (Wright, 1926)

Age of parents (in months)	Parent of polydactyl individuals in offspring				Whole population $c.v. \pm s_{c.v.}$
	Line A	Line B	Line C	Line D	
3	29.3	34.6	68.1	81.0	52.7±1.8
6	7.4	28.2	54.4	69.5	40.0±1.7
9	9.6	21.9	28.9	50.0	29.2±1.7
12	—	—	—	—	26.7±1.7
15	6.1	12.1	22.0	30.2	18.5±1.4
21—46	—	—	—	—	14.2±1.4
Average	11.9	21.4	38.4	55.8	31.1

Another example (Sawin, 1945) also shows how three different lines of rabbits differ in relative development of additional ribs and vertebrae (number of individuals are in %) :

Line	With 13 ribs	With 27 presacral vertebrae
III	95.4	95.3
IV	0	13.0
V	34.8	39.3

Finally, the last example concerning skeletal structures is taken from the work of J. Zejda (1960, 1965) on the occurrence of uncommon or "simple" form of upper third-molar teeth (M^3) in 14 populations of *Clethrionomys glareolus* at different heights above sea level (Table 55; Figure 6).

A specific interdependence is observed: There is an increase in the number of individuals with the "simple" M^3 when there is a decrease in the height of the place above sea level, though in certain instances

Table 55. Occurrence of "Simple" form of M^3 in a population of
Clethrionomys glareolus (**Zejda, 1960**)

Population	I	II	III	IV	V	VI	VII	VIII	IX	X	XI	XII	XIII	XIV
Height from sea level	750—1800					400—600			Less than 400					
Number of individuals with "simple" M^3 (in %)	12	13	13	14	18	19	14	3	24	26	37	47	44	62

(populations V and VIII), this dependence is vitiated. In this and the preceding examples, the relationship of variability of the epigenetic polymorphism type, with environmental factors is apparent. This relationship was experimentally proved by H. Grüneberg (1955), who showed diet dependence for 12 osteological traits in different lines of laboratory mice.

Body color of mammals is one of the most complex traits; it did not yield to objective quantitative evaluation for a long time. Because of an increasing interest in the recent past to study the morphology of populations, and to search for more efficient and stable traits which could serve as indicators of a population, some successful attempts in this direction have been made. V. N. Bol'shakov (1962) successfully used the colorimetric method for studying the color of mice in a genetical study of populations; [this method was previously used by F. Sumner (1909-1924), S. M. Gershenzon (1946), and others]. Voipio (1962) used the chi-square method to study color variations in martens in Scandinavia. However, the methods of colorimetry have not been used in investigations on coloration of those mammals like the Greenland seal which have large color patches on their bodies.

After examining a large number of animals obtained from all three regions of their habitat in the northern Atlantic, it was possible to separate six basic types of positions for dark "wings" on the side of the back. These types have been shown schematically in Figure 47.

It is known that the distribution of chi-square depends on the number of degrees of freedom. Hence, for a reasonably exact comparison, it is necessary to determine this number accurately as far as possible, for the character under investigation. In the present case, as a matter of a working hypothesis, it would be possible to postulate the number of degrees of freedom (at the most, say 15) keeping in mind that, in addition to the six types of coloration observed in the populations, some other variants could be expected (Figure 47, 7-14).

The comparison was carried out only on the males of the population to obtain as clean a sample as possible, because a preliminary comparison of coloration in males and females from the Newfoundland showed the presence of clear sexual dimorphism in this trait. All the calculations and a fuller comparison have been given in the work of A. V. Yablokov and V. Ya. Etin (1965). In analyzing the material, the frequency distributions showed that statistically significant differences were found among all populations:

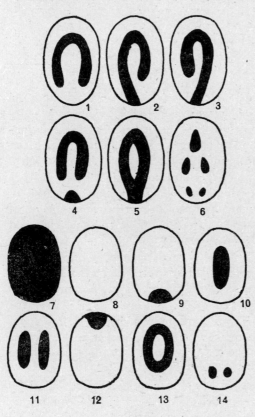

$$x^2_{1,2} = 85.9 \ (P<0.01)$$
$$x^2_{1,3} = 151.9 \ (P<0.01)$$
$$x^2_{2,3} = 39.2 \ (P<0.01).$$

The comparison shows that the largest differences in distribution of coloration types are found between seals from the Yan-Maien region and the White Sea; the least differences occur between seals from the Newfoundland region and the Yan-Maien region.

Unlike the chi-square method, an aggregate comparison using the criterion "lambda" of A. N. Kolmogorov and N. A. Smirnov, does not require a determination of degrees of freedom (Plochinskii, 1960).

A comparison of the same material on coloration of seals, carried out by the "lambda" method, confirms the results obtained by using the chi-square method. The differences between the distribution of color types in seals

Figure 47. Scheme of different types of hide color in adult males of the Greenland seal (*Pagophilus*): 1-6—*found in nature;* 7-14—*some possibilities.*

of the White Sea and Yan-Maien regions appear to be greatest ($\lambda_{1,3}=$ 1.313), and least between seals from the Newfoundland and Yan-Maien regions ($\lambda_{2,3}=0.524$). It is interesting to note that the magnitude of differences in the distribution of color estimated by the "lambda" method does not in a single case reach the level of significance.

The methodical importance of such a difference in the significance of the results lies, perhaps, in the reduced number of degrees of freedom when using the chi-square method. The number of different variants of coloration for which the differences between the populations of the Newfoundland and Yan-Maien regions could have been taken as non-significant with the given distribution, by using the chi-square method, should be close to 50 in number. We found only six variants in the natural population. It would be interesting to confirm through special observation the assumption that many more different types of coloration exist in the Greenland seal in nature than are presently known.[9]

It is interesting to note that a recently conducted study of polymorphism in blood proteins for three populations of the Greenland seal (Naevdal and Gunnar, 1966), completely confirms the conclusions about the degree of independence of individual groups drawn previously on the basis of quantitative (Chapter III) and qualitative (color) variability.

It is considered that the use of methods of the epigenetic polymorphism type for quantitative evaluations of coloration in mammals should find a larger usage in zoological investigations because these are incomparably clearer, throwing light on the exact similarities and differences between the populations under study.

In the work of A. I. Argiropula, data on the variability of chest spots in two populations of yellow-necked mice (*Apodemus flavicollis*) in Armenia are given. While comparing several variabilities, the author could only make the observation that "those traits variable for mice of one population are similarly variable for mice of another" (p. 206), i.e., the author indicated only the presence of variability. The analysis of the same data carried out by us using the chi-square method (the "lambda" method appeared inappropriate here because of the small number of samples), shows highly significant differences between the populations investigated with regard to the given trait; this allows one to draw more specific conclusions about its taxonomic and ecological importance. V. N. Pavlinin (1963) could have drawn much more significant conclusions had he resorted to analogical analysis while characterizing the coloration of sables and wild martens in the Sverdlovsk and Tyumen regions. Similarly, G. Markov (1957) who studied characteristics of tooth pigments while characterizing different populations of the common shrew, and G. Corbet (1963) who studied features of coloration at the tip of the tail while characterizing small mammals of England, could have drawn more significant conclusions had they resorted to similar analysis. Further, the data on different coloration of cetaceans could have been much more significant, had it been collected according to the above plan. There is no doubt that the coloration of cetaceans is a very favorable object for investigations of similar species. Many variations in the coloration of species like *Orcinus orca* (Figure 48), or the common dolphin (*Delphinus delphis*, Figure 49), expressed quantitatively and thus available for

---

[9] This proposal is well supported in recent years through new color-type findings (R. Sh. Khuzin, personal communication).

comparison, could answer many yet unanswered questions in ecology on the inter-relationships of different populations.

The structure of the circulatory system in mammals is another large section of variability where epigenetic polymorphism is widely manifested. In the case of the skeleton, anatomists had to deviate from the understanding of the term "norms," and similarly in the case of the circulatory system, because these "norms" do not exist in nature. There are many variations which can be grouped into a given classification and calculated and compared with the help of simple mathematical methods. Certain examples from the structure of the circulatory system are shown in Table 56. Two other examples, taken from the works of Tu Chin (1963) and P. Pšenička and J. Jurin (1964), are shown respectively in Figures 50 and 51.

An interesting example of epigenetic polymorphism in the structure of the circulatory system of foxes (*Vulpes vulpes*) has been given in the work of W. Cezariusz (1967). It was observed that in foxes brought up in captivity (platinum-colored and silver-black), there is a great asymmetry in the development

Figure 48.   Different variations of coloration in the body of *Orcinus orca* (Yablokov, 1963).

of the circulatory system of the brain. The possibility of a genetical analysis of variation in the structure of the circulatory system has been shown in this example.

Examples of epigenetic polymorphism in the numbers of different mammalian species are increasing day by day. It has to be admitted now that our understanding of the exceptional structural stability and sturdiness of chromosomal apparatus is erroneous. The intra-populational differences in the chromosomal apparatus relate to different numbers of acro- and meta-centric chromosomes [for example, in three populations of *Peromyscus* (Sparkes and Arakaki, 1967)], with regard to form of individual

Figure 49. Epigenetic polymorphism in the coloration of the common dolphin (*Delphinus delphis ponticus*) according to Barabash-Nikiforov; from Kleinenberg (1956).

Table 56. Variability of blood supply for different parts of the human heart (From right or left coronary artery; $n=82$) (James, 1960) (in %)

Right	Left	Blood supply from coronary artery					
		I	II	III	IV	V	VI
100	0	27	9	5	5	—	—
90	10	39	18	37	4	—	—
80	20	19	38	34	2	—	—
70	30	4	17	17	5	—	—
60	40	4	14	4	11	—	—
50	50	4	4	2	4	—	6
40	60	1	—	1	20	—	9
30	70	1	—	—	13	—	17
20	80	1	—	—	12	1	30
10	90	—	—	—	11	4	23
0	100	—	—	—	13	95	15

I—Posterior right ventricle; II—Anterior right ventricle; III—Free wall of right ventricle; IV—Posterior left ventricle; V—Free wall of left ventricle; VI—Anterior left ventricle.

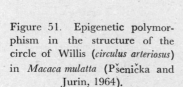

Figure 50.   Different types of branching in the femoral
artery of *Macaca* (Tu Chin, 1963):
F—a. femoralis;   P—a. poplitea;   S—a. saphena;   g—a.
articularis genu suprema;   mc—a. musculocutaneous distalis;
p—a. pergorans distalis.

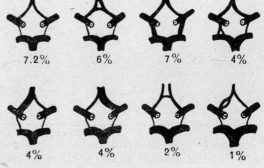

Figure 51.   Epigenetic polymorphism in the structure of the
circle of Willis (*circulus arteriosus*)
in *Macaca mulatta* (Pšenička and
Jurin, 1964).

7.2%   6%   7%   4%

4%   4%   2%   1%

chromosomes [data on laboratory mice (Bianchi and Molina, 1966)], and
so forth. The study of variability of karyotypes is especially interesting
because it can correlate studies on ecology and epigenetic polymorphism.

Some additional examples of epigenetic polymorphism, showing what
a great scope for studying variability exists in the approach, are yet to
be reviewed by us. In the commercial whale (*Delphinapterus leucas*) in
the northern seas, I studied the structure of the *uterus masculinus*. It was
observed that the degree of development in this organ can vary over a
wide range (Figure 52).

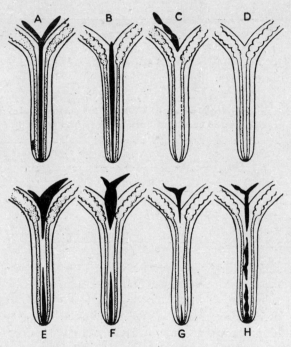

Figure 52.   Different varieties of development of the male uterus
(*uterus masculinus*) of the white whale (*Delphinapterus leucas*).

Another example is the frequency of the so-called "normal" configuration and possible deviations in the structure of the musculature in
the human hand (Basu and Hasary, 1960) (Table 57).

It is interesting that in this example symmetrical body structures are
investigated and there was more or less direct evidence of clear differences
in the frequencies of different morphs on different sides of the body.

Broadly speaking, the phenomenon of epigenetic polymorphism appears
to be more closely related to other manifestations of variability than it is
supposed to be. As seen from the work of E. Ford and H. Bull (1926),
who studied nearly 7,000 herring, deviation from the typical structure

**Table 57. Frequency of occurrence of different variations in the configuration
of human hand muscles (n=72) (Basu and Hasary, 1960)**

Type of configuration	Right hand	Left hand	Type of configuration	Right hand	Left hand
Norm	15	15	V	2	0
I	7	9	VI	1	0
II	1	1	VII	4	4
III	10	5	VIII	2	2
IV	3	6			

of vertebrae (i.e., the phenomenon of epigenetic polymorphism according
to modern classifications), occurs at greatly elevated frequencies in
individuals with extreme numbers of vertebrae (Table 58).

**Table 58. Epigenetic polymorphism in the construction of vertebrae
in herring (After Ford and Bull, 1926; from Fisher, 1930)**

		Number of vertebrae				
		53	54	55	56	57	58
Frequency of morph (%)	..	0.08	1.06	28.36	61.3	8.91	0.29
Frequency of deviations from "normal" (%)	..	45.5	4.1	1.2	1.1	2.6	10.0

In the detailed work of G. H. W. Stein (1963) on epigenetic polymorphism in the structure of the dental system in different populations
of European moles, certain data appear which allow one to assume that
the regularity observed by Fisher occurs in mammals also. It is necessary
to collect additional accurate data because the solution to this problem
will advance our knowledge about the peculiar phenomenon of epigenetic
polymorphism.

A deeper study of epigenetic polymorphism is important in population
genetics because genetical criteria, which are usually inadequate in morphology, can be used from this point of view. Epigenetic polymorphism
permits the study not only of quantitative but of qualitative differences.
This is one of the most important aspects of this type of variability.

Forms of Variability

Variability may manifest itself in different forms in relation to evolutionary factors. The following forms of variability have been examined
here : age, sex, chronological, biotopic, traumatic and teratological.

Variability of age

Within population age variability is considered to consist of : (1) the variability (of any dimension) of individuals in a similar age group; and (2) the differences in variability between different age groups.

The object of embryology is to study age changes in ontogenesis. However, attention has only very recently been paid to the existence of age variability in mammals, and I do not know if there are published works on this subject. This situation deepens interest in studying age variability as a separate form which undoubtedly plays a great role in the life of a developing population. I will cite certain factual data in order to make possible a review of this question (Table 59).

Table 59. Variability $(c. v. \pm s_{c.v.})$ **of body length of the Greenland seal**
Pagophilus groenlandicus (**White Sea, 1961**)

Sex		Sexually mature	New-born	t	P
Males	..	4.34±0.31	6.31±0.80	−2.29	0.05
Females	..	4,44±0.22	7.34±0.83	−3.02	0.01

There is a significant difference between the variability of the trait in question for newly-born and mature animals; moreover, the significance increases because of quite similar behavior in the coefficients of variation for the males and females.

Interesting data on the body length of fur seal embryos (*Callorhinus ursinus*) of different ages is given in the work of V. B. Scheffer (1962). The above-mentioned tendency toward decrease in variability with age, is clearly seen in Scheffer's data (see Figure 1).

The variability of tail length in female mice living in a hot room is not large, but it changes from the age of 1.5 months to 7 months (Sumner, 1909). The length of tail in females become a less variable trait with age in both the hot and the cold rooms (Figure 53). The differences between the final values of the coefficients of variation are quite significant.

There is no elimination of deviation by mortality in these experiments, and when the variability decreases it is clear that we observe the natural picture existing in the population. In other words, because of the irregular rhythm of tail growth in the young of the populations, a considerable difference is observed in animals aged 1.5 months relative to the adult stage, when a stability of the trait is reached in the population. All these changes take place on the background of tail-size development in both the hot and cold rooms This situation—the reversible dependence of the coefficient of variation on the size of the trait—is governed by primary regularities (Chapter V).

The data obtained as a result of analyzing the factual material of E. T. Popova (1941) on weight of sheep, show the importance of calculating a specific age-variability. It was observed that in half-bred flocks of sheep (both males and females) there was a regular decrease in variability with age (from 17.2 to 10.8%), whereas in pure-bred flocks such a decrease was not observed. The differences in individual populations (perhaps inbred to a great extent) in age-specific variability are significant. It is clear that any practical or theoretical investigation of these flocks will not be complete if these aspects of variability are not taken into account.

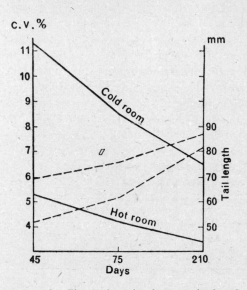

Figure 53. Fluctuations in the magnitude of variability of tail length for mice of different ages (the same population) in hot and cold rooms: *a—mean value of absolute length of tail (in mm)* (F. Sumner, 1909).

It can be seen from the data already presented (see Table 46) that the variability of the volume of the skull in one species of *Macaca* increases significantly with age, that the number of polydactyl offspring of guinea pigs increases with an increase in age of parents (Table 54), and that the variability in a number of traits of yellow-necked mice (*Apodemus flavicollis*) and common shrews (*Sorex araneus*) in one population decreases toward autumn—the season of general growth in the animal (see Table 41). According to Schwartz (1962), foot length and tail length in hibernating shrews are less variable than in the young; variability of body weight in four lines of rabbits decreased with age for both males and females (Castle, 1931); these data are confirmed by material obtained from nature by A. I. Kryl'tsov'a (1957) on lemmings (*Lagurus lagurus*) (Table 37).

But there are other data which show that decrease in variability of traits with age is not a uniform occurrence. According to Schwartz (1962), mentioned above, only two traits out of five in the common shrew show decrease in variability with age; Sumner ((1909-1924) did not observe a clear decrease in the variability of mice in experimental populations; and according to the data published by Roos and Shackelford (1955), the variability of weight in chinchillas (*Chinchilla laniger*) sharply decreases with age in males but remains at the previous level in females.

The work of McKeever and Quentin (1963) is interesting; here data show that the width of the *zona glomerulosa* in adrenals of mongoose (*Herpestes sp.*) in mature animals is half that in the young, the width of

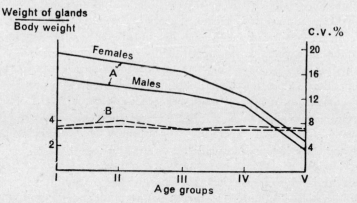

Figure 54. Coefficients of variation for relative weights of parotid glands in the common shrew (*Sorex araneus* L.) in different age groups: *a—Coefficient of variation; b—relative weight of the gland* (Buchalczyk, 1961).

the reticular zone is less variable in the young, and the *zona fasciculata* takes an intermediate place in variability. In Figure 54, data showing the presence of age variability in the weight of the parotid glands are

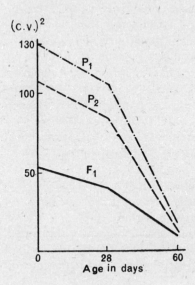

presented (Buchalczyk, 1961), and in Figure 8 data on the age variability for number of glial and nerve cells in the brain cortex of rats are given (Reiniš, 1964). It is interesting to note that the relationship of variability to age appears to be very complex in the experiments of King (1923), who studied a population of rats for more than two years, and also in the recently published work of Gebczynska (1964) on age variability for five different traits in field voles (*Microtus agrestis*). A fluctuation in the variability of body measurements (on the background of an absolute reduction in body length and an increase in tail length in very old males was observed by N. A. Ovchinikova (1966) for *Microtus oeconomus*.

Figure 55. Change with age in the coefficient of variation of body weight in two inbred lines of mice and F₁ hybrids (Chai, 1957).

A well-known "model example" of variability with age, which is known to geneticists and zoologists, should be given here. I refer to the results of the investigations of Chai (1957) on the variability of body weight in two inbred lines of mice and their hybrids. Variability was highest in all populations at birth; at four weeks the variability began to decline, until at 60 days of age it approached a single value for all three populations (Figure 55). According to R. C. Lewontin (1957) the dependence of magnitude of variability on age was "elegantly demonstrated" in this experiment. As can be seen from the examples given above, however, this dependence does not seem to be unquestionably constant.

In conclusion, it may be said that not only are all types of quantitative variability subject to age variation, but there are also some indirect relations of qualitative variability (for example, of epigenetic polymorphism) with the age of animals[10]. From this another important conclusion follows : While studying a population by morphological methods, it is always necessary to separate age variability so as not to disturb the actual situation of the structure under study with regard to evolutionary factors.

Sex variability

Sex variability considers : (1) the variability (for any dimension) of individuals of the same sex within a population; and (2) the presence of differences in variability between the sexes within a population.

The existence of sexual dimorphism in mammals is well-known. However, as in the case of age variability, for a long time researchers paid no attention to the presence of sexual dimorphism in variability itself or, in other words, to the existence of sex variability. This type of variability comes to notice rarely, but it occurs more or less frequently in nature. Although there are many cases where the variability of traits in males and females does not differ, there are a number of instances where sex differences in the magnitude of variability are manifested clearly.

The following examples of sex variability (Table 59a) have been selected from a number of comparable examples obtained during a study of pinnipeds.

The differences in the variability between males and females are clear-cut and indicate the force of different controlling factors in different sex groups. In fact, biologically, the degree of variability of organs like weight of lungs and weight of liver (Table 59a) cannot be the same. Direct observation of seasonal changes in the weights of these organs has shown a sharp development of the liver during pregnancy, which is caused,

---

[10] The determination of components of biological time, which generally do not coincide with the concept of physical time, is a promising approach for investigations in the field of age variability (Sikhlyan, 1960).

Table 59a. Sex variability of traits for certain species of pinnipeds*

Traits	Males	Females	$t\dfrac{\male}{\female}$	P
	$c.\,v.\pm s_{c.v.}$	$c.\,v.\pm s_{c.v.}$		
	Hooded seal			
	(*Cystophora cristata*)			
Sternal ribs	3.6±0.34	4.9±0.55	−2.08	>0.05
Body length	9.2±0.55	7.2±0.53	+2.74	>0.01
	Ringed seal (Okhotsk Sea)			
	(*Pusa hispida*)			
Body length of animals, 12 years old	5.0±0.72	1.4±0.20	+4.84	>0.01
Number of lip vibrissae	6.2±0.59	4.4±0.42	+2.39	>0.05
	Greenland seal			
	(*Pagophilus groenlandicus*)			
Weight of lungs	17.2±2.14	35.7±7.61	−2.34	>0.05
Weight of liver	41.9±5.32	15.6±3.47	+4.14	>0.01
Number of nasal vibrissae .	31.4±2.94	22.8±2.03	+2.41	>0.05

* The variability of only adult males and females obtained during the period of one season (2 to 3 months) has been compared, in order to avoid the effects of age, biotopical, and chronological variabilities.

perhaps, by general physiological changes in the body of females. It is clear that the control of the weight of the liver among females is rather stricter than among males. It is also clear that for normal functioning of the female organism, the intensity of liver function (to the extent that this can be judged from the weight of the organ) has greater role to play than in the same season for males. At the same time, the development of lungs (again, to the extent that this can be judged from the weight of the organ) is under greater control in males, who are compelled, perhaps, to hold their breath deeply for a long time when they go into deep waters after food. This statement could be confirmed by carrying out a comparative ecological analysis of feeding and other behavior in females during the period of caring for the young. I am sure that during this life period of the Greenland seal, there will be a specific difference in the feeding spectrum for males and females.

Considering the presence of different degrees of variability for nasal vibrissae, a trait hardly affected by significant seasonal variations, some more stable (and not merely seasonal) differences in the feeding and behavior of male and female Greenland seals can be assumed.

Because of the methods proposed for determining exactly the age of large mammals with long lives (Klevezal' and Kleinenberg, 1967), population studies of such animals have become relatively easy. Now, by obtaining a large sample of a population at one time and by determining the age of each animal to within half an year, the sample can be accurately divided by age.   This means that features of development in a number of year-classes can be studied from the material collected in one season. This method was used ѕy us (Potelov and Yablokov, 1966) during the analysis of data on the hooded seal (*Cystophora cristata*). The data were collected mainly during the two years of 1962 and 1963, but calculation of age allowed us to compare variability for animals of several ages (Table 60).

Table 60.   Sex variability of body length of the hooded seal (*Cystophora cristata*) (**Data of Potelov and Yablokov, 1966**)

Age	Males		Females		$t\overset{\circ}{\vec{\varphi}}$	P
	$c.\ v.\pm s_{c.v.}$	n	$c.\ v.\pm s_{c.v.}$	n		
New-borns ..	9.5±0.45	222	7.1±0.35	207	+4.21	>0.001
5 years ..	2.1±0.30	20	4.4±0.43	53	−4.60	>0.001
6 years ..	6.1±0.80	27	8.5±0.80	41	−2.12	>0.05
7 years ..	13.8±2.50	15	6.5±0.80	34	+2.78	>0.05
8-9 years ..	8.5±0.40	26	6.0±0.80	28	+2.77	>0.01
10-12 years ..	7.0±0.80	37	5.7±0.60	41	+1.30	>0.2
13-16 years ..	3.3±0.70	12	5.2±0.80	23	−1.79	>0.08
17 years and older ..	7.2±0.70	48	5.6±0.80	24	+1.15	>0.14

Sexual dimorphism in the trait studied was observed in all measurements; moreover, statistically significant results were obtained for the majority of the age groups.

Data on sexual dimorphism in variability can be found in many works. A few of the data are presented in Table 61.

Attention has not been given to sex variability in any of the works from which data have been taken on the different magnitudes of variability for males and females. This is the case, perhaps, with all zoological works and is a serious drawback to using data already obtained as well as planning experiments.

Data are presented on the weight of the adrenals in male and female palm squirrels (*Funambulus*) during different periods of sexual activity by K. Purohit, 1965. The author concluded that there is a considerable decrease in the weight of the adrenals in inactive animals. The result can be strengthened by the nature of the variability. The variability of the adrenals for both males and females is quite low (a range of 16.3 to 17.7 for males, and 10.2 to 24.4 for females), and is also low in inactive animals of both sexes.

Table 61.   Sex variability in certain traits of mammals*

Trait		Males c. $v. \pm s_{c.v.}$	Females c. $v. \pm s_{c.v.}$	$t\overset{\circlearrowright}{\underset{\circ}{}}$	P
Forest mice	Tail length	31.5±2.25	22.9±1.66	+3.05	0.001
(*Apodemus*	Height of skull	3.7±0.37	1.4±0.17	+5.46	>0.001
flavicollis)	Diastema	4.6±0.43	7.8±0.75	−3.82	>0.001
Sable	Width of skull at zygoma	5.4±0.74	3.4±0.53	+2.26	>0.050
(*Martes zibellina*)					
Mink	Volume of stomach	6.1±0.82	12.9±1.86	−3.33	>0.001
(*Mustela vison*)					
Macaque	Volume of skull	15.7±1.96	31.6±2.42	−5.11	>0.001
(*Macaca rhesus*)					

* All calculations have been carried out from original data presented in the works of K. 1 Adamczewska (1959), B. A. Kuznetsov (1944), E. A. Sokolov (1941), and J. Hromada and L. Strnad (1962).

Calculations carried out on the data published in the work of I. Bazan (1956) show that there is sex variability in body weight in different months in *Neomys fodiens* even though there is a complete absence of sexual dimorphism in the absolute measurements of the body.   Looking at the absence of sexual dimorphism in the absolute measurements of the traits, A. Dehnel (1949) rejected the presence of this type of variability in this species.   Dehnel carried out an analysis of his extensive and valuable data on population morphology for certain species of insectivores, but without taking into consideration their sexes.   Now, in the light of the data obtained here, the mistake in such an approach is clear.   Moreover, it can be definitely said that there is now a possibility of revealing some fine points in the biology of insectivores on the basis of the data of St. Borowski and A. Dehnel (1953).   Skoczeň (1962) presents data on a peculiar sexual dimorphism in the variability of behavior, manifested in the fact that the sex composition of groups of dead moles changed according to the time of day.

On the whole, it is important to note that sex variability occurs in quite different traits, for example in body measurements, number of ribs, vibrissae, skull measurements, weight of internal organs and behavior. All this shows how widespread this form of variability is in mammals and points to the importance of detailed investigations.

Chronological variability

Chronological variability is :   (1) the variability (of any dimension) of individuals of a group within a population in a given period of time (day, month, date, season, year, number of years, etc.); and (2) the differences in the variability of characteristics of a group in one population for different days, months, seasons, years, etc.

The concept of chronological variability was named first by S. S. Schwartz (1963), who included in it only the variability of seasons which he compared with generational variability. Such a narrow concept of chronological variability is not proper. Seasonal variability is without doubt only one of the forms of variability in traits of a population during a particular time, and generational variability cannot be completely chronological.

While studying mammalian populations, many researchers have examined seasonal changes. The attention of zoologists was drawn toward seasonal variation in the morphology of a population after the appearance of a series of works by Polish investigators (Dehnel, Petrusevich, Puček, and others) showing that apparently stable traits like form and size of the braincase and weight of the brain are also affected by seasonal variation. But even after these investigations, particular attention of research workers was not attracted toward the phenomenon of seasonal variability. The existence of groups in a population differing in variability for a single trait at different periods of time, can play an important role in the life of the population.

As the first example, we will present some data on variability of body parameters for forest mice (*Apodemus flavicollis*) (Table 62).

Table 62. Variability of certain traits of forest mice (*Apodemus flavicollis*) (**Calculated from the data of Adamczewska, 1959**)

Sex		August $c. v. \pm s_{c.v.}$	November $c. v. \pm s_{c.v.}$	$t_{VIII-XI}$	P
		Tail length			
Males	..	31.5 ± 2.25	11.4 ± 0.91	$+8.27$	0.001
Females	..	23.0 ± 1.66	10.9 ± 0.87	$+5.98$	0.001
		Body weight			
Males	..	24.0 ± 1.65	15.9 ± 1.24	$+3.92$	0.001
Females	..	24.6 ± 1.71	15.1 ± 1.20	$+4.53$	0.001

The high degree of differences in the variability of the same traits between August and November attracts attention in the data presented. It is also interesting that the variability of all traits appears to be considerably less during autumn. This conclusion is confirmed, in general, by other data obtained from the work mentioned in Figure 56 and from the data of W. Serafinski (1965).

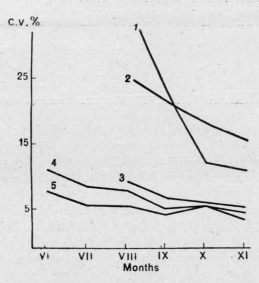

Figure 56.   Seasonal variability of measurements of forest mice
(*Apodemus flavicollis*) (Calculated from the data of Adamczewska, 1959):
1—*Tail length;* 2—*Body weight;* 3—*Body length;* 4—*Ear length;* 5—*Foot length.*

An analysis of data on variability of body weight for field voles
(*Microtus agrestis*) in different seasons (Newson and Chitty, 1962) shows
significant specific differences in the variability of this trait between different
years (Table 63).

**Table 63.   Variability of body weight for adult males of
the field vole** (*Microtus agrestis*) **in different years
(Analyzed from the data of Newson and Chitty, 1962)**

$c. v. \pm s_{c.v.}$	$c. v. \pm_{c.v.}$	t_{56-57}	P
September, 1956	September, 1957		
6.2 ± 0.95	9.2 ± 1.01	-2.14	>0.05
December, 1956	December, 1957		
5.3 ± 0.63	8.4 ± 0.90	-2.79	>0.01

While studying any type of variability, it is important to obtain a
homogeneous sample so that the effect of unaccounted for factors is
reduced to a minimum.   This common requirement fully applies also to
the study of the phenomenon of chronological variability.   A good example
in this respect is of the data on time of sexual maturity in *Lagurus lagurus*
under laboratory conditions (Pokrovskii, 1962).

	$c.\,v.\pm s_{c.v.}$	t	P
January	28.6±4.22		
		2.90	>0.01
May	14.4±2.47		
		2.61	>0.01
October	35.7±7.77		

A number of examples of chronological variability are given in the sections that follow. The most significant among them are those obtained from the data of E. Z. Kogteva (1963) concerning the length and thickness of hair of such ecologically different species as the white hare (*Lepus timidus*) and the European mole (*Talpa europaea*). Different living conditions and different approaches to sampling, led to very different behavior in the variability of parameters of hair according to seasons.

There are large quantities of data on seasonal variability but data on yearly variability are much scarce; they are still scarcer for variability over a cycle of years or for a century. Of these few works, the one by K. Ya. Fateev (1962) devoted to studying the same population of moles for three continuous years should be presented (Table 64).

Table 64. Year-to-year variability $(c.\,v.\pm s_{c.v.})$ **for certain traits of adult males of moles** (*Talpa europaea*)

Weight	1958	1959	1960	t_{58-59}	t_{58-60}	t_{59-60}
Body	16.1±2.07	13.3±1.23	8.5±1.23	+1.16	+3.16	+2.47
Heart	39.5±5.28	20.8±2.00	17.3±2.49	+3.30	+3.77	+1.09
Liver	28.4±3.79	18.7±1.80	13.7±1.98	+2.31	+3.42	+1.85

It is seen from the parameters presented that there is clear yearly variability. All the traits in the year 1958 are more variable than in the year 1959 or in the year 1960; furthermore, these differences are quite large.

While studying chronological variability in mammalian populations, the continuity of life for individuals of the species under study has to be taken into consideration. The mean natural lifetime of the small rodents and insectivores is a few months to, at the most, a year, so when we investigate a population at half-yearly or yearly intervals, we investigate entirely different animals belonging mainly to different generations. Each such generation may have individual characteristics in structure and reflect the specific influences under which it developed and which continue to exert influence at the time of investigation.

The situation changes when studying long-lived mammals, such as large ungulates, pinnipeds, cetaceans or large carnivores. Sexually and physically mature members of a population may comprise individuals of several generations (in cetaceans, up to ten generations). Such a situation significantly changes the reaction of the total population to the influences of environmental factors (Yablokov, 1961c). The stock of individual ethological information which has accumulated for such a complex population seems to be quite large, for "foreseeing" a number of influences and accordingly, adapting behavior in case of a change in some external factor, without altering the morpho-physiological structure, as happens in mammalian populations of "ephemera".

It is known that an organism is most affected by various influences in its early development. Because of the fact that, depending upon age, there are several cohorts in a complex population (each developing in different years and accordingly in different conditions), a great phenotypic differentiation among individuals is but natural in such a many-aged population. In order to test the statement, it is necessary on the one hand to compare variability of the same trait in different species of long-lived mammals with ephemera, and on the other hand to compare variability of different cohorts of large animals. The first type of comparison (Table 65) shows that the variability of homogeneous traits is quite comparable for sables (*Martes zibellina*), beavers (*Castor fiber*), seals, white whales (*Delphinapterus leucas*), and small rodents (*Mus, Sicista, Apodemus*).

The second type of comparison gives interesting results, due possibly to the exact determination of age in large mammals (Laws, 1956; Chapskii, 1952; Klevezal' and Kleinenberg, 1967) :

Age	Variability of body length of ringed seal* $(c. v. \pm s_{c.v.})$	Age	Variability of body length of ringed seal $(c. v. \pm s_{c.v.})$
10 years (year of birth, 1952)	3.4 ± 0.46	12 years (year of birth, 1950)	1.4 ± 0.20
11 years (year of birth, 1951)	3.8 ± 0.53	All ages (7 years and older)	6.2 ± 0.77

*From data of Fedoseev, Okhotsk Sea, 1964, females.

It can be seen that the variability of seals born in the same year is considerably less than for animals of all ages. Besides this, the variability of animals sharply fluctuates from year to year; the cohorts born in 1950 and 1951 are close to each other in variability of body length (3.4 and 3.8%), but the 1949 cohort is considerably less variable in this trait.

Table 65.   Comparison of variability $(c.\,v.\pm s_{c.v.})$ **of certain mammals with various longevities**

Species	Condylo-basal length	Body length	Body weight	Author
House mouse (*Mus musculus*)	2.6±0.64	9.5 ±1.86	23.3±5.22	Dinovskii, 1963
Birch mice (*Sicista betulina*)	2.3±0.38	6.6 ±0.38	—	Kubik, 1953
Forest mice (*Apodemus flavicollis*)	4.1±0.63	5.7 ±0.43	15.9±1.24	Adamczewska, 1959; Ursin, 1956
Sable (*Martes zibellina*)	2.3±0.34	2.81±0.63	—	Kuznetsov, 1941
Greenland seal (*Pagophilus groenlandicus*)	3.9±0.39	4.3 ±0.31	9.0±2.01	Own observations
Ringed seal (*Pusa hispida*)	2.3±0.49	6.2 ±0.7	—	Own observations
White whale (*Delphinapterus leucas*)	—	3.99±0.60	22.4±2.45	Own observations

And so, two different approaches to solving the same problem give quite different results. The comparison of variability for long-lived animals and ephemera shows a great similarity in the variability, and the analysis of individual cohorts of population for long-lived species shows that each generation is considerably less variable than the population as a whole. However, in studying the populations of ephemera, only one cohort was compared which effectively constituted the population. Could it be said on the basis of these data that small animals are more variable than large ones? Of course, the data presented are insufficient to answer this question, but it can be assumed that large animals are more "protected" during individual development, and are less affected by the direct influence of those environmental factors which easily change the structure of the individual in the populations of smaller animals (the factor of obtaining food, or the stability of the ecological niche in a broad sense). It is also possible that the comparison made was not sufficiently "clear" that way; there are always certain individuals born in the beginning, in the middle and at the end of one breeding period in a population of ephemera.

Returning to the analysis given by the example of the ringed seal (*Pusa hispida*) as to the fact of different variability among individual cohorts of large animals, it can be concluded that the data on the variability of different cohorts of the hooded seal, like those presented previously (see Table 60), confirm the opinion of I. I. Sokolov and V. L. Rashek (1961) that variability in animals of the same age, born in the same year, and consequently developing in identical conditions, is less than in animals of the same age brought up in different years. There are almost no examples of chronological variability in which the variability of the same populations, or group of populations, has been studied for long periods of time.

Among the few available examples[11] are the work of Elga and Hall (1962) on Pleistocene and recent populations of bats of the genus *Tadarida*; the data of Simpson (1948) on the variability of certain traits of fossil horses; the data of Hysing-Dahl (1959) on the variability of recent and Pleistocene populations of otters (*Lutra lutra*) in Scandinavia; and the works of Derums (1964) on the variability of human skull traits in south Russia one to three thousand years ago and in the 15th to 18th centuries. In summarizing such data, the opinion of Simpson is that the variability of fossil forms is very close in magnitude to that of present-day forms; this can be fully confirmed.

The relatively stable variability in the evolutionary development of groups for quite a considerable period (Simpson's example considers a period of millions of years) allows one to pose a still broader question about the meaning of chronological variability. Perhaps a number of phenomena concerned with this concept exist which we cannot examine separately. With our knowledge deepening in the field of ecology and the genetical structure of a population, modern concepts of chronological variability should be separated into some individual components. It is possible that the recently discovered properties of endogenous periodicity in the functioning of organisms (the presence of a "biological clock") (Byunning, 1964), will play an important role in this separation. It is usually thought that the phenomenon of "biological clocks" should be considered only in ecological, physiological, and biochemical investigations. However, it would also be completely incorrect not to consider this phenomenon during the study of morphological variability. It is very possible that we would be able to carry out exact comparisons between two samples by considering this "biological" time and remove conflicts between data obtained in apparently identical conditions. This observation holds good particularly for morphological material obtained during the study of experimental populations "under similar living conditions." It is possible that these other "similar living conditions" are not, in fact, "similar." Shnoll' (1964) well observed in this regard : "A doctor should be accustomed to the thought that the same therapeutic preparations give different effects depending upon the time of the day they are administered....He should always keep in mind that the results of clinical analysis also depend upon this time factor. Agronomists, veterinarians,

[11] In the work of Paaver (1965), there is an excellent analysis of epochal changes and variability of many south-Russian mammals. Unfortunately this monograph was published after the final touches were given to the present book and I was deprived of the opportunity of using the interesting factual data presented in it.

bee-keepers, physiologists and biochemists should also decide their own approach toward the 'constant' conditions—continuous lighting and constant temperature are also not normal conditions. In conformity with the concept of endogenous periodicity, during a study on the effect of some factor on an organism the approach to the principle of 'other similar conditions' must be very cautious. The conflict in the 'other' conditions may put the 'control' and 'experimental' into a quite unrealistic comparison" (p. 9).

Hence, while studying mammalian populations, we should not forget about a number of phenomena based on reversible and irreversible processes differing in different periods, going on in each organism, and in a population as a whole, which are characterized not only by changes in morphological structures but also by changes in the magnitude of variability.

Birth-order variability

Birth-order variability is the variability of different traits among individuals in a population by the order of birth and not related to age nor to time. One example is of the data on variability of number of new-borns in a litter in *Clethrionomys* depending upon the ordinal number of pregnancies (Olavi Kalela, 1957). An analysis of these data shows a tendency toward greater variability in number of new-borns in the first pregnancy. This trait has been shown to be quite invariable in the second pregnancy. It is possible that this example is not very promising, but there should be no doubt of the existence of such a type of variability in nature, related specifically to the order of offspring produced by animals and plants.

Biotopic variability

The term "biotopic variability" was proposed by Schwartz (1963). This concept should include the variability manifested within one population or between micro-populations and caused by somewhat different sets of conditions. It is clear from the above that this type of variability could be equally classified as micro-population or within-population variability. But here there is a serious contradiction. By the definition of population used in this work (see Introduction), all the so-called micro-populations within which there is panmixis and which, during a given period of time, are isolated from other such groups, should be taken as populations having an independent significance in evolution. If these requisites—panmixis and isolation—are not observed, then the group cannot be separated as a population and it will not be possible to talk about the independent significance of variability for the structure of such a group.

It is well known that isolation can be temporary and partial. This situation makes more difficult any single solution to the problem of classifying the variability of individual micro-populations within a population. This phenomenon logically seems to be related to that of geographical variability. Geographical variability is the same variability of individuals of different groups, situated in a definite set of conditions—like biotopic variability, only at a little higher level. Perhaps, it would be more proper to consider the phenomenon of geographical variability as between-population variability (down to the level of micro-population variability); and to take biotopic variability as only within-population variability (or between-micro-population variability). An insufficient resolution of the general theory of population (Naumov, 1958; Beklemishev, 1960; and others), makes it difficult to solve the problem.

Both geographical and biotopic variability represent a phenomenon of the same type caused by a specific adjustment of a population to its living conditions. Factors like climate and biotic relations, as well as the nature of the genetical structure of the populations, will fall under such "specific living conditions" in both these cases.

Considering that the classification of type of variability proposed here is preliminary and does not claim any final solution to the problem, it is better to show the presence and the role of such variability in mammalian populations without going into further detailed differences between biotic and geographical variabilities (Table 66).

Table 66. Biotopic variability $(c. v. \pm s_{c.v.})$ **of a number of traits in the common hamster** (*Citellus citellus*) **in Bulgaria (Analyzed from the data of Straka, 1963)**

Character of biotope		Length of			
		Body	Tail	Foot	Ear
Height above sea (meters)	$t*$				
50	19.7	6.0±0.46	12.1±0.93	4.3±0.33	9.3±0.71
650	15.7	5.0±0.37	9.7±0.71	4.6±0.34	9.6±0.34
1900	7.9	6.0±0.66	8.2±0.90	5.2±0.57	9.7±1.06

*The mean monthly temperature in the active period of life of the population.

While analyzing absolute indices of the traits studied, F. Straka (1963) confirmed Allen's rule on the material presented by him. A comparison of variability for these populations (micro-populations) allows one to conclude that there is a considerable stability in range of variability for all the groups for all the traits except tail length. The variability of tail length is considerably less in hill hamsters than for sea-level ones. It is not possible to relate these differences specifically to the height of the habitat or to temperature because there are really a large number of factors which can determine the character of the trait.

A. K. Lee (1963) studied the utilization of oxygen and water in desert and river-bank populations of *Neotoma lipida*; his data are concerned equally with the phenomena of biotopic and geographical variabilities. The range of variability for these traits (water and oxygen utilization) is considerably higher in the desert type than in the river-bank type of *Neotoma lipida*.

However, the data of Clark (1940) give the most detailed example of this type of variability; Clark studied absolute indices and indices of variability for nine body traits (body and skull measurements) in 30 (!) populations of *Peromyscus maniculatus*, 8 populations of *P. leucopus*, and 4 populations of *P. eremicus*. Analysis of these data shows that there are significant differences in variability for at least some of the populations studied. This is one of the few works (if not the only one) where the phenomenon of population variability has been given independent importance in a zoological investigation.

An experimental study of geographical variability was carried out by Sumner (1924), who studied the changes resulting from the transfer of two different populations of *P. maniculatus* to other ecological conditions in the habitat zone of a third population (subspecies). The results are quite intriguing. Only the absolute indices appeared to be of interest to Sumner in this experiment and the variability was left unstudied. This lacuna can be filled in however, because the factual data presented by Sumner suffice for the calculation of a detailed characterization of variability in the original and the transferred groups. The findings are very significant. Firstly, there is a reduction in the variability of almost all traits studied—in some to a lesser degree and in others to a greater degree (of the total number of 16 traits from both groups, only three traits remained unchanged in variability with the transferred group, and there was a significant increase in variability for one trait). Secondly, this reduction in variability was rather sharply expressed in the population of the subspecies *P. m. rubidus*, where a high degree of difference exists for five of the eight traits studied. What factors brought about such a behavior of variability is totally unclear. It may be observed, as concluded by Sumner, that the changes did not go in the direction of the third subspecies living on this territory. Unfortunately, data are lacking for an exact comparison of these three subspecies with regard to their original variability.

That many factors control variability is well seen from this example. The genetic mechanisms which, perhaps, determined these changes in the given case, may occupy an important place among these factors.

The number of examples of biotopic variability could be considerably increased; several are given in other places of this work.

Traumatic variability

Traumatic variability is the variability of any dimension manifested as a result of some trauma sustained by an organism. The manifestation of traumatic variability can be linear, of weight, of volume, meristic, colorimetric, or in the form of epigenetic polymorphism, for any organ or structure. But the importance of an independent treatment of traumatic variability lies in the fact that first, it allows one to investigate more exactly the above-mentioned manifestations of variability; and second, traumatic variability covers a specific number of natural phenomena and can serve as a particular character of a population. A change in the structure of the host caused by parasites is known. Such changes could be and should be taken into account while describing the general variability of a population, because they represent specific correlations existing in the "environment-population" system.

It is possible that the concept of traumatic variability should be broadened and should be transformed into a concept of variability caused by the so-called mechanical reasons. Then variability like that from grinding down of teeth, which occurs for all mammals but in various intensities depending upon different ecological reasons, could be classified with this variability. One of the complex types of such grinding down of teeth forms a number of typical "scissors" from the initial non-differentiated dental system in cetaceans (Yablokov, 1958). The number of examples of such types could be increased.

Teratological variability

Teratological variability is the variability of any dimension arising as a result of congenital abnormalities. Usually this type of variability comes under epigenetic polymorphism (undeveloped individual organs, like the instances of kidney and adrenal reductions in the Indian gerbil, *Meriones hurrianae* described by Kaul, 1966). Examples of such variability are numerous in man also. Recently, special attention has been given to this kind of variability because of widespread mutagenic factors in natural populations.

The proposed classification of variability ends with this account of teratological variability. Such a classification will inevitably broaden according to the modes and methods of study of the structure of mammals, and according to the selection of traits for which variability may be calculated in exact units.

Conclusion

The basic classes, types, appearances and forms of variability which should be taken into consideration while studying mammalian populations, have been examined in this chapter. On the basis of the data presented and from an analysis of the schemes of classification suggested before, I propose the following classification for the phenomena of population variability (Table 67).

Table 67.   Classification of within-population variability

Manifestations (kind of measurement)

Variability of time
Variability of weight
Linear variability
Variability of volume
Variability of surface area
Angular variability
Colorimetric variability
Meristic variability
Variability of temperature

Category

Continuous or quantitative	Discontinuous or qualitative (polymorphism)

Type

Structural (morphological)
Functional (physiological)
Biochemical
Ethological (variability) of behavior

Form

Age
Sex
Chronological
Birth-order
Biotopic
Traumatic
Teratological

Numerous examples of different types, forms, and manifestations of variability presented in this chapter show how varied and elaborate is the phenomenon of variability. This complexity of the phenomenon shows the importance of exactly observing the class, type, form, and manifestation of variability and considering the possible relationship of each to the sample under study. An unexpected cause could be from unintentional mistakes in the sampling of material. It has been shown in the work of Adamczewska (1959) that there are clear differences in variability (and in other traits) between animals caught in cylindrical traps and in other kinds of traps. It is clear that some sampling methods are better than others. Let us imagine that the variability of animals caught in a cylindrical trap in the virgin forest of Belovezh is being compared with the variability of animals caught in some way in the Rostov region. It is clear that, although we may observe all rules (same age, sex, selection at the same time), such a comparison may not give good results because the variability with regard to the behavior of the animals was not studied.

At times, very good data on population morphology are spoiled by insufficiently clean sampling. V. S. Smirnov (1962) analyzed changes due to age in the skulls of males and females. Coefficients of variation calculated from Smirnov's data on the differences due to age in the skulls of male and female Arctic foxes in Yamal, show no clear-cut trends other than some sexual dimorphism. However, it appeared that data from two different years were combined; in each of the age groups, which had been separated with great care, animals of different ages and not just one age were included. The development of these animals might have occurred under different conditions. It is very possible that in this case the conflicting results in the variability obtained could be explained by the fact that yearly (chronological) and generational variabilities were not considered.

I clearly understand that my proposed classification for the phenomena of variability cannot be final. But such a temporary "working" classification is more or less necessary for further developments in the study of the problem of variability.

CHAPTER V

SOME REGULARITIES OF VARIABILITY

Elementary Regularities in the Variability of Traits

The interrelations of individuals within a population and the relations of the population as a whole to the biogeocenose are so complex that at our present level of knowledge we are unable to comprehend these processes. It follows from this situation that the long-term need for formalization of biological interrelations among populations and the biogeocenose has not yet yielded fully to calculations.

However, in all types of biological investigations which are carried out with the help of formalized methods (during statistical analyses of biological material, a known formalization or abstraction—large in some cases and small in others—always takes place), it is important to know fully the results of formalization so as not to attribute this or that property to natural processes when it has arisen only as a result of using some particular method. In the present case, while studying variability by the method of coefficients of variation, it is necessary as far as possible to consider fully the properties of this expression that arise out of mathematical and other simple regularities. It can be assumed that these regularities are not now directly correlated with the effect of natural selection, and hence they can be termed "elementary."[1]

It is evident that these elementary trends or regularities of a population, in relation to environmental and within-population interactions, cannot reflect all the complexities of these interactions and should only be considered as constantly present parts of these complicated interactions.

[1] Analogous to the term "elementary correlation" proposed by A. A. Malinovskii, 1948.

The available data allow one to examine the dependence of the coefficient of variation of a trait on the absolute value of the trait and on the relative and absolute values of the trait.

Some of these questions have attracted the attention of researchers (Schmalhausen, 1935; review by Roginskii, 1959), but these questions were not considered of primary importance for the study of variability given here.

Relationship of Variability to Dimensionality of Traits

To understand the relation of variability to the dimensionality of the trait, it is necessary to compare data on the variability of the same organ or structure, expressed in different dimensions.

Proceeding from the existence of different manifestations of variability, it is at first desirable to analyze at least two traits which are biologically close but of different dimensions (which will also serve as a basis for further general conclusions about the relation of variability to the dimensionality of traits in more complex series). Logically, the first step will be to compare different manifestations of variability :[2]

Variability of weight	.. Variability of time
do	.. Linear variability
do	.. Variability of volume
do	.. Meristic variability
do	.. Colorimetric variability
do	.. Variability of area
do	.. Variability of angle
Variability of time	.. Linear variability
do	.. Variability of volume
do	.. Meristic variability
do	.. Colorimetric variability
do	.. Variability of area
do	.. Variability of angle
Linear variability	.. Variability of volume
do	.. Meristic variability
do	.. Colorimetric variability
do	.. Variability of area
do	.. Variability of angle
Variability of volume	.. Meristic variability
do	.. Colorimetric variability
do	.. Variability of area

[2] See the classification of variability phenomena in Chapter IV.

Variability of volume .. Variability of angle
Meristic variability .. Colorimetric variability
do .. Variability of area
do .. Variability of angle
Colorimetric variability .. Variability of area
do .. Variability of angle
Variability of area .. Variability of angle

There are no factual data as yet to examine all these variations. There is an absence of such comparable data even in the usual investigations in variability. All this makes it difficult at present to prepare a full arrangement of the relations of the various manifestations of variability.

More than 30 years ago, while examining methodological problem, I. I. Schmalhausen (1935) drew attention to the incorrectness of a direct comparison of variability values of weight, volume, and linear traits. These observations (made in the basic text of this subject) assume importance in the context of studying variability problems; I will fully quote the opinion of I. I. Schmalhausen :

"In the most recent literature, especially American literature (Schneider and Dunn, 1924; Asmundson, 1932; Angulo and Gonsālez, 1932), it is indicated that coefficients of variation of the same material appear to be greater for weight measurements than for linear ones, and on this basis a statement is made about how much more exact linear measurements are in comparison with weight measurements. This conclusion is based on a misunderstanding. The values of coefficients of variation for linear, surface, and volume traits should not be compared among each other in the same way, as for one-, two- or three-dimensional correlations and values in general. It can be proved with the help of some comparatively easy mathematical calculations that for the same measurements of the same objects (when the surface and volume expressions are obtained through an analysis of linear measurements of a geometrically proportional body), there is a specific relationship between the coefficients of variation for linear, surface, and volume values. For example, where there is not a very large individual deviation (on the average less than 10%), the relation is 1 : 2 : 3. In this way, with relatively identical accuracy of measurement, the coefficient of variation of weight values should be three times larger than for linear ones....Hence, to compare the degree of accuracy or variability of data on linear and weight measurements, it is better to transform all individual weight data to conventional linear values by extracting the cube root" (Schmalhausen, 1935, pp. 11-12).

There is a known interest in carrying out comparisons of various manifestations of weight, linear, and volume variability. It may be noted here that the relation of variability of weight, linear, and volume values in the work of Schmalhausen (1935) is concerned with a comparison of parameters of variability of geometrically proportional bodies and cannot exactly reflect the situation arising during studies of morphological traits in animals.

A comparison of the variability of weight and body length for the common house mouse (Table 68) shows that the variability of body weight is two to three times greater than the variability of body length in all the sexually mature groups. A similar situation is observed in almost all cases studied among the most different groups of mammals (Table 1 in the Appendix). The variability of body length appeared to be less variable than the variability of body weight in all cases.

Of all the data presented in this work, the variability of weight appeared to be equal to or greater than the variability of body length in just two cases : in the population of moles studied by K. Ya. Fateev in 1960 in the Kostrom region, and in hybrid populations of white mice (Law, 1938). It is important to note in the first case that during two other years (1958 and 1959), the variability of weight in the same population of moles was, as usual, a few times greater than the variability of body length. This shows, perhaps, that in 1960 some unusual changes took place in the "environment-population" system.[3] The last proposition holds good because of the fact that the year 1960 was unusual also for other traits in this population. The variability of almost all traits sharply declined (see Table 64).

Table 68. Variability ($c. v. \pm s_{c.v.}$) **of length and body weight of house mice (Calculated from data supplied by Dynowski, 1963)**

Age group	Variability of weight	Variability of length	Age group	Variability of weight	Variability of length
	Males			Females	
II	25.0±1.70	9.9±0.66	II	30.9±2.28	10.0±0.71
III	15.9±1.26	7.7±0.53	III	22.2±2.34	9.5±0.93
IV	18.5±3.28	6.9±1.19	IV	23.3±5.22	9.5±1.86

The second instance of greater variability of body length compared to variability of body weight, in inbred populations of laboratory mice, is in my opinion one of those exceptions which confirm the general rule. In fact, the above-mentioned deviation in the behavior of coefficients of variation takes place in a complex hybrid population maintained under

[3] This proposition is true in this instance only if the effect of accidental errors or change in method of collection and analysis of the material is totally excluded.

198   *Variability of Mammals*

unusual conditions. The mixing of genetically different populations vitiates any general relationships in the development of traits. And the fact that there is such a relationship between weight and length in genetically pure lines is shown by many genetical works.

But could it be that the variability of length is less than the variability of weight only when comparing length of body and body weight? The comparison of weight and linear characters of different organs shows that this is not so. Thus, the variability of weight of the intestines appears to be a few times more than the variability of length of the intestines :

$c.\,v. \pm s_{c.v.}$ Length of intestine .. 4.2 ± 1.11 8.4 ± 1.1 25.7 ± 44

$c.\,v. \pm s_{c.v.}$ Weight of intestine .. 19.7 ± 3.87 45.3 ± 6.0 46.0 ± 15.3

Species and author   ..   (*Delphinap-*   (*Talpa*   (*Macropus sp.*)
                                         terus leucas)   *europaea*)   Tribe and
                                         Own data   Fateev, 1962   Peel, 1963

Data on the variability of linear and weight characters for the skull of the fur seal are interesting (Table 69).

These data show clearly that variability of weight is always greater than the linear variability of the same organs.

Table 69. Variability of weight and linear characters for certain skull traits of the fur seal (*Callorhinus ursinus*) **(According to data obtained from V. F. Muzhzhinkin)**

Weight $c.\,v. \pm s_{c.v.}$	Length $c.\,v. \pm s_{c.v.}$	$t_{\text{weight-length}}$	Sex	Age
		Skull		
17.3 ± 0.84	4.7 ± 0.23	$+14.4$	Males	2=3 years
16.8 ± 3.30	3.0 ± 0.76	$+\ 3.8$	,,	4=5 years
10.3 ± 2.31	4.2 ± 0.98	$+\ 2.5$	Females	2=3 years
11.5 ± 2.60	3.2 ± 0.71	$+\ 3.1$	,,	4=5 years
9.7 ± 1.82	2.5 ± 0.47	$+\ 7.6$	,,	10+ years
		Lower jaw		
20.8 ± 1.02	5.3 ± 0.26	$+15.0$	Males	2=3 years
20.0 ± 3.93	4.4 ± 0.87	$+\ 3.9$	,,	4=5 years
11.7 ± 2.63	3.6 ± 0.80	$+\ 2.9$	Females	2=3 years
13.0 ± 2.91	3.7 ± 0.83	$+\ 3.1$	,,	4=5 years
13.5 ± 2.56	2.7 ± 0.51	$+\ 4.1$	,,	10+ years

To summarize all the data comparing linear and weight variability presented here, the following conclusion can be drawn : Weight variability is significantly higher than linear variability. It should be emphasized once again that this conclusion is applicable only to the variability of the same organs or structures; it is reasonable that the variability of body length may appear to be significantly higher than the variability of weight for the crystalline lens of the eyes. Instances showing deviations from this rule should indicate shortcomings in methodology or unusual relationships in the population-environment system.

Certain data permit a comparison of linear and volume variabilities for the same organs and structures (Table 70).

Table 70. Variability in volume and linear characters of intestines of foxes and minks (Calculated from data of Sokolov, 1941)

Sex	Volume $c.v.\pm s_{c.v.}$	Length $c.v.\pm s_{c.v.}$	$t_{volume-length}$
Foxes			
Males	8.6 ± 1.26	12.5 ± 1.97	-1.71
Females	5.6 ± 0.66	12.6 ± 1.71	-3.93
Minks			
Males	9.7 ± 1.27	13.6 ± 1.92	-1.69
Females	10.5 ± 1.55	13.6 ± 1.92	-1.25

It can be seen from these data that the variability of volume was less than the variability of length in all cases without exception. Unfortunately, this conclusion is not sufficiently reliable, as other such examples are lacking.

A comparison of weight and volume variabilities can be carried out by analyzing the data of J. Hromada and L. Strnad (1962). From their data, in 12 out of 13 comparable groups of different sex and age in two species of *Macaca* (*M. rhesus* and *M. cynomolgus*), the variability of weight was greater than the variability of volume for the skull; moreover, in ten cases the differences were statistically significant.

According to the hypothesis developed by Schmalhausen (1935), the weight and volume variabilities should coincide for the same trait. It is seen from the example of variability of parameters for arboreal nests of golden mice (*Peromyscus nuttalli*) in the data of Packard and Garner (1964), that this assumption is true in some cases :

Trait		c. v.
Length, width, depth	..	10.3-14.3%
Volume	..	27.0%
Weight	..	38.1%

On the other hand, a difference in the variability of linear, volume, and other traits of the organ under study, indirectly denotes the accuracy of the methodology used. It is seen from the above data of Hromada and Strnad that the precision of measurement of the volume traits of skull appears to be higher than the precision of the weight traits.

Data comparing meristic and linear variabilities for tail length and number of caudal vertebrae in mice are given in Table 71. In the example studied, the meristic variability appeared to be two to four times less than the linear variability in 16 different samples. However, data on the variability of number of teeth on each side of the jaw, and the length of jaw, in Black Sea dolphins do not particularly confirm these conclusions. Nevertheless, it is quite possible that in the last case it would be better to compare variability of the number of teeth in a quadrant with the variability of length of only the dental lamina, and not the whole jaw.

Table 71. Variability $(c.v. \pm s_{c.v.})$ **of tail length and number of caudal vertebrae in different phenotypes within one back-crossed population of mice (Calculated from data of Law, 1938)**

Phenotype	Sex	Tail length	Number of caudal vertebrae	Length of 15th vertebrae
Black I	♂♂	16.5±2.38	2.9±0.42	7.0±1.01
	♀♀	10.6±1.67	3.6±0.57	5.6±0.88
Blackish-spotted I	♂♂	23.6±3.40	3.3±0.48	8.6±1.24
	♀♀	21.5±3.24	6.2±0.93	12.0±1.80
Black, waltzing	♂♂	18.0±2.58	4.3±0.62	6.3±0.91
	♀♀	12.9±1.94	4.9±0.74	11.5±1.73
Blackish-spotted, waltzing	♂♂	21.6±3.04	4.4±0.63	11.2±1.58
	♀♀	18.0±2.77	4.0±0.60	7.8±1.21
Brown	♂♂	15.7±1.45	3.1±0.28	7.6±0.70
	♀♀	17.4±1.59	11.7±1.06	11.1±1.01
Brownish-spotted	♂♂	16.4±1.70	7.0±0.73	13.7±1.42
	♀♀	15.8±1.68	7.8±0.83	7.8±0.83
Black II	♂♂	16.1±1.40	4.4±0.37	7.0±0.60
	♀♀	19.2±1.58	8.6±0.70	7.6±0.62
Blackish-spotted II	♂♂	16.6±1.73	2.9±0.30	9.3±0.97
	♀♀	17.8±1.70	6.5±0.62	7.6±0.73

The data of Hall and Schaller (1964) on *Enhydra lutris* make possible a comparison of time and meristic variabilities. A sea otter spends different amounts of time breaking up the armored shells of sea urchins, etc., depending upon what catch the individual surfaces with. Naturally, the time taken on the surface for eating food can be compared with a high degree of significance as a homogeneous character of its behavior; also comparable are the total number of strokes and the individual series of those strokes inflicted to convert food material (crabs, sea urchins, and shells) into an edible condition. The variability of time taken on the surface with these objects ranges from 52.2 to 59.4%, and the variability of number of strokes and series of strokes is respectively 55.1±3.53% and 56.3±1.24%. As can be seen, the meristic and time variabilities completely coincide with each other.

A comparison of meristic and colorimetric variabilities is possible if it is presumed that the quantity of hemoglobin (estimated with the help of a colorimeter) and the number of erythrocytes can measure the same trait—the hemoglobin content of the blood in the given species. It appears that the variability $(c. v. \pm s_{c.v.})$ for number of erythrocytes is considerably higher than the variability for quantity of hemoglobin:[4]

Breed of sheep	Hemoglobin quantity according to Sali	Number of erythrocytes in millions	^{t}colorimetric-meristic
Romni-Marshi	1.76±0.23	3.10±0.40	−2.91
Tsigeiskie	1.59±0.25	2.26±0.36	−1.52
F_1 hybrids	2.28±0.36	3.06±0.48	−1.15

As seen from the data presented, there is no possibility of comparing the majority of manifestations of variability, but the data already obtained allow one to draw conclusions in principle for an analysis of variability of any form and type. Though the coefficient of variation is a dimensionless number and hence can formally allow a comparison of traits with any type of measurements, it should be remembered that the nature of those measurements has an effect on the magnitude of variability. It follows from this that the variability of a trait under study is, perhaps, accurately comparable with the variability of another trait, measured in different measurements, only after considering additional corrections.

Relationship of Variability to Absolute Size of Trait

The first problem confronting us in relating variability to the absolute size of a trait is the need for comparing measures of body size in different species. It should be clear in the light of recent studies on seasonal, age, oon, and biotopic variabilities (Chapter IV) that the assertion of Ya. Ya.

[4] Calculated from data presented in the work of Kh. F. Kushner, 1941.

Roginskii (1959) is doubtful, that there should be relatively close values of coefficients of variation for the same trait in different species. In fact, if the coefficient of variation varies considerably in the same population in different seasons and years, and depends upon many specific factors, then how can it coincide with indices of other species ?

For a clean comparison, it would have been better to compare co-efficients of variation from data which are collected specifically in the same years, seasons, and months, and belonging to absolutely identical age groups. But, as a rule, there are no such data available for comparison. Anyway, let us try to compare the variability of one trait in species belonging to different orders (Table 72).

It is seen from this table that the statement of Roginskii about the relative constancy of coefficients of variation for one and the same trait in different species is wrong. In *Sorex minutus* (body length, about six cm), the coefficient of variation of body length appears to be the same as in sables (body length, more than 40 cm), but the coefficient of variation of length of the skull is closer to that of beavers and moles; in the hedgehog (body length, 26 cm) the variability of body length appears to be the same as that of hamsters, forest mice, bank voles, and certain seals, but the hedgehog excels all the other mammals presented in the table in variability

Table 72. Comparison of variability of body length and basal length of skull in different animals (Adult males)

Species	Body length, mm		Condylo-basal length	Data from
	$\bar{x} \pm s_{\bar{x}}$	$c.v. \pm s_{c.v.}$	$c.v. \pm s_{c.v.}$	
Sorex minutus	59.6±1.60	2.8±0.42	1.1±0.09	Dolgov, 1963
Sicista betulina	65.4±0.996	7.8±1.08	2.3±0.38	Kubik, 1953
Clethrionomys glareolus	101.0±0.98	6.7±0.69	3.6±0.37	Bol'shakov and Schwartz, 1962
Apodemus flavicollis	105.1±0.64	5.7±0.43	4.1±0.63	Adamczewska, 1959
Talpa europaea	140.5±1.68	4.9±0.85	1.8±0.31	Markov, 1957
Citellus citellus	202.5±1.31	6.0±0.46	—	Straka, 1963
Erinaceus europeus	260.5±4.24	6.5±1.15	13.1±2.34	Markov, 1957
Martes zibellina	412.7±2.50	2.8±0.42	2.3±0.34	Kuznetsov, 1941
Castor fiber	—	—	1.7±0.32	Hinze, 1950
Pusa hispida ochotensis	1169.0±12.60	7.2±0.76	2.3±0.49	Own data
Pusa hispida hispida	1185.0±14.40	9.1±0.86	3.1±0.32	Own data
Cystophora cristata	2208.0±17.0	9.2±0.55	4.3±0.51	Own data
Delphinapterus leucas	4028.0±32.30	4.9±0.57	—	Own data

of skull length. Thus, the variability of the same trait may be different in different species.

Going to another aspect of the problem, let us compare the variability of different traits within one population. In the opinion of Roginskii (1959) there should be a negative relationship between the absolute size or magnitude of a trait and its variability value.

It is seen from Table 73 that if all the traits of organs of different systems are combined and examined, no negative relationship between the magnitude of the trait and its variability is observed either in the meristic or the linear traits. Thus, the variability of body length is close to the variability of width of snout (the absolute values of these measurements differ more than 40 times), but the variability of skull width between the orbits appears to be inseparable from the variability of the "anus-navel" measurement (the differences in the absolute values are more than 50 times). Many examples of this type could be cited.

Table 73. Relation of variability to absolute size of trait (Ringed seal of the Okhotsk Sea, *Pusa hispida;* **adult males from Summer collections of 1963)**

Trait	Absolute size	Coefficient of variation
Meristic (in numbers)		
Eye vibrissae	3.0±0.15	28.0±3.7
Sternal ribs	10.0±0.02	1.4±0.1
Caudal vertebrae	13.4±0.29	8.1±1.9
All lip vibrissae	50.6±0.42	6.2±0.6
Tracheal rings	91.0±1.03	5.7±0.8
Linear (in mm)		
Skull width between orbits	5.9±0.17	15.4±2.0
Width of snout	26.9±0.30	5.7±0.7
Length of lower jaw	108.0±0.55	2.9±0.4
Length of skull	166.0±0.74	2.4±0.3
Anus-navel measurement	319.0±7.80	13.6±1.7
Body length	1169.0±12.60	7.2±0.8

Therefore, in general, the statement about the negative relationship between the magnitude or size of a trait and its variability, when comparing different traits of one population, appears to be incorrect. However, this statement would appear to be correct for organs of one system.

If the variability for number of all vibrissae in the rows of the nasal group in the Greenland seal is compared with the absolute number of vibrissae in each row (Figure 57), it appears that a smaller number of vibrissae per row completely coincides with a greater coefficient of variation. This observation is confirmed by all other data on the variability of vibrissae in pinnipeds of all ages, male and female, for all species studied (Yablokov, 1963a, 1963b; Yablokov and Klevezal', 1964; see also Table 3 in the Appendix).   The data of Huestis (1925) confirm these observations with regard to meristic traits.

But this rule is true not only for meristic traits.   It appears that the negative relationship between the magnitude of a trait and its coefficient of variation occurs also in linear traits of one organ or a system.   Many examples of this type of variability for different animals can be found in the data already presented.

But it must be said that for some traits this regularity rarely occurs in a typical way.   It can be seen from Figures 18, 21, and 22 that there is no clear-cut relationship between the magnitude of the traits and their coefficients of variation according to the rule indicated. However, a specific trend is observed in the behavior of the majority of traits which, briefly, is that the traits of greater size have generally smaller coefficients of variation.

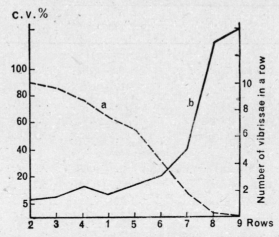

Figure 57.   Relationship of coefficients of variation to the absolute number of vibrissae in the lip group in the Greenland seal:
a—Number of vibrissae in a row; b—Coefficient of variation.

The data of Lowrance and Latimer (1957) show not only the dependence of coefficients of variation of length on the absolute size of the trait, but also the correlation of traits of weight with their absolute values at the same time.   As seen from Figure 58, the hyoid bone, with the lowest weight, appears to be the most variable bone in the human skeleton, and the skeleton as a whole has the lowest variability.   However, it is seen from the same figure that a number of measurements do not fall in the framework of this rule. Thus, for example, a comparatively low variability occurs for the weights of the lower jaw, the pelvic bones, and the vertebral column, while the weights of the ribs and scapulae have a comparatively high variability. But the part having the least length, the manubrium of the sternum, has the greatest variability of length, and the part having the greatest length, the hip, has the least variability.

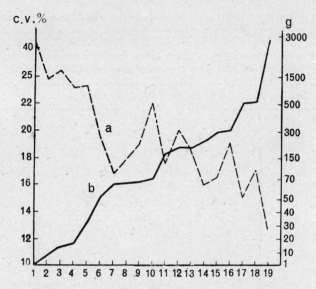

Figure 58.   Relationship of absolute magnitude of weight for parts of the human skeleton with the magnitude of the respective coefficients of variation (according to the data of Lowrance and Latimer, 1957):

a—Weight; b—Coefficient of variation.   Individual bones, in order of increase in weight, are shown on the abscissa.

Data exist on the relation between the magnitude of colorimetric variability with the absolute value of the trait (Table 74), and on the relation between time variability and the magnitude of the trait (Littlepage, 1963). These data generally confirm the conclusion of the presence of a negative relationship between the size of the trait and the magnitude of its variability. Therefore it appears that during a comparison of functionally similar traits or the characters of organs of one system, *there is a negative relationship between the size of the trait and the magnitude of its variability; the higher the absolute value of the trait, the lower its variability.* This regularity or dependence occurs in nature only in a general way, and in large series of measurements quite a few deviations are observed.

Such deviations from these regularities are not accidental. It is already clear from the general situation explained in the beginning of this chapter, that there must exist some more complex regularities of the appearance of variability of traits in a population, in addition to the primary trends or regularities. And it would be difficult to assume that these primary regularities could be brought to light in pure form in natural material. It becomes necessary to examine them through the complex mesh of other relationships. There could be cases where primary regularities absolutely do not appear. But such cases cannot prove the absence of such primary regularities; they only show the resultant of the total situation in nature.

Table 74. Variability of back color in *Peromyscus maniculatus* **of Florida and Alabama (Absolute data from Klein, 1964)**

Population	Red	Green	Bluish-violet	
I	18.9 ± 0.74	15.3 ± 0.82	13.9 ± 0.60	$\bar{x} \pm s_{\bar{x}}$
	17.9 ± 2.76	24.8 ± 3.81	19.8 ± 3.05	$c.v. \pm s_{c.v.}$
II	14.1 ± 0.40	10.5 ± 0.20	8.9 ± 0.30	$\bar{x} \pm s_{\bar{x}}$
	16.5 ± 2.03	11.1 ± 1.36	21.2 ± 2.62	$c.v. \pm s_{c.v.}$
III	22.4 ± 0.48	9.5 ± 0.31	7.6 ± 0.29	$\bar{x} \pm s_{\bar{x}}$
	17.4 ± 2.58	14.7 ± 2.33	17.2 ± 2.73	$c.v. \pm s_{c.v.}$
IV	11.1 ± 0.28	8.1 ± 0.31	6.7 ± 0.39	$\bar{x} \pm s_{\bar{x}}$
	23.5 ± 1.78	16.2 ± 1.23	20.3 ± 1.53	$c.v. \pm s_{c.v.}$
V	13.7 ± 0.33	9.8 ± 0.36	7.2 ± 0.36	$\bar{x} \pm s_{\bar{x}}$
	30.4 ± 2.23	36.3 ± 2.77	49.4 ± 3.63	$c.v. \pm s_{c.v.}$
VI	10.7 ± 0.22	8.1 ± 0.31	6.7 ± 0.39	$\bar{x} \pm s_{\bar{x}}$
	17.9 ± 1.45	33.3 ± 2.54	50.6 ± 4.11	$c.v. \pm s_{c.v.}$
VII	8.8 ± 0.51	6.9 ± 0.31	5.5 ± 0.24	$\bar{x} \pm s_{\bar{x}}$
	57.9 ± 4.08	44.8 ± 3.16	43.7 ± 3.07	$c.v. \pm s_{c.v.}$
VIII	7.7 ± 0.26	6.0 ± 0.19	5.2 ± 0.16	$\bar{x} \pm s_{\bar{x}}$
	24.6 ± 2.39	23.1 ± 2.24	22.4 ± 2.17	$c.v. \pm s_{c.v.}$
IX	7.4 ± 0.86	5.5 ± 0.63	5.2 ± 0.52	$\bar{x} \pm s_{\bar{x}}$
	66.2 ± 8.70	65.3 ± 8.16	67.9 ± 8.49	$c.v. \pm s_{c.v.}$

The question of relating the absolute value of a trait to the magnitude of its coefficient of variation appears to be far from simple and specific, as it seemed from a superficial examination. It is seen from the formula for the coefficient of variation,

$$c.v. = \frac{\sigma . 100}{\bar{x}}$$

that in fact the coefficient of variation must decrease with an increase in the absolute value of the trait $(\bar{x})$ in the denominator (except when the standard deviation itself increases proportionately with the mean value).

Because this rule is not observed in a natural sample, a speculation arises that some powerful forces capable of changing and regulating variability of structures, act beyond simple mathematical regularities. The generally understood ecological and genetical factors must be the first of such forces.

After examining more carefully the graphs of the relationship of the absolute value of a trait with the magnitude of variability in a sufficiently large number of traits, and by restricting the higher and lower peaks, it is possible to obtain the general nature of this range of real variability for the group of traits in the organ under study, a "variability drift" in which the most variable traits form the lower border of the drift, and a certain number of traits of intermediary significance appear. It is better from a practical point of view to introduce into this "drift" a certain hypothetical "mean drift," in relation to which it would be possible to calculate more exactly the deviations both on the side of increased and that of decreased variability, and which to a certain extent can show the magnitude of deviations from the influence of the elementary regularity between the magnitude of the trait and the magnitude of variability.

Such "drifts" of variability in the skull measurements for a number of species of pinnipeds have been given in Chapter III (see Tables 15, 18, 19, 31, etc.).

It is necessary to compare data belonging exclusively to one organ, one system of organs, or with a functional complex of similar measurements, for a practical analysis of this drift. Sufficiently large amounts of data (not less than 15 to 20 traits) are a necessary prerequisite so that the upper and lower boundaries of the variability drift are brought out; and finally, it is necessary to arrange at least a large majority of the traits in an ascending or a descending order of their absolute values (and not group them around one or a few traits close to them in absolute value). This method of finding out the "variability drift" attains a special significance for analyzing structures with a greater or lesser variability, and for a morphological-ecological study of population.

Relationship of Absolute and Relative Variability Values (Indices)

The study of indices (relative values) sometimes makes it possible to eliminate the effect of the largeness or smallness of an animal (Filipchenko, 1916) during comparisons, and brings to light more vividly the specific properties of the organ under study, or of the animal as a whole. This method of indices is widely used in modern taxonomy (Mayr, Linsley and Usinger, 1956) and in studies of the ecology and physiology of mammals (summary of data by Schwartz, 1960). However, as far as I know, the variability of relative values has not especially attracted the attention of researchers. Because of the widespread use of indices in zoological investigations, the question of comparing the magnitude of variability for relative and absolute indices should be taken into account during the study of morphological variability as a whole.

The variability of indices is in abstract numbers without dimensions, and Ya. Ya. Roginskii (1959) observed that instead of calculating the coefficient of variation, the standard deviation may be calculated directly. However, the formula is

$$\sigma^2_{\frac{a}{b}} = \frac{a_0^2}{b_0^2}\left(\frac{\sigma_a^2}{a_0^2} + \frac{\sigma_b^2}{b_0^2} - \frac{2r\sigma_a\sigma_b}{a_0 b_0}\right),$$

where σ^2 is the variance of the index $\frac{a}{b}$, a_0 and b_0 are the means of the measurements a and b ; and r is the coefficient of correlation of a and b. We see that the magnitude of the index is influenced by the standard deviation itself, and the coefficient of variation has to be used. "By dividing the standard deviation by the mean index, we rid ourselves of the influence of the latter" (Roginskii, 1959; p. 86).

To develop the viewpoint of Roginskii, it would appear proper to propose that for a complete study of the variability of an index, it is necessary to know these two parameters: (1) the coefficient of variation for each separate trait; and (2) the coefficient of correlation between the traits under study. And then (in case the indices under study are similar in magnitude and there is a considerable correlation between the traits), the coefficient of variation of the index will be small even if the value of variability for each trait is large or small or however diverse. With a low correlation between the two traits under investigation, it is possible that the variability of each trait will be comparatively low while the coefficient of variation for the index appears to be very large. But then what does calculating the coefficient of variation for the index reveal if we already know the separate coefficients of variation for each trait and the correlation coefficient which expresses the relation between the traits ?

Ya. Ya. Roginskii concludes that "the coefficients of variation give an idea of the structural mode of variability of indices" (1959; p. 86), and in this the role of coefficients of variation differs considerably from the one they play in the study of any individual trait.

After these general observations, let us compare some appropriate data on the magnitude of variability for absolute and relative values of a trait; then let us make an attempt to determine the relation between them by looking at specific examples.

Data on the variability of body length and length of intestines for the Greenland seal (Table 75) show that the variability of body length has comparatively low values (3 to 4%), that the variability of intestinal length is three to four times higher (11 to 12%), and that the variability of intestinal length in relation to the body length is about 11 to 12%, i.e., is retained on the level of variability of the more variable member of the comparison. The variability for length of large and small intestines has values quite similar (15 to 17 and 11 to 12% respectively); the variability of the ratio of length of large intestines to that of small intestines is very different in males and females (11 and 24%); moreover, in this case, the variability of the index in females is retained on the level of the less variable member of the comparison, while in males it somewhat exceeds the level of the more variable member of the comparison. The sexual dimorphism in variability of body length did not influence the variability of the index during the determinations of variability of the relative length of the intestine, but the sexual dimorphism, which was not reflected in the variability of absolute traits, clearly appeared during the determination of the variability value for the small intestines relative to that of the large intestines.

Table 75. Variability $(c.\,v. \pm s_{c.v.})$ **of absolute and relative values of length of intestines of adult Greenland seals** (*Pagophilus groenlandicus*), **Yan-Maien region, 1962**

Length of	Males	Females
Body	4.0 ± 0.28	3.1 ± 0.24
Intestines	12.0 ± 2.35	11.7 ± 1.89
Small intestines	12.2 ± 2.40	11.1 ± 2.03
Large intestines	17.2 ± 2.30	15.3 ± 2.54
Intestines/body length	11.6 ± 2.46	10.6 ± 1.81
Small intestines/body length	12.6 ± 2.80	11.0 ± 1.88
Small intestines/length of large intestines	24.0 ± 5.37	11.3 ± 1.93

Data on the variability of absolute and relative weights of musculature for six different groups of rabbits are available (Latimer and Sawin, 1955). The variability of absolute muscle weight appeared to be practically the same as the variability of body weight (11.7 to 21.5 and 12.5 to 21.0% respectively), and the variability of relative muscle weight was three to four times less than any of these parameters (3.9 to 5.5%).

As seen from the data given below, the variability of the index of intestinal length (in relation to the body length) in white whales (adult males, Novaya Zemlya, 1957) appeared to be twice the variability of either of the components in the comparison :

Length of	$c.v. \pm s_{c.v.}$	$\bar{x} \pm s_{\bar{x}}$
Body	4.0 ± 0.60	397.3 ± 4.22
Intestine	4.2 ± 1.11	29.6 ± 0.47
Intestine/Body	8.6 ± 2.30	7.7 ± 0.25

In this case, there is a reverse situation from the one observed for the variability of height index for muscles in rabbits.

The data on variability of relative length of the feet of yellow-necked mice (Table 76) also show the complex behavior of the index of variability (in relation to the variability value of each of the traits in the given index).

Table 76. Variability of yellow-necked mice
(Calculated from data of Ursin, 1956)

Population $c.v. \pm s_{c.v.}$	Body length $c.v. \pm s_{c.v.}$	Foot length $c.v. \pm s_{c.v.}$	Foot length/body length	
			$c.v. \pm s_{c.v.}$	$\bar{x} \pm s_{\bar{x}}$
Latvian	4.8 ± 0.28	10.5 ± 0.61	1.5 ± 0.34	20.7 ± 0.10
Danish—1	4.6 ± 0.49	8.8 ± 0.96	3.5 ± 0.27	20.8 ± 0.08
Danish—2	4.4 ± 0.35	8.6 ± 0.88	6.1 ± 0.88	20.8 ± 0.26

It is seen from the data presented in Table 76 that the coefficients of variation for body length and foot length are practically the same in the three populations, whereas the variability of indices of these measurements differ. It is interesting that the indices of absolute values are unequivocally the same in all populations.

The distribution of the variability values for indices of intestinal length in four sexually mature groups of hooded seals (*Cystophora cristata*), may depict a still more complex picture (Yablokov, 1963). The variability of the index for intestines (length of intestines/body length) in mature females is greater than that for absolute length of intestines in new-born males and females, but in mature males the situation is the reverse. The variability of the index of intestines (length of small intestines/length of large intestines) appears to be greater than the variability of absolute measurements for large intestines in both mature males and new-born females. Since it is true that all the differences mentioned here are insignificant, it can be said that the variability value of the index in these cases approaches the variability of absolute values of the trait.

It is important to examine large numbers of measurements in their absolute and relative expressions so that the relationship between the variabilities of the absolute and relative values becomes clear. An example of this is found in the work of Lowrance and Latimer (1957), where the variability of weights of bones of the human skeleton is given. Out of 16 traits, the coefficients of variation for 13 indices appear to be lower than the corresponding absolute values of the traits; moreover, in the majority of cases, the differences are considerable. However, the disposition of the coefficients of variation of the indices in order of ascending variability remains exactly the same for the coefficients of variation of the absolute weight of the skeleton and its parts.

A comparison of the variability of absolute and relative values for a number of traits in a laboratory population of mice (data of Sumner, 1909) shows a different tendency. The variability of indices throughout appeared to be higher than the variability of absolute measurements. The length and weight measurements are exceptions to this (weight of hair/ square of body length). But even this behavior of coefficients of variation of indices is not constant; thus, for example, the variability of the weight of the eyeball is significantly less than the variability of the index of the weight of the eyeball (according to Latimer, 1951).

The last example in this series is from the data of V. I. Tsalkin (1960) on the variability of metapodials in horned cattle (*Bos taurus*). It appeared that the variability of all indices of the metacarpus and metatarsus of bulls, bullocks, and cows of Kalmitskii cattle was, in all cases, lowest in cows and greatest in bullocks. A similar distribution is observed also for the variability of height at withers in the groups under study.

The examples presented here and in other chapters allow one to draw certain conclusions.

First, the variability of indices is not always governed by those general tendencies which are characteristic of the variability of the absolute values of traits. Second, specific trends in the behavior of variability of indices, characteristic of all the appearances of a variability of this type, are not found. Both of these conclusions confirm the assumption that the variability of indices reflect relations and regularities different from those which express variability in absolute values.

Attempts are often made to use different traits as independent variables in a determination of relative characteristics in order to discover general regularities in the variability of indices. Wood *et al.* (1965) showed that indices obtained on the basis of dividing the weight of an organ by the body weight were not sufficiently accurate, and they proposed that in such calculations it is better to use heart weight than body weight. Talbot, Lee, and McCullich (1965) think that weight of the heart is not the most useful independent variable but rather perimeter of the heart, whereas in many other works the relative weights of organs are calculated in weight units per 100 kg (or 100 g) body weight (for example, Kramer, 1964). All these attempts reflect a non-specificity and insufficiency of determination of the relative parameters of organs.   It is not possible to say how closely the variability of indices is related to the micro-evolutionary processes in populations, unless some special critical investigations are carried out. And to carry out such an analysis, large quantities of factual data on all types, forms, and appearances of variability are necessary.

It is quite likely that the data on variability only seem heterogeneous and can be explained by the complexity of the whole phenomenon, which does not yield to interpretation from the viewpoint of the study of absolute values.   In any case, the variability of relative values (indices) is not comparable in magnitude to the variability of absolute values.

Comparative Variability and its Importance in Population Biology

In the previous chapters, from II to IV, the variability values of traits characterizing one system of organs or an individual organ were examined separately without reference to the variability of other traits in the population.   This problem—the correlation of variability of different traits in the same population—has also not been examined by other research workers. This has happened possibly because data for even posing the question were not then available.

Data on two basic aspects are needed to obtain a unified picture of comparative variability in a population : Data from the same population at different times (after months, seasons, years, a number of generations, etc.),[5] and data on variability of a number of the same traits in different populations of close species in the same season and during a number of seasons.

In the work of K. Adamczewska (1959), data appear which characterize a population of yellow-necked mice (*Apodemus flavicollis*) in different months of one year.   Absolute measurements and coefficients of variation calculated on the basis of factual data are presented in Figure 56.

Let us try to distribute the coefficients of variation in each monthly series in declining or increasing order of variability, and then compare the data obtained for different months.   It appears in all cases (not only for males as shown in Figure 56, but also for females) that with regard to the lowest coefficient of variation, "length of feet" (trait 5) comes first, "length of ear" (trait 4) second, "body length" (trait 3) third, and "tail length" (trait 1) in fourth place.   It seems that, according to the magnitude

---

[5] Strictly speaking, by investigating the animals at the same place after sufficiently large intervals of time, exceeding the lifetime of one generation, we investigate not one but two different populations.   It is quite logical to restrict a population by time, and in future developments of population morphology such an approach of demarcating the concept of population by the life of one generation will perhaps be widely used.

of variability, each of the traits maintains its place in the series. It is important to note that the "maintenance (of place) in the series" is observed in spite of the considerable overlapping of absolute values of coefficients of variation from month to month. Thus, the coefficient of variation for ear length in males varies more than twice—from 5% in September to 10.5% in June; the coefficient of variation for length of feet varies almost as much—from 4% in November to 7.1% in June; the coefficient of variation for tail length varies almost three times (Table 77).

Table 77. Seasonal variability of body measurements for male and female forest mice (*Apodemus flavicollis*) **(Collected 1955; calculated from the data of Adamczewska, 1959)**

Month	Sex	$\bar{x}\pm s_{\bar{x}}$	σ	$c.v.\pm s_{c.v.}$	n
		Body length			
August	♂♂	100.0±0.88	8.98	8.98±0.63	104
	♀♀	97.0±0.73	7.39	7.61±0.53	102
September	♂♂	102.0±0.48	6.81	6.67±0.27	248
	♀♀	99.0±0.40	6.73	6.79±0.29	279
October	♂♂	103.6±0.95	6.47	6.25±0.65	46
	♀♀	96.6±1.14	6.54	6.77±0.83	33
November	♂♂	105.1±0.64	5.96	5.67±0.43	86
	♀♀	98.2±0.70	6.29	6.41±0.51	80
		Body weight			
August	♂♂	28.7±0.67	6.88	23.97±1.65	105
	♀♀	25.6±0.62	6.29	24.57±1.71	103
September	♂♂	29.8±0.37	6.34	21.28±0.87	301
	♀♀	26.3±0.31	5.14	19.54±0.83	278
October	♂♂	30.8±0.89	5.60	18.18±2.03	40
	♀♀	24.0±0.79	4.47	18.63±2.33	32
November	♂♂	32.4±0.57	5.15	15.90±1.24	82
	♀♀	26.2±0.45	3.96	15.11±1.20	79
		Tail length			
August	♂♂	102.0±3.24	32.12	31.49±2.25	98
	♀♀	101.0±2.37	23.18	22.95±1.66	96
September	♂♂	107.9±1.48	23.08	22.06±0.97	259
	♀♀	104.1±1.77	27.17	26.10±1.20	235
October	♂♂	105.9±2.18	13.05	12.32±1.45	36
	♀♀	102.3±2.01	10.05	0.00±1.00	21
November	♂♂	107.9±1.39	12.29	11.39±0.91	78
	♀♀	103.1±1.28	11.14	10.81±0.87	76

(*Contd.*)

Month	Sex	$\bar{x} \pm s_{\bar{x}}$	σ	$c.v. \pm s_{c.v.}$	n
		Ear length			
June	♂♂	17.6±0.22	18.50	10.51±0.87	73
	♀♀	17.2±0.18	1.58	9.19±0.74	77
July	♂♂	17.4±0.09	1.39	7.99±0.36	245
	♀♀	17.2±0.09	1.44	8.37±0.38	240
August	♂♂	17.5±0.13	1.33	7.60±0.52	105
	♀♀	17.4±0.11	1.14	6.55±0.46	101
September	♂♂	17.8±0.05	0.89	5.00±0.21	292
	♀♀	17.7±0.05	0.91	5.14±0.22	282
October	♂♂	18.1±0.15	1.03	5.69±0.60	45
	♀♀	17.8±0.17	1.01	5.67±0.69	34
November	♂♂	18.1±0.10	0.90	4.97±0.38	85
		Foot length			
June	♂♂	24.49±0.21	1.74	7.10±0.60	70
	♀♀	23.60±0.16	1.41	5.97±0.48	78
July	♂♂	24.80±0.008	1.27	5.12±0.23	250
	♀♀	24.20±0.09	1.41	5.83±0.27	241
August	♂♂	25.40±0.13	1.31	5.16±0.36	104
	♀♀	24.60±0.11	1.09	4.43±0.31	101
September	♂♂	25.30±0.06	1.04	4.11±0.17	295
	♀♀	24.70±0.07	1.11	4.49±0.19	286
October	♂♂	25.20±0.22	1.47	5.83±0.62	44
	♀♀	24.90±0.17	1.00	4.02±0.49	34
November	♂♂	25.30±0.11	1.02	4.03±0.31	86
	♀♀	24.60±0.11	0.97	3.94±0.31	80

And thus, in each moment of the life span of a population (in the given example, in each month), the coefficients of variation for the same traits are distributed in exactly the same order : 5-4-3-1.

In the work of Sumner (1924), the same four traits were studied in four populations of *Peromyscus maniculatus* : in two original populations of different subspecies (*P. m. sonoriensis* and *P. m. rubidus*), and in transplanted populations of these subspecies. In the first case, the experimental population was studied after seven generations, and in the second case, after 12 generations of development in captivity.

The absolute values of coefficients of variation for a number of traits considerably overlapped, as in the above-mentioned case of forest mice. But if we distribute the traits according to the coefficients of variation at one time, it appears that the disposition of all traits relative to each other is fixed absolutely specifically in all cases :

P. m. sonoriensis		*P. m. rubidus*	
Wild population	3 4 1 2	In nature	3 4 1 2
After 7 generations	3 4 1 2	After 12 generations	3 4 1 2

As in the case of forest mice, in all the contemporary samples, tail length (trait 2) appears to be the most variable. Then in the order of reduced variability follow body length (1), ear length (4), and length of feet (3).

It can be seen from the two comparisons cited above that the same traits in taxonomically remote species are exactly similar with regard to variability. As will be shown below, such a situation is not characteristic in general of the given traits. This is shown by the analysis of data obtained by us on house mice sent by Dynowski. The traits arranged themselves in the following manner with regard to variability in one population:

Age group	Males	Females
II	3 4 2 1 0*	3 2 4 1 0
III	3 — 2 1 0	3 4 2 1 0
IV	3 4 2 1 0	3 4 1 2 0

* The nomenclature of traits is the same; 0—Body weight.

In the majority of cases (and without exception in males), the disposition of the traits in the series is absolutely specific, but it differs from the disposition of the same traits in yellow-necked mice and deermice in that the variability of body length appears to be less than the variability of tail length. It is important to emphasize again that, on the average, all the variabilities for all the traits considerably overlap (6.9 to 10%, body length, 6.1 to 10.4%, tail length; 5.7 to 7.3%, ear length). This means that it appears to be impossible for traits to maintain their disposition in the samples with regard to variability because of specificity of coefficients of variation.

There are data in the above-mentioned work of Adamczewska which allow one to compare variability not only of body measurements, but also of six different measurements of the skull in one population in different months. The results obtained are not as uniform as those secured in the comparison of body measurements, but the presence of a general trend toward a similar disposition of traits is undoubtedly there:

	Males	Females
October	1 6 5 4 3 2*	6 1 5 4 3 2
November	5 6 1 3 4 2	1 5 6 4 3 2

* 1—condylobasal length; 2—diastema; 3—length of palate; 4—width between orbits; 5—skull height; 6—height of braincase.

In these samples it is seen that traits 1, 6, 5 are always positioned in the left half of the series and traits 4, 3, 2 are always in the right half.

It should be remembered here that the coefficients of variation for a number of traits are very similar and an accidental change of place in traits is possible (see below).

In the work of K. Ya. Fateev (1962) on the morphology of moles from the Kostrom region, data on weight of different organs of males and females caught by the same method in different seasons during 1958, 1959, and 1960 are presented. In Table 78 the calculated error $(\pm s_{c.v.})$ of coefficients of variation is added in each case to the coefficients of variation presented in this work (a necessity when comparing coefficients of variation of samples which differ considerably in their values).

Table 78. Variability $(c.\,v.\pm s_{c.v.})$ **of weights of certain organs in one population of moles in different years (According to Fateev, 1962, with calculated error** $s_{c.v.}$)

Weight of organ	1958		1959		1960	
	Males	Females	Males	Females	Males	Females
1–Body	16.1±2.1	23.8±3.1	13.3±1.2	13.8±1.3	8.5±1.2	5.7±0.8
2–Heart	39.5±5.3	44.3±5.9	20.8±2.0	26.6±2.6	17.3±2.5	16.7±2.4
3–Liver	28.4±3.8	32.5±4.3	18.7±1.7	23.6±2.3	13.7±2.0	19.6±2.8
4–Lungs	23.6±3.2	17.8±2.4	19.5±1.9	17.2±2.9	21.2±3.1	15.7±2.3
5–Kidneys	30.5±4.1	34.0±4.5	17.6±1.7	13.3±1.3	19.7±2.9	21.1±3.1
6–Spleen	—	—	43.2±5.1	29.9±3.5	37.7±5.2	18.2±2.6
7–Stomach	51.8±6.9	27.8±3.7	26.9±2.6	47.2±4.5	38.9±5.6	18.2±2.6

Let us try to compare the variation of weights of different organs in different years.

If the traits are arranged in the order of increasing value characterizing their variability, the following picture emerges :

	Males	Females
1958	1 4 3 5 2 7 *	4 1 7 3 5 2
1959	1 5 3 4 2 7 6	5 1 4 3 2 6 7
1960	1 3 2 5 4 6 7	1 4 2 7 3 5 6

* Character 6, spleen weight, was not recorded in the year 1958.

Without disturbing the traits in the series, these series could be divided as follows for analytical convenience:

	Males				Females			
	1 4 3	5	2 7 —		4 1 7	3	5 2 —	
	1 5 3	4	2 7 6		5 1 4	3	2 6 7	
	1 3 2	5	4 6 7		1 4 2	7	3 5 6	

On examining these series, the following conclusions may be drawn:

1. In the left half of all the series the males have traits 3 and 1; the females have traits 1 and 4;

2. In the right half of all the series, the males have traits 6 and 7; for females, only trait 6 appears in the right half of all the series;

3. The series of the traits arranged according to absolute values of coefficients of variation are more similar within each sex group than between the sexes.

To analyze these samples further it is necessary to determine somehow the "reliability" of disposition for each of the traits in a particular place in one or another series, because many coefficients of variation differ from each other. Even with considerable differences in the mean values of coefficients of variation, the differences could seem insufficiently reliable because of large errors caused by the size of the samples examined. For example, traits 3 and 4 seem to differ from each other appreciably in the year 1958, 28.4 and 23.6% respectively, but their larger errors (3.8 and 3.2%) make these differences less clear-cut and in fact insignificant.

Let us say that the differences could be considered "significant" if $c.\,v._1 - c.\,v._2 > s_{c.v.1} + s_{c.v.2}$, i.e., if the conditions were deliberately made to give more significant differences than do the ones usually used in statistics.

The following picture emerges if the series are rewritten after considering the significant differences between variability values of individual traits:

	Males	Females
1958	1 (3, 4, 5) 2 7 —	4 1 (3, 5, 7) 2 —
1959	1 (3, 4, 5, 2) 7 6	(1, 5, 4) (3, 2, 6) 7
1960	1 3 (2, 4, 5) (6, 7)	1 (2 ,3, 7, 4, 5, 6)

Now, taking into consideration the possibility of a chance in place of the traits put into parentheses (because of the absence of detectable differences in the values of their coefficients of variation), let us do the final possible rearrangement :

	Males	Females
1958	1 3 4 5 2 7 —	4 1 5 3 7 2 —
1959	1 3 4 5 2 7 6	1 4 5 3 2 6 7
1960	1 3 4 5 2 7 6	1 4 5 3 2 6 7

These lines make it possible to draw more specific conclusions, in principle, coinciding with those which have been drawn above for the linear measurements of forest mice and deermice. The disposition of traits in variability during the period of three years is practically the same in males; such a conclusion is not completely correct in the case of females but it cannot be overlooked that, even in this group, the sequence of variability of traits is specific and quite similar from year to year.

A question arises of whether such a uniform distribution of variability of a trait is merely a reflection of a constant coefficient of variation for every trait. However, a simple comparison of the coefficients of variation for traits in different years shows that this hypothesis is not correct. Thus for males, the variability value of body weight ranges in three years from 8.1 to 16.1%; of the heart, from 17.3 to 39.5%; of the liver, from 13.7 to 28.7%, etc.

And the large variations in variability notwithstanding, the causes ordering the majority of the traits in the series have a tendency to keep constant from year to year. Hence, though the absolute value of coefficients of variation for the same trait in the same population can vary considerably in different years, the relative value of coefficients of variation (the position of a given trait in the sequence of other traits with regard to variability value) has a tendency to remain constant.

On the basis of this conclusion, I now propose that the phenomenon of comparative variability, or the variability of disposition of traits, be singled out from the usual study of variability of organs and structures in animals.

Analysis of Comparative Variability for Some Mammals

The parallels in the comparative variability of the same body measurements of mammals like forest mice and *Peromyscus*, have already been seen. In these species, the comparative values of coefficients of variation for four body measurements completely coincided. The results of other researchers (Clark, 1940) are in accord with this:

P. maniculatus (30 populations)

I subspecies	6 5 3 4 1 2	II subspecies	6 5 3 1 4 2
III subspecies	6 5 3 4 1 2	IV subspecies	6 5 3 4 1 2
V subspecies	6 5 3 4 1 2	VI subspecies	6 3 5 4 1 2
VII subspecies	6 5 3 4 1 2	VIII subspecies	6 3 5 4 1 2

P. leucopus (8 populations)

6 5 3 4 1 2

P. eremicus (4 populations)

6 5 3 4 1 2

(Length of : 1—body; 2—tail; 3—feet; 4—thigh; 5—lower jaw; 6—skull).

In the few instances of some other disposition of coefficients of variation (1, 4 in one case, and 3, 5 in another two cases), it seems that the values of coefficients of variation are so close to each other that there are no detectable differences between them (4.3±0.26% and 4.2±0.30% in one case, 2.88±0.21% and 2.92±0.22% in another case). Only in one case is there a formal difference in the values from the general disposition of coefficients of variation, and that is for the VIII subspecies of *P. maniculatus*; the coefficients of variation for the third and fifth traits are 2.75±0.07 and 3.05±0.4% respectively.

A comparison of these data with those presented above (Sumner, 1924) shows that the disposition of the same traits is similar in the sequence of variability. However, the data presented do not agree with the data of D. Hoffmeister (1951) on another species, *P. truei*, in which the arrangement of the traits in order of variability is : 6, 2, 1, 3 (traits 4 and 5 were not investigated). The data of Hoffmeister and Lee (1963) shows that in one more species of this same genus, *P. merriami*, the arrangement of the traits corresponds well with the data of Clark and Sumner : 3, 4, 1, 2 (traits 5 and 6 were not investigated).

Many times the variability of incomparable traits has been investigated in different species of mammals. Such a situation restricts the comparison of comparative values of variability to only closely related forms as a rule. But even such a comparison appears to be interesting.

From the data sent to me for analysis by J. Dynowski, it is possible to compare variability of traits in six age and sex groups for a series of measurements of the body and skull of house mice (Table 79). First of all, we shall examine those groups of traits concerned with body measurements (2–body length, 3–length of tail, 4–length of feet, 5–length of ear):

Age group	Males				Females			
II	2	3	5	4	2	3	5	4
III	2	3	–	4	2	3	5	4
IV	2	3	5	4	3	2	5	4

It is seen that the arrangement of coefficients of variation coincides well in the first two age groups in both males and females. In the third age group, traits 2 and 3 change places for females but, as has happened in examples presented previously, the differences between the values of coefficients of variation are so insignificant compared to the error (6.9±1.2 and 6.1±1.0% in females) that such an arrangement of the coefficients of variation could even be accidental.

The analysis of distribution of coefficients of variation for skull traits shows a generally similar picture (Table 80).

Table 79.   Variability of some traits of male and female house mice (Calculated from data obtained from Dynowski)

Age group, Sex		$\bar{x} \pm s_{\bar{x}}$	σ	$c.\,v. \pm s_{c.v.}$	n
			Body weight		
II	♂♂	11.9±0.29	2.98	25.0±1.70	108
	♀♀	12.6±0.41	3.89	30.9±2.28	92
III	♂♂	14.4±0.26	2.31	15.9±1.26	80
	♀♀	15.7±0.52	3.48	22·2±2.34	45
IV	♂♂	15.8±0.73	2.93	18.5±3.28	16
	♀♀	15.0±1.11	3.50	28.3±5.22	10
			Body length		
II	♂♂	74.9±0.70	7.38	9.9±0.66	110
	♀♀	75.3±0.75	7.50	10.0±0.71	99
III	♂♂	80.6±0.61	5.42	7.7±0.53	80
	♀♀	83.6±1.10	7.90	9.5±0.93	52
IV	♂♂	82.8±1.39	5.72	6.9±1.19	17
	♀♀	84.8±2.22	8.02	9.5±1.86	13
			Tail length		
II	♂♂	67.0±0.58	6.07	9.1±0.61	110
	♀♀	68.0±0.56	5.63	8.3±0.59	100
III	♂♂	72.2±0.56	5.04	7.0±0.55	80
	♀♀	73.4±0.83	5.97	8.1±0.81	50
IV	♂♂	73.9±1.09	4.50	6.1±1.04	17
	♀♀	76.5±2.21	7.96	10.4±2.04	13
			Foot length		
II	♂♂	16.8±0.06	0.65	3.9±0.26	108
	♀♀	16.9±0.07	0.66	4.0±0.29	94
III	♂♂	17.0±0.07	0.62	3.7±0.29	80
	♀♀	16.8±0.09	0.66	3.9±0.39	52
IV	♂♂	17.1±0.12	0.50	2.9±0.50	17
	♀♀	17.0±0.16	0.58	3.4±0.67	13
			Ear length		
II	♂♂	12.5±0.08	0.83	6.6±0.45	110
	♀♀	12.5±0.09	0.91	7.3±0.55	97
III	♀♀	13.3±0.11	0.76	5.7±0.57	50
IV	♂♂	13.1±0.19	0.75	5.7±1.01	16
	♀♀	13.4±0.27	0.98	7.3±1.43	13

It is seen from the final data obtained as a result of rearranging coefficients (after taking into account the possible errors), that even the skull measurements may well be ordered quite similarly in the first two age groups of males and females and in a very close but somewhat changed order in the third age group. The values of coefficients of variation of comparable skull measurements overlap considerably ; this means that it is impossible to explain a regular arrangement of coefficients of variation in a sequence by an absolute variability inherent in each trait.

Together with such easily calculable data, more complex cases have been met which show that the concept of a comparable variability is far from complete in spite of the general regularities already noticed and some other reasons yet unknown which influence the regularities previously observed.

In the work of Saint Girons and van Bree (1962), factual data are presented on variability for a number of traits in three populations of forest mice (*Apodemus sylvaticus*) of North Africa.

Table 80. Arrangement of skull measurements in different age groups of a population of house mice in decreasing order of coefficients of variation (Calculated according to the data of Dynowski)

Age group	Distribution according to absolute value, *c. v.* (uncorrected data)	
	Males	Females
II	7 6 10 9 11 8	6 7 10 9 11 8
III	6 7 9 10 11 8	7 6 10 11 9 8
IV	6 10 7 11 8 9	7 9 10 6 8 11
	Distribution after taking error into consideration, *c. v.*	
II	7 (6, 10) (9, 11) 8	(6, 7) 10 (9, 11) 8
III	(6, 7) 10 (11, 9) 8	(6, 7, 9, 10) 11 8
IV	(6, 10) (7, 11) 8 9	(7, 9) (10, 6) (8, 11)
	Final possible distribution	
II	7 6 10 9 11 8	7 6 10 9 11 8
III	7 6 10 9 11 8	7 6 10 9 11 8
IV	6 10 7 11 8 9	7 9 6 10 11 8

The coefficients of variation for body measurements calculated on the basis of these data (Table 81) are arranged in two populations in exactly the same way as they were in the Polish population of this genus : 3, 4, 1, 2. The arrangement of the coefficients of variation in the third population is different : 1, 2, 4, 3. Even after a possible rearrangement of traits 1, 2, and 4, the comparative variability of this population will differ from the one which is characteristic for the rest of the populations of the species. The comparative variability of skull traits also seems irregular (Table 82).

It can be said only in a most general form that there are certain common characters between the variability of the populations (traits 7 and 5 are always on the left and traits 10, 11, 8 are on the right). However, the coincidence of arrangement for coefficients of variation is far from complete.

Table 81.　Variability of body and skull measurements of three populations of forest mice (*Apodemus sylvaticus*) of North Africa (Calculated from data in the work of Saint Girons and van Bree, 1962)

Trait	$c. v_{\cdot 1} \pm s_{c.v.1}$	$c. v_{\cdot 2} \pm s_{c.v.2}$	$c. v_{\cdot 3} \pm s_{c.v.3}$
Length of			
Body	6.7±1.93	8.9±1.06	5.5±1.03
Tail	6.9±2.17	9.2±1.09	6.1±1.19
Feet	3.7±1.05	5.9±0.68	9.5±1.79
Ear	4.3±1.24	6.7±0.85	6.5±1.22
Condylobasal length	2.7±0.85	4.9±0.63	3.8±0.77
Width of skull			
Zygomatic	3.6±1.44	5.2±0.67	3.6±0.77
Maximum	1.0±0.32	2.7±0.34	2.7±0.65
Minimum	3.7±1.18	4.3±0.49	4.2±0.83
Diastema	2.9±0.83	6.3±0.73	3.4±0.66
Length of lower jaw	3.8±1.08	5.6±0.65	3.8±0.75
Upper dental row	4.8±1.37	5.0±0.57	5.0±0.98
Lower dental row	3.3±0.94	3.9±0.44	4.6±0.90

Table 82.　Comparative variability of skull measurements for three populations of forest mice of North Africa

Population	Order of arrangement of traits
	According to absolute values, $c. v.$
I	7　5 9 12　6 8 10 11
II	7 12 8　5 11 6 10　9
III	7　9 6　5 10 8 12 11
	With calculation of error, $s_{c.v.}$
I	7 (5, 9, 12) (6, 8, 10) 11
II	7 12 (5, 6, 8, 11) 10 9
III	7 (5, 6, 9, 10) 8 (12, 11)
	Possible final
I	7　5 9 12 10　6　8 11
II	7 12 5　6　8 11 10　9
III	7　5 9　6 10　8 12 11

Data on variability of some traits in 11 populations of bank voles (*Clethrionomys glareolus*) have been presented in the work of V. N. Bol'shakov and S. S. Schwartz (1962). Because of the small size of some samples, I have analyzed data for only seven populations (Table 83).

Table 83. Geographical variability ($c. v. \pm s_{c.v.}$) **of adult bank voles** (*Clethrionomys glareolus*) **(Calculated from the data of Bol'shakov and Schwartz, 1962)**

Population	Region	body	Length of tail	bar
I	Kuvandik	8.7 ± 1.07	11.0 ± 1.40	7.1 ± 0.87
II	Bashkiria	3.7 ± 0.55	6.2 ± 0.92	8.1 ± 1.19
III	Raskuikha*	6.7 ± 0.69	12.6 ± 1.30	9.5 ± 0.98
IV	Pishminik .	5.6 ± 0.74	8.0 ± 1.05	9.9 ± 1.28
V	Verkotur'e**	6.3 ± 0.85	8.5 ± 1.16	5.6 ± 0.76
VI	Deneshkin Kamen	6.0 ± 0.83	11.8 ± 1.63	7.3 ± 1.01
VII	Komi ASSR	5.0 ± 0.67	5.4 ± 0.72	8.3 ± 1.10

* Perhaps, males and females together.
* Sverdlovsk region.

A comparison of coefficients of variation for body measurements shows that the comparative variability is similar in five of the seven populations:

	According to observed values, *c. v.*	After rearrangement with calculation of error $s_{v.c.}$		According to observed values, *c. v.*	After rearrangement with calculation of error $s_{c.v.}$
I	3 4 1 2	3 1 4 2	V	3 4 1 2	3 1 4 2
II	3 1 2 4	3 1 **2 4**	VI	3 1 4 2	3 1 4 2
III	1 3 4 2	3 1 4 2	VII	3 1 2 4	3 1 **2 4**
IV	1 3 4 2	3 1 4 2			

Let us note, as an aside, that the sequence of variability of body measurements in bank voles differs from that in forest mice and deermice. The differences in the absolute values of coefficients of variation are so great, as is the case also in all the instances examined above, that it seems impossible to relate their arrangement to a general variability of individual traits.

A general analysis of variability for eight measurements of the skull in the same populations of bank voles (*Clethrionomys glareolus*) confirms the presence of a specific similarity in the disposition of coefficients of variation for these traits between different populations which as before, could not be related to a constancy of the variability values of different traits:

Population	After correction with standard error, $s_{c.v.}$							
I	12	11	5	8	10	7	9	6
II	12	11	5	8	10	6	7	9
III	8	12	5	11	10	6	7	9
IV	11	3	5	10	6	12	7	9
V	12	5	8	11	10	6	7	9
VI	12	11	5	8	7	6	9	10
VII	12	5	8	10	7	9	12	6

It should be noted that the populations studied up to now include males as well as females. This undoubtedly makes it difficult to understand the natural situation, because in the data presented for the house mouse and mole it was always observed that the comparative variability in males is not similar to that in females. In addition, the authors do not give the date of collection of material for each of the populations. Judging from the geographical distances between the populations—South Urals to Sverdlovsk region and Komi, USSR—it is very probable that the data were collected in different years; if this is the case, the natural picture could have been distorted by the effect of varied differences in elements of geographical, biotopic, and chronological variabilities. These same observations are similarly applicable to the following data on red-backed voles (*Clethrionomys rutilus*) by the same authors (Table 84).

Table 84.   Variability of body and skull measurements ($c.v. \pm s_{c.v.}$)
of mature red-backed voles (*Clethrionomys rutilus*)

Trait	Kurgan region $n=69$	Shipitsino, Sverdlovsk region $n=40$	Denezhkin Kamen $n=94$	Yamal R. Polui $n=105$	R. Khadita $n=53$
Length of					
Body	7.0 ± 0.60	5.9 ± 0.56	9.9 ± 0.72	6.3 ± 0.43	9.5 ± 0.92
Tail	13.6 ± 1.16	7.7 ± 0.86	9.1 ± 0.66	14.6 ± 1.00	13.8 ± 1.34
Feet	4.7 ± 0.40	3.4 ± 0.38	11.4 ± 0.83	4.8 ± 0.33	6.0 ± 0.58
Ear	11.1 ± 0.94	7.9 ± 0.38	10.5 ± 0.77	—	—
Condylobasal length	3.3 ± 0.28	7.3 ± 0.82	5.8 ± 0.42	3.1 ± 0.21	4.5 ± 0.44
Diastema	5.9 ± 0.50	5.2 ± 0.58	6.6 ± 0.48	4.4 ± 0.30	7.3 ± 0.71
Width between orbits	4.4 ± 0.37	3.2 ± 0.36	4.9 ± 0.36	5.4 ± 0.37	3.7 ± 0.36
Zygomatic width	5.2 ± 0.44	4.8 ± 0.54	5.1 ± 0.37	6.3 ± 0.43	6.2 ± 0.60
Height of zygoma	3.8 ± 0.32	2.8 ± 0.31	3.2 ± 0.23	3.5 ± 0.24	2.5 ± 0.24
Length of dental row	5.4 ± 0.46	2.7 ± 0.30	4.1 ± 0.30	4.4 ± 0.30	3.2 ± 0.31

The pattern of coefficients of variation in body measurements (traits 1 to 4) differs sharply only in population III from that which characterizes the other three populations. The skull measurements show, as before, a more mixed picture of comparative variability for the red-backed vole. Traits 11, 5, and 12 are little variable in all populations and traits 6 and 8 are more variable. The places for the rest of the measurements are not exactly fixed in the sequence:

Population													
			Corrected data with calculated error, $s_{c.v.}$										
I	3	1	4	2	11	5	7	9	6	12	10	8	
II	3	1	4	2	11	12	9	7	10	5	8	6	
III	2	1	4	3	11	12	9	5	6	10	7	8	
IV	3	1	2	—	11	5	12	7	6	8	9	10	
V	3	1	2	—	11	12	9	5	7	6	10	8	

Viewed from a general analysis of the comparative variability of skull measurements, an assumption can be made to some extent explaining the irregular arrangement of coefficients of variation in a series. When the body measurements are compared, traits having different relations to the controlling factors are undoubtedly compared (length of ear helix, length of feet, length of tail—each of these measurements has a specific ecological importance). When one compares many measurements of the skull, it is possible that traits having "equal relation" to natural selection are compared, the variability of which is controlled to a great degree by, say, genetical factors. It is natural that in such a case the relative variability, controlled by natural selection, will not be manifested so regularly.

To continue the analysis of comparative variability of traits in mammalian populations, I shall consider the results obtained during a comparison of variability for three populations of common hamsters (*Citellus citellus*), calculated from data by Straka (1963) (Table 66). It appears that the variability for length of body (1), of tail (2), of feet (3), and of ear (4), form identical sequences of comparative variability (3, 1, 4, 2) for the populations living at 50, 650, and 1,900 meters above sea level. The positions of the coefficients of variation in the sequence are maintained in all cases despite appreciable differences of absolute values of organs and despite a scattering of values of the coefficients of variation.

All the above cited examples of comparative variability belonged to various species of rodents. The material presented in the work of V. A. Dolgov (1963) makes possible an analysis of comparative variability for body and skull measurements in populations of three species of insectivores (Tables 85, 86, 87).

Identical sequences of variability are observed in each of the three species of shrews from the data on comparative variability. There are also identical sequences of comparative variability between the common shrew (*S. araneus*) and *S. isodon* while the lesser shrew (*S. minutus*) differs from the first two species in the sequence of traits in variability (the position of coefficients of variation for body measurements and the position of

Table 85. Variability ($c.\ v.\pm s_{c.v.}$) **of some traits of the common shrew** (*Sorex araneus*) **(Calculated from data of Dolgov, 1963)**

Trait	Males		Females	
	Immature	Mature	Immature	Mature
1. Body weight	8.2±0.37	9.7±0.68	9.2±0.41	9.7±1.08
2. Body length	2.8±0.12	3.1±0.21	2.9±0.13	3.5±0.31
3. Tail length	5.4±0.24	6.0±0.41	5.7±0.24	6.4±0.68
4. Foot length	3.4±0.15	3.4±0.23	3.5±0.15	3.5±0.31
5. Condylobasal length	1.5±0.07	1.6±0.11	1.7±0.08	1.7±0.15
6. Maximum width	1.9±0.09	1.9±0.13	1.9±0.08	1.8±0.17
7. Height	2.4±0.11	2.4±0.17	2.6±0.12	2.5±0.22
8. Inter-orbital width	3.0±0.14	3.8±0.26	3.6±0.15	3.8±0.33
9. Pre-orbital width	3.9±0.17	3.5±0.23	3.6±0.16	3.5±0.31
10. Upper dental row	1.9±0.08	1.9±0.14	1.9±0.08	1.9±0.14

Table 86. Variability ($c.\ v.\pm s_{c.v.}$) **of some traits of the lesser shrew** (*Sorex minutus*) **(Calculated from data by Dolgov, 1963)**

Trait	Males		Females	
	Immature	Mature	Immature	Mature
1. Body weight	5.8±0.80	6.5±0.56	7.5±1.14	—
2. Body length	3.2±0.47	2.7±0.23	2.4±0.43	2.3±0.66
3. Tail length	3.8±0.53	5.8±0.50	4.2±0.69	4.5±1.20
4. Foot length	2.5±0.35	2.4±0.20	2.7±0.45	1.7±0.45
5. Condylobasal length	1.6±0.25	1.3±0.11	1.3±0.25	1.6±0.42
6. Skull width	2.4±0.43	1.6±0.14	2.0±0.40	2.6±0.69
7. Skull height	2.1±0.36	2.9±0.25	3.3±0.68	2.7±0.72
8. Inter-orbital width	2.3±0.34	2.6±0.22	3.0±0.51	1.5±0.40
9. Pre-orbital width	3.8±0.57	3.6±0.31	3.7±0.40	3.7±0.98
10. Upper dental row	1.6±0.24	1.3±0.12	1.7±0.30	1.9±0.51

Table 87. Magnitude of variability $(c.\,v.\pm s_{c.v.})$ **in a shrew** (*Sorex isodon*)*

Trait	Male	Female	Trait	Male	Female
1. Body weight	6.7±0.97	6.7±1.19	7. Skull height	2.0±0.30	2.0±0.37
2. Body length	3.1±0.43	1.3±0.22	8. Inter-orbital		
3. Tail length	4.9±0.60	3.1±0.55	width of skull	3.4±0.48	3.7±0.65
4. Foot length	3.4±0.47	1.9±0.34	9. Pre-orbital width		
5. Condylobasal			of skull	4.2±0.59	2.7±0.47
length	1.7±0.27	1.9±0.33	10. Upper dental row	1.7±0.25	2.0±0.35
6. Skull width	1.6±0.24	1.9±0.36			

* Only immature.

coefficients of variation for some measurements of skull). Characters 1 through 4 of Tables 85 through 87 differ from those in the sequence diagram.

```
        Sorex minutus                        Sorex araneus
   3  1  2  4    5  10  6  8  7  9       1  3  2  4    5  6  10  7  8  9
   3  1  2  4    5  10  6  8  7  9       1  3  2  4    5  6  10  7  8  9
   3  1  2  4*   5  10  6  8  7  9       1  3  2  4    5  6  10  7  8  9
   3  1  2  4    5  10  8  6  7  9       1  3  2  4    5  6  10  7  8  9
```

```
                          Sorex isodon

                 1  3  2  4  5  6  10  7  8  9
                 ─────
                 1  3  2  4  5  6  10  7  9  8
```

* After corrections.

Data characterizing the skull measurements of four types of shrews from Yamala are given in the work of Schwartz (1962). Parameters of variability calculated on the basis of these absolute measurements are presented in Table 88.

The samples under investigation are not of similar sex and age and are not very large, all of which makes one approach the results rather cautiously:

```
                    Without correction           After correction
S. minutus          9   5   6   10   8   7       9   5   10   6   8   7
S. arcticus         5   6   8   10   9   7       5   10   6   8   9   7
S. daphaenodon      5   —   10   9   —   8       5   10   —   8   9   —
S. araneus          9   10  8   6   7   9        5   10   6   8   9   7
```

Table 88.   Variability $(c. v. \pm s_{c.v.})$ **of traits for shrews from Yamala**
(Calculated from data by Schwartz, 1962)*

Trait	*Sorex araneus* Segoletki	*S. daphaenodon,* females breeding in Segoletki	*S. arcticus*	*S. minutus*
5. Condylobasal length	1.9±0.30	2.1±0.48	2.9±0.46	1.4±0.26
6. Skull width	3.2±0.50	—	3.4±0.55	3.2±0.59
7. Skull height	4.6±0.71	—	6.3±0.99	5.2±0.94
8. Inter-orbital width	3.1±0.45	6.6±1.4	4.1±0.64	4.4±0.80
9. Pre-orbital width	5.0±0.72	5.5±1.16	5.5±0.86	1.1±0.19
10. Upper dental row	2.7±0.41	2.8±0.63	5.1±0.81	3.6±0.66

* The time of collection of the data has not been mentioned exactly; for the third graph, the males and females are combined.

As can be seen, after correction, all the traits correspond well in all species except trait 9, which retains its position at the head of the line for *Sorex minutus* (which itself has to head the line).   The non-coincidence of this trait is so significant that it appears that an accidental mistake may have (unwittingly) been committed while calculating the material.

A comparison of these data with the data obtained by Dolgov from the Oksk region shows that in the Yamala samples, the comparative variability of the same traits appears to be similar in all the four species investigated, and is similar to only *Sorex minutus* of the Oksk collection. Whether this is caused by specific natural conditions of Yamala—an extreme region for all *Sorex*—or can be explained by an insufficient study of the within-species taxonomy, is not fully clear.   But it looks as though the study of the phenomenon of comparative variability permits one to throw light on relations which have slipped from the attention of ecologists and morphologists.

All the series of comparative variability presented above were concerned with body measurements, skull measurements, and weights of individual organs.   It appears that variability of color in different populations within a species polymorphic for color, has a similar tendency to maintain the sequence of traits.   In Chapter IV, data on variability of photometrical indices for the posterior and lateral sides of *Peromyscus maniculatus* are presented.   After a small number of rearrangements, the individual color indices for eight different populations arrange themselves (in order of increase in variability) in the following manner:

I	RT	Y	G	B	BV		V	RT	Y	G	B	BV
II	RT	Y	G	B	BV		VI	RT	Y	G	B	BV
III	RT	Y	G	B	BV		VII	RT	Y	G	B	BV
IV	RT	Y	B	G	BV		VIII	RT	Y	G	B	BV

(RT—Reddish tinge; Y—Yellow; G—Green; B—Blue; BV—Bluish-violet).

For all populations together, the values of the coefficients of variation for all the shades overlap each other considerably : RT—11.0 to 16.6; Y—11.3 to 16.3; G—13.0 to 18.3; B—13.8 to 21.3; BV—14.7 to 26.1%. This means again that such maintenance of trait positions cannot be explained through constantly very low or very high values of variability for a given trait. It is interesting to note here that the comparative variability of color shades of the back does not show as much uniformity as has been observed for the variability of color shades on the sides of the body.

Interesting data on variability of color are presented in the work of Hayne (1950), who studied photometrical indices of color for nine different populations of *P. maniculatus* from Florida and Alabama. A comparison of absolute photometrical indices shows an identity in the position of bluish-violet, green, and red shades in all the populations (red has the greatest value, and bluish-violet has the least).

A comparison of variability values shows practically full overlapping of coefficients of variation for all three shades in different populations. But in comparing positions in order of increased coefficients of variation for shades within each population, a more complex situation appears:

I	RT	B	G			V	RT	G	B
II	G	RT	B			VI	RT	G	B
III	G	B	RT			VII	B	G	RT
IV	G	B	RT			VIII	B	G	RT
		IX	G	RT	B				

(RT—Reddish tinge; G—Green; B—Blue).

It can be seen that populations II and IX, III and IV, V and VI, and VII and VIII appear to be the same in the sequence of traits in order of variability. There is reason for thinking that such similarity is not accidental but is determined by common features of the environment, and here the analysis of comparative variability values points to phenomena which are overlooked in other approaches.

An examination of variability for a number of traits within one population, as well as the comparison of relative variability of traits between different populations, is part of the widespread subject of "comparative variability." The phenomenon observed is not universal and it is not completely specific in some cases. The available facts of course are insufficient to describe comprehensively the character of this phenomenon, but based on the general conclusions it is possible to advance an hypothesis of "comparative variability," the basic aspects of which can be formulated in the following manner :

1. In mammalian populations, variability of all traits is in a mutually coordinated condition during each moment of evolution;[6] and

2. The variability value of each trait changes for different specific reasons, but these changes are related to changes of variability of other traits also, as a result of which the position of this trait has a tendency to keep constant in the series of traits.

The corresponding positions of coefficients of variation of the same trait in the sequence of variability of all traits in some populations, and their different positions in other populations and species, allow one to assume that there are specific reasons for the existence of such a phenomenon. It is possible that these reasons play a major role in the formation of the whole morphological appearance of different populations.

It is obvious that a parallel detailed ecological analysis of the group under study is necessary for analyzing these reasons. The experimental-ecological approach could throw light on the relationship of variability to structures having some importance to the life of separate individuals as well as to the whole population. The study of micro-evolution could not even be thought of without such an analysis.

But on the other hand, even the most exact experimental-ecological analysis appears to be incapable of solving evolutionary problems without subsequent extrapolation of ecological data obtained in the field of population morphology, and without testing by genetical methods the results obtained. Hence the essential aspects of the study of micro-evolutionary processes are population morphology, genetics, and ecology.

The hypothesis of comparative variability advanced above is an example of such a situation, when the regularity discovered by morphological data cannot be understood without an ecological understanding of the morphological material, and without testing the results thus obtained by exact genetical experimentation. The importance of a morphological approach to population biology is thus confirmed.

---

[6] This situation has something in common with the phenomena observed by P. V. Terent'ev (1959) under the name of "correlation pleiades" because it is possible that the correlation pleiades of the traits underlie their mutual variability.

Chapter VI

VARIABILITY AND THE PROBLEM OF VESTIGIAL ORGANS

After an examination of the problems of "selection and variability," a chapter devoted to the manner of phylogenetic formation of organs and structures—namely, vestigiality and vestigial organs—follows naturally. An attempt must be made to show that population morphology can throw light on a number of confused problems of evolutionary morphology.

A Short Historical Account of Viewpoints on the Problem of Vestigial Organs

The concept of "vestigial organs" is often encountered in the morphological literature. Modern understanding of this concept was mainly formulated by Charles Darwin, and in order to study the problem objectively it is logical first to draw attention to his work. "Useful organs, however little they may be developed, unless we have reason to suppose that they were formerly more highly developed, ought not to be considered as rudimentary" (Charles Darwin, *Sbor. soch.*, Volume II; p. 637; ed. 6, p. 440).[1] A few lines later, Darwin adds: "Rudimentary organs, on the other hand, are either quite useless, such as teeth which never cut through the gums. . . . They have been partially retained by the power of inheritance, and relate to a former state of things" (p. 638; ed. 6, p. 440).

Darwin also lists the wings of penguins, milk glands of male mammals, the reduced portion of lungs in serpents, teeth in the embryos of baleen whales and ungulates, as further examples of vestigial organs. He comes to this general conclusion: "It would be impossible to name one of the higher

---

[1] The 1939 edition has been referred to here and hereafter.

animals in which some part or other is not in a rudimentary condition" (p. 636; ed. 6, p. 439).

There are some contradictions in the understanding of the concept of vestigial organ even in the above-cited statements.   In the first citation which determines an organ as "rudimentary," stress is given to the peculiarities of its structure, and whether it was well developed before—its usefulness, its functional importance, is not the deciding factor.   In the second citation, complete emphasis is given to another criterion, the functional utility of the organ.   This concept of a primacy of form in the definition of vestigial organs becomes more difficult: "An organ, serving for two purposes, may become rudimentary or utterly aborted for one, even the more important purpose, and remain perfectly efficient for the other. . . . An organ may become rudimentary for its proper purpose, and be used for a distinct one: in certain fishes the swim-bladder seems to be rudimentary for its proper function of giving buoyancy, but has become converted into a nascent breathing organ or lung" (p. 637 ; ed. 6, p. 440).

Such mixed functional and morphological criteria in the understanding of the concept of vestigial organs has been retained even to this day in many works.   A. N. Severtsov observes that "Vestigial organs are absolutely useless, more or less dwarfed and secondarily simplified" (1939, p. 554). I. I. Schmalhausen gives essentially the same specifications: "Vestigial organs are those organs which have lost their significance, and are represented in the form of insignificant remnants; their position, correlation, development, and sometimes even their structure indicate their origin from the more developed organs of their direct ancestors, in which they played a more significant role" (pp. 13-14).   A few pages later, Schmalhausen again turns to this problem and writes: "Strictly speaking, of course, it could not be said that vestigial organs have no function at all.   They remain to a less extent as the active point of some aspect or other of morphogenetical regulations . . . ."   Further on he states: "Vestiges preserved in the adult state usually have a specific function, even though it may be insignificant and generally has nothing really in common with the previous function" (p. 30).

There is no point in pondering over many such definitions occurring in various works.   The above-given definitions suffice to reflect clearly the existing conditions.   And the reader is no wiser for knowing that there are about 100 vestigial organs in man because here again there is a very imprecise definition of the concept: ". . . remnants of the fully developed organs of ancestors" (Villey, 1959; p. 588).   Such vague definitions of the concept of vestigial organs are characteristic of works in the field of evolutionary morphology and general biology.   A. A. Malinovskii (1939) writes: ". . . However, besides the traits vital for life, there should also exist such traits which do not have any significance for the organism"

(p. 609). Later he adds: ". . . Actually, each small organ, if it has no advantage for the animal, is in itself harmful" (p. 610).

It is clearly seen in all these examples that the vague or imprecise understanding of the concept of vestigial organ present in the works of Darwin, persists to the present day.

Recently, comparatively speaking, there has been a renewed interest in the problem of vestigial organs in the works of S. G. Kryzhanovskii (1950), G. V. Nikol'skii (1955), G. V. Nikol'skii and V. A. Pikuleva (1958). G. V. Nikol'skii writes: "All the organs considered to be useless (vermiform appendix, wing of ostrich, small feathers in flying birds, visceral vessels in the embryos of all vertebrates) appear to have an adaptive significance after detailed investigations" (p. 725).[2] G. V. Nikol'skii nowhere directly rejects the presence of vestigial organs, but from his discussions (especially in the work of 1955, p. 978), this conclusion is almost evident.

It is understandable that the problem of vestigial organs can only be examined confidently by taking some concrete examples of the structures of organs belonging to the category "vestigial." A number of structures of marine mammals will serve as such examples.

Structure of the Pelvic Girdle in Toothed Whales

From the time of Charles Darwin to the present, the two small bones in whales in the place of the well-developed posterior extremities of terrestrial mammals, have been considered to be a fine example of vestigial organs (Prout, 1964). What are these pelvic bones and should they really be considered vestigial ? To answer these questions, let us examine the structure of pelvic bones in the common small whale of our northern and southern seas—the white whale, *Delphinapterus leucas*.

The pelvic girdle so characteristic of all terrestrial mammals is practically absent in the white whale as well as in all other cetaceans, because there are no posterior extremities and the small bones are not in direct contact with the vertebral column.

The pelvic bones in the male differ in position and structure from those in the female. In the male they are larger (in similar-sized animals), more curved, and their surface is rather raised (Figure 59). The pelvic bones of the female are rather smooth, without sharp crests, and have a generally rather round form. The difference between the absolute measurements of these bones for males and females is not large proportionately: the maximum length is 13 to 15 cm in males and 8 to 10 cm in females (when the length of the animal is 3.5 to 4 meters).

[2] It is best to understand that this viewpoint is rather close to the one held by I. I. Schmalhausen (1947), who also considers that the vestiges always have a function however insignificant.

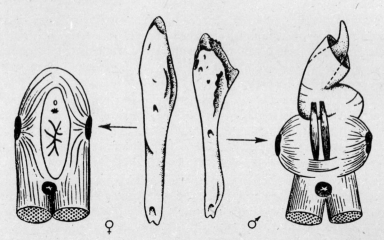

Figure 59.   Construction and position of pelvic bones in male and female white whales (*Delphinapterus leucas*).

The pelvic bones in the male are situated on the ventrolateral surface of the bulb of the penis, at the base of the corpus cavernosum (Figure 59). In the female, the pelvic bones lie on the posterior part of the abdomen between the wall of the vagina and the mammary gland, as in other cetaceans. The pelvic bones in the male are connected to the bulbocavernosus muscles at the base of the penis; in the female they are connected to the muscles of the vagina.

The presence of the pelvic bones makes penis erection possible in the male; they help in the effective contraction of the vagina in the female. These muscles make it possible to close the anal aperture in both sexes. For these reasons, they are important functional structures.

In the evolution of cetaceans, as the aquatic mode of life became prominent the tail became the main organ for locomotion. Initially the pelvic bones served as a support for the posterior extremities. Many muscles related to other systems of organs were attached to these bones. Gradually, the function of this support had to dwindle and the morphological readjustment of the bones progressed, under the new conditions, in the direction of more successfully carrying out the functions concerned only with the muscle activity of the urogenital system and the anal aperture. In present-day toothed whales (both male and female), the pelvic bones have lost all contact with the function of body movement and appear to be related only to the urogenital and digestive systems.

It seems that we have a typical example of principal function change in an organ as understood by A. Dorn (1936). On the whole, the pelvic bones as an organ do not lose their significance for the organism but simply change this significance. As a result, it would appear that the significance of the pelvic bones under the new conditions of existence is also vital for the whole organism. The existence of these structures in cetaceans is perhaps not less important than the presence of hind limbs for other mammals, because the process of copulation and the normal function of the digestive tract is only made possible by these "vestiges."

From the viewpoints of Charles Darwin, A. N. Severtsov, and I. I. Schmalhausen, the pelvic bones of cetaceans should, no doubt, be labeled vestigial organs because they were more developed in the ancestors of these animals. But, as seen from the brief analysis of their structural and functional significance, these structures not only retained their significance for the organism, but their presence has been proved essential for the normal functioning of life. It follows logically therefore that these organs should not be labeled incipient, embryonic, or "rudimentary" (*"rudimentum"*—unformed) on the one hand, or vestigial on the other.

Structure of the Vibrissal Apparatus in Cetaceans

It is possible to arrive at the same conclusions (i.e., those given in the preceding paragraph), after examining the so-called "remnants of hair cover" in baleen cetaceans. It is known that there are individual "hairs" on the head of whales and these are usually considered a very clear example of vestigial organs (Kükenthal, 1909; Beddard, 1900). However, the work of A. Jafha (1910) shows that these "vestiges" have a very complex structure and well-developed nerve supply for each "hairlet."

According to Jafha's calculations (1910), about ten thousand nerve fibers, combined in big bundles, approach each of the vibrissae of the blue whale (*Balaenoptera musculus*). Based on this fact, and also the observations of A. Malm (1866) regarding the behavior of shoaling blue whales on touching their vibrissae, Jafha concludes that W. Kükenthal's opinion (1909)—that the vibrissae are only "remnants of a previous hair cover"—was wrong. In Jafha's opinion, the vibrissae can play a large role in the life of the animal as tactile organs. A still more specific statement about this has been made by Nakai and Shida (1948): ". . . the vibrissae have a very important significance in the life of baleen whales because they use them as instruments for feeling out food" (p. 47).

Recent investigations (Yablokov, 1963b; Yablokov and Klevezal', 1964; Solntseva, *in litt.*) have confirmed the observations of Jafha and Nakai and Shida. Results of histological investigations of vibrissae for five species of baleen whales show tha it is a complex organ.

The general structure of this organ is shown in Figure 60. The hair follicle extends deep into the dermal layer of the skin and is well embedded in the connective tissue fibers. These fibers differ considerably in size and disposition from similar ones in the connective tissue of the

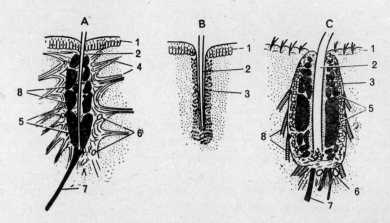

Figure 60.   Diagram of structure of vibrissae and hair follicle (longitudinal section) of (*A*) Fin whale (*Balaenoptera physalus*); embyro of common dolphin (*B*) (*Delphinus delphis*); Greenland seal (*C*) (*Pagophilus groenlandicus*):

1—*Epidermis;* 2—*Core of vibrissae;* 3—*Hair follicle;* 4—*Bundle of connective tissue fibers;* 5—*Blood sinuses;* 6—*Cross-sectioned blood vessels;* 7—*Bundle of nerve fibers* (*Yablokov and Klevezal'*, 1964).

dermis.   While protecting all sides of the hair follicle, they connect the follicle with the surrounding dermis and fix it in the hide to make it immovable.   The thickness of the wall of the hair follicle varies somewhat in the different species of cetaceans investigated; it is greatest in the hooded whale and least in the sei whale.

Between the core of the vibrissae and the inner edge of the hair follicle there are wide spaces separated by partitions.   These wide spaces are located all along the portion of the vibrissae embedded in the dermis in the fin whale and the blue whale, but are considerably less developed in the hooded whale and the grey whale.   In the sei whale, these spaces are wide, asymmetrical, and found only in the upper half of the hair follicle immediately beneath the epidermis.   Many small blood vessels pass through the walls of the hair follicle from the sides and from underneath the follicle.

In all the species examined, there are well-marked nerve tracts in the base of the hair follicle, the endings of which are lost in the thickness of the wall (Figure 61).   At the bottom of the hair follicle there are epithelial layers in the form of glands, which cause continuous growth in the vibrissae.

In baleen whales the vibrissae are found only on the head, where they form separate groups.   The first and the most significant group in its numbers is situated at the end of the lower jaw (see Figure 4).   In the blue whale, about 42% of all vibrissae are found here; in the sei whale and the fin whale, about 46 to 47%.   In rorquals, the vibrissae in this region are situated in two vertical rows.

The second group of vibrissae is arranged along the external edge

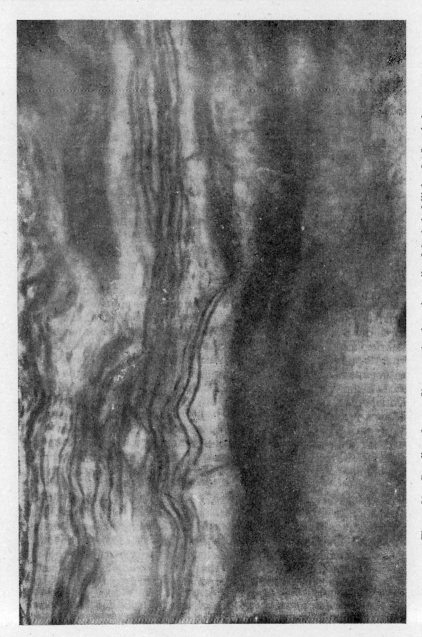

Figure 61. Bundles of nerve fibers passing into the walls of the hair follicle of a fin whale (*Balaenoptera physalus*) vibrissae. Photo by author from sample prepared by G. N. Solntseva.

of the lower jaw beginning about 0.5 to 1.0 meter aborally from the first group of vibrissae. Here the vibrissae are usually arranged in one row though there are instances (fin whale) in which the vibrissae are arranged in two rows; a second lower row of vibrissae always has fewer hair than the upper row. Usually, vibrissae of this group extend to the end of the lower jaw. A relatively larger number of vibrissae in this group are found in the blue whale (38% of the total); in the fin whale, 31%; and in the sei whale, only 24%.

The third group of vibrissae is situated on the dorsal surface of the head and usually comprise four more or less well-defined parallel rows located on both sides of the central crest formed from the intermaxillary bones, and in certain rare cases, a number of vibrissae situated in the region of the external nares. The greatest number of vibrissae in this group, both relative and absolute, are in the blue whale (up to 50 in number; on an average, 38% of the total); the fin whale comes next (36 in number; average, 31%); and finally, the sei whale (18 in number; average, 24.6%) (Table 89).

Table 89.   Vibrissa distribution on the head of whales (*Balaenoptera*) **(In % of total) (From Yablokov and Klevezal', 1964)**

Species	End of mandible	Sides of mandible	Upper jaw
Blue whale (*B. musculus*)	29.2	18.5	52.0
Fin whale (*B. physalus*)	47.7	23.3	29.0
Sei whale (*B. borealis*)	45.2	31.6	23.9

It is interesting that in the sei whale, vibrissae were not even once observed between the external nares, while in the blue whale and the fin whale, vibrissae were found there quite frequently.

The data presented above on the anatomical structure of vibrissae and the manner of their disposition on the body of animals correspond well with the already known ecological characteristics of different species of baleen whales. Of the species investigated, the blue whale requires plankton and crustaceans for food (Nemoto, 1959; Betesheva, 1961); hence for it, the development of a tactile apparatus which permits an accurate orientation to the surrounding food field is most significant. Also, the blue whale vibrissae are arranged in a very uniform manner on the surface of the head; this fulfills the requirement of obtaining uniform information about the disposition of an object which can be accidentally met in front, at the sides, and under or above the head.

Plankton and crustaceans are found in the food of fin whales regularly, but apparently not in as large a quantity for sei whales, whose stomach content in the region of the Kuril'skii Islands is mostly small fish. Correspondingly, the number of vibrissae sharply increases at the end of the lower jaw, on the very front receptor portion.[3] Of course, the concentration of a number of vibrissae on the end of the jaw in the sei whale (and to a lesser degree in the fin whale), should be considered as an adaptation for collecting more accurate and quick information about the quicker and more elusive fish and squid shoals.

Thus, the differences in the distribution of vibrissae in ecologically different types of whales are such that the characteristics of their distribution can be viewed as adaptations to feeding habits.

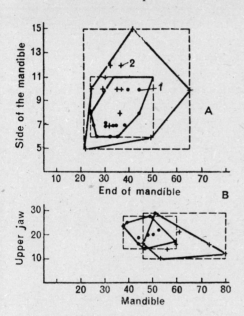

Figure 62. Scatter diagram of distribution of whiskers on the side and at the end of the lower jaw (*A*) and in the upper and lower jaws (*B*) of the fin whale: 1—*Males*; 2—*Females*.

Specific differences in the mode of distribution of vibrissae are observed between the sexes in the same species. As seen from the data presented in Figure 62, the limiting line of the scatter diagram of male fin whales completely includes the scatter diagram of females, showing considerably less variability for number of vibrissae in females. In the ecology of large cetaceans, it is difficult with our present knowledge to point to a specific biological significance for these traits, though some basis for this is available in the work of T. Nemoto (1959), who observed specific food differences between male and female baleen whales. In principle, sexual dimorphism in the development of organs that are considered to be "vestigial" is of great significance.

It is difficult to imagine that an organ which has no significance for an organism develops to a different degree in the different sexes; on the contrary, it seems more probable that the presence of sexual dimorphism in the development of an organism points to an important functional significance for that organ.

In view of the above arguments, it is absolutely incorrect to consider

---

[3] It should be noted that sight is excluded during the catching of a fish; the whale sees nothing in his direct vicinity (for details, see Slijper, 1962; Yablokov, 1964).

the "remnants of hair cover" growing on the body of whales as vestigial organs. They comprise a complex and specialized receptor which helps in a special way in the finding of food.

Specialization and Vestigiality

The two examples of the so-called "vestigial organs" presented above show that not only do these vestigial organs have a function in the organism but they are highly specialized structures, perfected for carrying out complex and delicate functions as in the case of the pelvic bones in the present toothed whales, or vibrissae in baleen whales. The structure of these organs was modified by a significant change in function at some time in their evolution.

The basic criterion for defining vestigial organs, based on their relatively poor development as compared to similar organs of their ancestral forms, does not serve the purpose adequately, because it does not distinguish between the specialized organ and the vestigial organ.

If the pelvic bones of cetaceans are to be considered "vestigial," then why not also consider as vestigial the front limbs of these animals, which have a simpler construction (in the number of muscles retained and the absence of movement by different parts of the limbs, the structure of skeletal, circulatory, and nervous systems, etc.) when compared to the limbs of the present and past terrestrial mammals which are the direct ancestors of cetaceans ?

Proceeding from these principles of determining the "vestigial" nature of an organ from morphological criteria, why not consider as vestigial the few remaining digits so characteristic for mammals but mostly lost by the majority of ungulate mammals ?

Such examples can be increased considerably, and moreover, as shown by A. N. Severtsov (1939), the reduction of an organ is caused by those very processes (substitution of organs and functions, change of functions, and decrease in the number of functions) which cause the specialization of an organ. This situation serves as one more argument for the impossibility of an exact demarcation between specialized organs and vestigial organs as they have been understood in the past.

One example from the already presented data on the structure of the vibrissae in cetaceans, illustrates this conclusion. The embryo of *Delphinus delphis* has some vibrissae on its upper jaw arranged in two erect rows. After birth, or possibly before it, these vibrissae fall off.

The study of the characteristics of these vibrissae in the dolphin embryo (Yablokov and Klevezal', 1964) showed that the depth of the vibrissae in the skin of the embryo is relatively less than that for all the baleen whales. The hair follicles of the vibrissae of the dolphin have only a weak attachment to the connective tissue (see Figure 54); the core of the hair is completely free in the follicle, does not have any contact with the wall of the follicle, and looks like a foreign body. There are no blood sinuses in the hair follicle characteristic for the vibrissae not only in cetaceans but in all mammals, and there are no traces of blood vessels passing through the hair follicle. Unlike baleen whales and pinnipeds, there is no epithelial papella at the base of the hair pouch in dolphins, which indicates that the processes of growth have stopped. Nerve fibers were not observed in either the hair follicle or the surrounding parts of the dermis.

But there are other facts too. It appears that there are many vibrissae on the body surface of mature river dolphins of the Amazon (*Inia geoffrensis*) and the Ganges (*Platanista gangetica*). The functional and morphological analysis of the vibrissae of these species has not yet been done, but coupled with the factors connected with their habitat in very turbid waters of tropical rivers, and full or partial blindness in this type of dolphin, the vibrissae of these species should be taken as important functional devices.

The question arises as to when (depending upon the nature of their construction) vibrissae should be considered specialized organs, and when vestigial organs ? The possibility is not excluded that the developing vibrissae in the embryo dolphin play a specific functional role in the early stages of its development. This hypothesis cannot be ruled out completely.

On the whole, it is very clear that vestigial organs cannot be distinguished from specialized ones with the help of morphological criteria. The use of a mixed morpho-functional criteria is not correct in principle; first, because it is not possible to calculate exactly the "part taken" by one criterion or the other in the determination of an organ as "vestigial," and second, because it is not possible to find a functional criterion of a phenomenon without knowing the significance of that phenomenon. Having examined the data presented here and elsewhere, a question arises as a logical consequence of this material: Do vestigial organs exist at all ?

In all the usually cited examples of vestigial organs, the organ is present in all the individuals of a given species. Further, it is observed in all cases that such organs or structures, inherited by the whole population have a functional significance and logically cannot be named as vestigial. But should not those structures be taken as vestigial which develop in some individuals but are not characteristic of the whole population ? It has been known for a long time that such organs exist in animals. The following can be cited as examples: the appearance of additional mammary glands; bregmatic bones in the mammalian skull (Manville, 1959; Puček, 1962); the development of the palatopharyngeus muscle only in some individuals of such species as horses and dogs (Gimmel'reikh, 1962); and the development of posterior extremities and a male uterus in toothed whales. I will discuss the last two in detail as I have been involved in their study.

It is known that in some individual cetaceans underdeveloped posterior extremities—like small fins or protuberances—are visible on the underside of the body. Such instances have usually been described as proofs that once the posterior extremities in the ancestors of whales were more significantly developed.

Such findings among toothed whales have been made in dolphins (Slentsov, 1939) and in sperm whales (Ogawa and Kamia, 1957). To-date, only six instances of remnants of posterior extremities have been found in the sperm whale (*Physeter catodon*).

In June, 1962, V. I. Borisov observed a sperm whale with well-developed protuberances on the ventral region of the body,[4] while working in the whale factory at "Skalistii" (Central Kuril Islands). One of these protuberances could even be X-rayed. Aided by already known facts, this helped us to separate some types of construction in sperm whales (Figure 63). The first type is represented by a single pelvic (?) bone found without

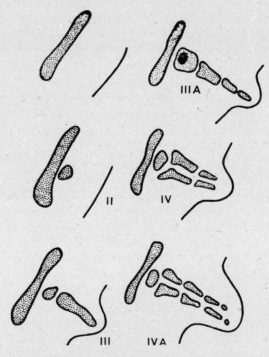

Figure 63.   Known variants of the structure of pelvic girdle ("vestiges of posterior extremities") in the sperm whale, *Physeter catodon*:

I—Usual variant; II—From author's data; III—Data of Ogawa and Kamia (1957); *IIIa—Data of V. I. Borisov; IV-IVa—Data of A. A. Berzin and V. A. Zemskii* (1960).

[4] V. I. Borisov kindly passed all the material of this find on to me.

exception in all the animals of this species and playing an important role in the function of the urogenital and digestive systems (see above). The second type is the pelvic bone with additional bony elements (perhaps, remnants of a femur), observed by me in June, 1959, in a male sperm whale in the whale factory at "Podgornyi," North Kuril Islands.[5] The third type of posterior extremity in sperm whales was found and described by T. Ogawa and T. Kamia (1957); a variant of this type was found by V. I. Borisov which differed only in being more complex in structure. A fourth type of extremity, also from the North Atlantic, has been described by A. A. Berzin and V. A. Zemskii (1960); in this instance, the metatarsus and remnants of phalanges had developed.

The presence of so many types of extremities in the sperm whale can be taken as a clear proof of the fact that the evolution of this organ in cetaceans is far from complete and we observe only a particular stage in this process. Much material passing through the hands of investigators (almost tens of thousands) has made it possible to examine extremely rare variants in such mammals that would have otherwise been left undetected. Such findings point to the fact that in the mobilized reserve of variability of sperm whales, the possibilities of evolution in other than modern directions have been preserved in the evolutionary "memory" of the species. Given some condition or other, these evolutionary directions, characteristic of the distant ancestral forms, which have apparently been discarded because of adaptive evolution, could be realized once more.

Another example of the same kind is the development of a male uterus (*uterus masculinus*) in certain toothed whales. Many authors have found significant variations in the development of a male uterus, including its complete absence, while studying the male reproductive system of different species of cetaceans (review by Yablokov, 1961b). The degree of development of a male uterus has been advanced as a taxonomic criterion not only for the species, but also for larger taxonomic units even up to the level of family and sub-order.

As a result of works on the morphology of the white whale (*Delphinapterus leucas*), it was possible to investigate the structure of the male uterus for tens of thousands of this type of whale (Yablokov, 1961a, 1961b; Kleinenberg, Yablokov, and others, 1964). In some animals, a well-developed male uterus was found which opened into the seminal vesicle, ventral to the opening of the vas deferens. A tube two to three mm wide and up to 100 to 150 mm long (depending upon the size of the animal) ran up to the bifurcation (Figure 52). After bifurcation, the horns of the uterus were symmetrically arranged on the common mesentry of the vas deferens. Such a

[5] Because I had no data on the variations in the construction of the pelvic girdle at that time, this find did not attract much attention and was recorded in the diary as "normal."

structure of the male uterus is conventionally taken as the normal and is found in some individuals of the species under study.

In the majority of individuals of the species, the male uterus develops with different deviations from this "average" type. One of the commonly occurring deviations is the absence of horns. In some cases, the horns are completely absent; in others, they are considerably reduced (see Figure 46). The most usual variant is the division of the internal lumen of the organ into various isolated ones; usually, the division is observed up to bifurcation, but it has been observed farther than this also. In a few animals there were absolutely no traces of the uterus. None of these deviations were related to the age of the animal in any way.

Most of the various stages of reduction of the male uterus were observed in the white whale. The functional importance of this organ is not clear at present. It can only be assumed that the lymphatic fluid contained in the cavity of the male uterus points to some relation of this organ to the function of the lymphatic system of the sex apparatus. Whatever the case may be, the development of this organ in some animals and its complete absence in others, shows that this organ is certainly not needed by some members of the population during their normal life span.

The organs described above—posterior extremities of the sperm whale, and the male uterus of the white whale; similarly the bregmatic bones, additional milk glands, and the palatopharyngeus muscle—could perhaps fall into the category of atavism, i.e., organs appearing in the development of present forms and indicating the condition of their ancestors (*"atavus"*— ancestor in Latin).

I feel that the solution to the problem of vestigial organs is closely related to the phenomenon of atavism. It is impossible to imagine that an organ developing in an organism in conjunction with other organs, is not related to it in various other ways. In the case of so-called "atavisms" appearing for reasons not yet known, the morphogenetical processes followed the path characteristic for ancestral forms. But because the development occurred by such an old path, the corresponding structures would necessarily appear to be essential and important for the given direction of morphogenetical processes.

It is difficult to imagine that such a disturbance in development would take place uniformly in many systems of organs at once. We should not forget the system of control that acts by selective elimination, influencing all the developmental stages of individuals and destroying greatly deviating forms (Schmalhausen, 1943), but individual organs and parts of organs could change (as is observed in nature) in a similar way. If during this the individual as an object of selection successfully passes the test of natural selection, then such "ancestral" types will also be observed in nature.

In any case, each such organ, developing in an uncommon way, happens to be an active participant of specific morphogenetical processes and carries out a specific function, significant only for that organism. Such functions are important for that very organism in which such a structure exists, but are not significant for the population.

It is easy to imagine that genetic mechanisms play an important role in the appearance and distribution of such structures. It is possible that, after some given time, it would be significant to have such a useless organ subject to selection, and then those individuals with, let us say, a male uterus, will either be eliminated or, on the other hand, will have distinct advantages; and according to the rule of genetics, this trait will either vanish or spread widely in the population.

Here we approach a most interesting problem, i.e., the usefulness of an organ retained in a state of considerable variability, which is likely to be compared with a stage of typical pre-adaptation. An organ which has become useless at some stage of evolution does not vanish immediately and completely, but is transformed into a potentially hidden stage with the help of genetical mechanisms and, after a lapse of quite a considerable period, may again be "picked up" by natural selection if the evolutionary direction of the group changes.[6] In this way, the considerable variability inherent in the vanishing organ and structure becomes understandable (Simpson, 1948; and many others), and finds expression in a well-known conclusion: "It is so commonly true that degenerating structures are highly variable that this may be advanced as an empirical evolutionary generalization" (Simpson, 1948; p. 74; 1944, p. 39). The proposed explanation of the phenomenon may perhaps help to transform this empirical generalization into a theoretical one.

The phenomenon of increase in the variability of vanishing structures may be a consequence of the slowing down of the elimination of alleles from a population as a result of weakening the selection on particular traits. Such a decreased elimination of alleles theoretically may lead to an increase in phenotypic variability, especially that part of it which is controlled by genetic mechanisms.

And so, it is proposed to examine the functional significance of an organ or a structure not "generally" but relatively, either to the population as a whole (as an object of evolution) or to the organism (as an object of selection).[7] Thus a discrepancy may arise regarding the interpretation

---

[6] This aspect of the relation of natural selection to variability is examined in greater detail in the next chapter.

[7] I wrote about the possibility and the necessity of such a division of an organism and a population in an evolutionary study incorporated in my review of M. M. Kamshilov's book (1959, see *Zoologicheskii Zhurnal*, 1962; vol. 41: 1438-1441). This article concerns the process of micro-evolution; species and genera could become objects of selection during the process of micro-evolution.

of the concept of "vestigial organ" proposed by previous investigators : Vestigial organs do not exist and cannot exist in relation to an organism; such organs exist only in relation to a population and are carried by some members of that population. In such cases, their relative insignificance for the life of the population at a given moment of evolution serves as a criterion for describing them as vestigial.

Proceeding from the fact that the function (in its wider sense) determines the structure of an organ, would it not be more correct to look first at the process of the evolution of vestigiality primary changes (the changes in functions), and not the secondary changes (the changes in organs)? In such an approach it is more logical to talk about the vestigiality of functions rather than the vestigiality of organs. In the first place, to talk about the vestigiality of an organ it would be necessary to know clearly with regard to which function a degeneration of an organ has taken place. It is natural that all the general conditions which were put forth for determining the concept of vestigial organs and the criteria for defining such an organ, should accordingly be fully applicable to the concept of the vestigial function. Such an approach is justified because it is not correct to relate the changes of a whole organ exclusively to the changes in one function of this organ (which happens when the organ is said to be a vestigial one).

In conclusion, it is necessary to note the close relationship of the problem of vestigiality to the problem of morphological variability (epigenetic polymorphism type). The majority of the examples presented in this chapter belong to that type of variability—epigenetic polymorphism. This shows once again the outstanding importance of the phenomenon of epigenetic polymorphism for analyzing the problems of evolution.

With such widely differing ideas about populations, it becomes necessary to revise many of the basic hypotheses of evolutionary biology. This need is recognized by leading present-day investigators: Beklemishev, 1960, 1964; Livanov, 1960; Berg, 1957-1964; Schmalhausen, 1958-1965; Timofeev-Ressovskii, 1965a, 1965b; Simpson, 1953; Russell, 1958; Collin, 1960; Lewontin, 1961; Mayr, 1962; and many others. Such a revision is going on incessantly through the impact of revolutionary ideas from contiguous biological fields, i.e., molecular biology, genetics, cybernetics, physiology, and others.

CHAPTER VII

VARIABILITY AS AN ADAPTATION

"Study is more hopefully directed to variability for its own sake, directly observable and a primary factor in evolutionary rates and modes."

(Simpson, 1948; p. 79; 1944, p. 44)

The specific material presented in the previous chapters allows one (in my opinion) to define precisely the well-known position that population variability is an independent evolutionary factor closely related to the effect of natural selection.[1]

This statement, in such a general form, can hardly be objected to. But the interaction of the processes of natural selection and variability in populations are areas which have had almost no investigation and offer great possibilities for new ideas and new methods of approach.

The study of populations by morphological methods inevitably leads the researcher to pose general questions regarding the place and role of the study of variability in evolutionary biology. What is variability from the viewpoint of evolution ? What is the nature of the relationship of variability as a leading evolutionary factor to natural selection ? The answer to these fundamental questions does not lie, of course, only in the field of study of within-population variability to which the present work

---

[1] "Selection" is, by definition, the result of specific relations (see Introduction). However, the process of differential elimination by the reproduction of organisms comes under selection. In a third approach, selection can be defined as an important factor of evolutionary processes. All three approaches are useful and show once more that the categories of formal logic ("either—or") cannot be used in analyzing the phenomena of biological order. In this chapter, the third approach to "selection" has been used—that it is an important factor of evolutionary processes.

has been devoted.   But the important problem in all such investigations of this type, is to discuss at least some such questions, out of so many, on the basis of available factual material.

The problem, unfortunately, is not only inevitable but also ignoble, as its solution lies somewhere in the future and cannot yet be realized. Some hypotheses and speculations have to be advanced which will be rejected sooner or later.   However, Simpson is very correct in saying that factual data will never be sufficiently complete and hence it is cowardly to withdraw efforts to determine solutions to the problems of today simply because tomorrow those efforts may be evaluated as insufficient.

There can hardly be any opposition to the point of view that variability is an important evolutionary factor, standing in close relationship to the evolution of specific populations.   An important conclusion from many works devoted to the study of variability of different organisms is a hypothesis regarding the relationship of variability to the degree of its influence on evolutionary factors.

Darwin wrote: "Heretofore, I said that variations—so common and so manifold in organisms under domestication and rare under natural conditions—were more or less accidental.   Such a statement is, of course, quite incorrect, but it clearly shows our lack of understanding of each individual variation" (*Sbor. Soch,* Volume IV; 1951, p. 641).   Thus, by taking variations in an organism and afterwards even the variability in a population as his basis for reasoning, Darwin took a major step toward the solution of this problem.

The idea, based on Darwin's theory, that all the variations are actually adaptations, was theoretically developed in the 1920's by R. A. Fisher.   It is noteworthy that this conclusion not only offered a possibility for conducting a study of population from qualitatively new positions, but even happened to be (as has been admitted by Ashby) an original source for the development of cybernetics (Russell, 1958).

By the 1940's development of this situation had taken place in all the fields of biology concerned with populations. And,   more important, experimental evidence for this idea is accumulating.   The presence of a relationship between the intensity of selection and the frequency of appearance of a particular mutation can be shown by genetical investigation. "The rate of mutation in each species is an adaptive trait determined by natural selection" (Dubinin, 1940).   Simpson (1948, p. 77; 1944, p. 42), while summarizing data on paleontology, comparative anatomy, and genetics, observes that "the extent and nature of variability are themselves important group characters subject to natural selection and other evolutionary factors."   These points of view express a general trend in progressive evolutionary ideas.   On this R. L. Berg said well: "The concept of group adaptation is more and more occupying the attention of scientists" (1957, p. 133).

It is generally accepted by researchers that the magnitude of variability is definitely related to the intensity of the evolutionary processes going on in nature.   But a simple comparison of different points of view shows that the nature of this relation is understood quite differently by different researchers.   To compare different viewpoints, it is considered reasonable in the first stage to simply cite excerpts from various works.   Of course, it is impossible to include here all the scientific works concerning this problem, but a sample of 25-30 individuals is usually considered sufficient to understand the morphological features of a population, and similarly, to attempt to show the contradictory opinions of biologists, zoologists, paleontologists, morphologists, ecologists, and geneticists.

An examination of the material presented below shows that all the possible combinations can be stated in terms of the following four variants:

Weak selection leads to strong variability,
Strong selection leads to strong variability,
Weak selection leads to weak variability,
Strong selection leads to weak variability.

According to one point of view, the variability in "favorable" conditions (under which comes a longer life span due to free access to food resources, i.e., a general weakening of the pressure of natural selection) increases considerably.   In "unfavorable" conditions (correspondingly, during intense selection), the variability decreases.

According to another viewpoint, variability decreases in "favorable" conditions.   During intensive selection, variability increases—which is to say that during unfavorable conditions an increase in variability takes place.

But before considering the different viewpoints presented in the next few pages, it is necessary to mention that Simpson pointed out in 1944 that one of the reasons for obtaining exceptionally low or exceptionally high values of variability may be an insufficient genetical homogeneity of the sample.   If we are working on a sample genetically more homogeneous than the whole population, then the variability may be considerably less than that really existing in nature.[2]

---

[2] Here and henceforth, while determining the relation of variability to selection pressure, I do not propose to examine the genetical control of any variability, accepting an important role for such control in the formation of a mobilized reserve of variability in mammals. The study of the regulation of the formation of such reserves and variability is in the province of genetics and cannot be carried out from the position of population morphology. But the ways in which this reserve of variability manifests itself in the process of evolution, should be simultaneously studied through the genetics, morphology, and ecology of populations. The present work, as has been mentioned many times before, is supposed to be the morphological part of such a common investigation.

On the other hand if we are working with a sample where the genetical heterogeneity of the population has been artificially increased (for example, by rearranging variants within classes and reducing the number of common variants), the magnitude of variability could be increased. But to make consideration of the problem easier, let us assume that the samples with which we are working are sufficiently accurate to reflect the real situation of a population.

Relation of Variability to Intensity of Selection
(According to Different Authors)

Weak selection (increase in numbers)—high variability

1. "On the other hand, vestigial and non-functional characters—those with *low selective value*—have higher average variability" (Simpson, 1948; p. 135; 1944, p. 83; Italics mine).

2. "It is clearly seen from this, that the more favorable the living conditions, the greater appears the within-population polymorphism" (Sinskaya, 1948; p. 71).

3. "The first phase—increase in numbers in favorable conditions when the influence of natural selection is weak—is correlated with an accumulation and recombination of mutations (with an increase in individual variability)" (Schmalhausen, 1946; p. 190; 1949, p. 116).

4. "Under favorable conditions, with a weakened struggle for existence and a decrease in the intensity of elimination of deviations, mutations accumulate rapidly and reach rather high frequencies. Individual differences accumulate great diversity and to a rather considerable extent" (Ibid., p. 195).

5. ". . . The degree of within-species diversity to a considerable extent depends on the total intensity of selection; to be exact, of its stabilizing form. Moreover, even in the most homogeneous conditions, in a micropopulation with weak stabilizing selection, the genetic heterogeneity sharply increases. Because of this, the number of aberrant individuals increases" (Olenov, 1961; p. 107).

Strong selection—high variability

1. "Intense selection for deviations (i.e., against the previous norms) may lead to an increase in the variability" (Schmalhausen, 1943; p. 196).

2. "Increased variability in populations living under unfavorable conditions . . . has been recorded" (Ibid., p. 207; 1947, p. 125).

3. "The amount of variability increases when the food supply diminishes" (Naumov and Nikol'skii, 1962; p. 1137).

Weak selection (reduction in numbers)—low variability

1. "In a very small population an almost stable *insignificant variability* and weak selection is observed. Therefore a static situation, disturbed from time to time by accidental occurrences of rare mutations inevitably leading to degeneration and death, is likewise seen" (Wright, 1931, cited by Klein, 1964; Italics mine).

2. "Variability decreases in favorable conditions" (Naumov and Nikol'skii, 1962; pp. 63-64).

Strong selection (reduction in numbers)—low variability

1. ". . . functional, integrated structures of adaptive significance— i.e., those that are under strong *selective pressure* tend to have low, although still appreciable, variability. . . ." (Simpson, 1948; p. 135; Italics mine).

2. "All these facts demonstrate that the more intense the selection under certain conditions, the smaller is the number of visible variations" (Schmalhausen, 1946; p. 190; 1949, p. 117).

3. "The second phase—a relative stability associated with the conditions of competition and also a type of direct struggle of a species for existence—is related to an *effective selection* of more favorable combinations with a *decreased variability*. The third phase—a more or less sharp decrease in numbers under the influence of powerful eliminating factors (usually not having any selective significance)—may be associated with a further decrease in variability. . . ." (Ibid., p. 190; 1947, p. 116; Italics mine).

4. ". . . a *rigid* individual *elimination* leads to a decrease in variability" (Schmalhausen, 1939; p. 213; Italics mine).

In noting the possible reasons for an increase in variability in natural populations, we have to consider fluctuations in numbers (analysis by I. I. Schmalhausen, 1946; summary by N. P. Naumov, 1945). During a period of increase in numbers, the variability of all populations inevitably increases. The mechanism of such an increase in variability is adequately understood: In the period of increasing numbers, there appear in great quantities diverse extreme variants which get eliminated under other conditions. The genetical heterogeneity of the population increases with an increase in numbers and increases the chance of accidental influences affecting the development of a considerable number of individuals. After a sharp decrease in numbers, brought about by non-selective elimination as shown by Schmalhausen (1946), the genetical constitution of the population is likely to change qualitatively, and in the new growth period with an increase in numbers there appears a population with a different gene pool. This complex cycle of phenomena, now yielding to only a most general analysis, shows that there are considerable possibilities in a close collaborative study of the problem of micro-evolution from the ecological, genetical, and morphological points of view.

Some contradictions in the statements of different authors can be eliminated if we consider that during unfavorable conditions, and under great pressure of selection, these conditions would not affect all organs and traits of the animal to the same extent. Elimination, or the final removal of the individual, in other words, of the whole ontogeny, will always have individual traits as focal points. This means that during the most intense selection, despite pressure on one trait or on a group of traits, the variability of other traits could not even be affected. And it is known that the majority of authors, although realizing the inaccuracy of biological terminology, use the concept of variability in conjunction with the whole organ; strictly speaking, this is not possible and cannot be done without qualifications.

But despite all this, many viewpoints still remain contradictory. This contradiction shows that the generalized concept of "natural selection," "pressure of natural selection," "improvement" or "deterioration" of living conditions, etc., seems to be inadequate for the analysis of the phenomenon observed.

One of the most important achievements in the development of Darwin's theory was separation of a unique process of natural selection into different forms (Wright, 1931; Schmalhausen, 1939). And the explanation of the above-mentioned controversial viewpoints is obscured without observing the influence of different forms of selection on variability.

Modes of Selection and Variability

Arising out of elimination, natural selection manifests itself in two basic modes: directional and stabilizing (Schmalhausen, 1939, 1946).

The directional mode of selection is caused by the occurrence of a selective advantage in changed environmental conditions with specific deviations from the "normal" (that characteristic of the previous living conditions). This form of selection is also named "centrifugal" or "linear" (Wright, 1931; Simpson, 1948). Selection in this mode (with intermediate types also considered) is graphically shown in Figure 64, taken from the works of I. I. Schmalhausen and G. G. Simpson.

The stabilizing mode of selection appears when there is a selective advantage for the "normal" organization above all the deviations. This type of selection, also called "centripetal" (Wright, 1931), counteracts any displacement in the character of a population. This type of selection is likewise graphically shown in Figure 64. An examination of these graphic representations of different modes of selection permits one to assume that, with regard to a specific trait, the directional mode of selection can be taken as basic. Thus directional selection, if directed uniformly in different directions away from the central point, gives centrifugal selection and

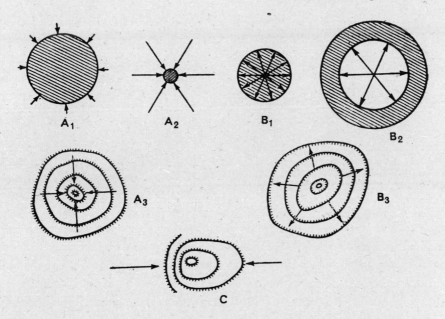

Figure 64. Schematic representation of centripetal (A_{1-3}) and centrifugal (B_{1-3}) selections:
A_3, B_3 and C—*"landscape" of selection; C—variant of an asymmetrical centripetal selection.
Arrows—pressure and direction of selection (Simpson, 1948).*

selective vectors directed from various points toward the center give rise
to centripetal selection. A linear selection in different directions gives
rise to an asymmetrical type of selection (which has been known before).
This subsuming of the graphical representations of different types of selection under the linear mode makes the study of further theories on the structure
of variability rather easier to understand.

From the viewpoints of different investigators given above, it can
be seen that variability may be similar at different selection pressures and,
contrarily, it may be different during similar selection pressures. S. Wright
(1931) and Schmalhausen (1939), who have described different types of
selection, showed that variability decreased only with an increase in the
centripetal selection, or "stabilizing" selection, to use the terminology of
I. I. Schmalhausen. When directional (centrifugal) selection increases,
the variability increases. These well-established facts are unfortunately
not always remembered in zoological research. The authors of these works
continue to use the word "selection" from only one point of view, and it is
imperative that they should indicate which form of selection is being dealt
with.

To summarize, it can be said that the magnitude of variability depends
not only on the intensity of selection, but also on its direction. Different

modes of selection, similar in magnitude but different in direction, can give rise to variability of different amounts.

After such general comments, let us now analyze the manifestation of variability under the influence of different forms of natural selection.

Stabilizing selection and variability

The relation between the stabilizing mode of selection and variability is expressed by the same normal Gaussian curve which serves as a base for the overwhelming majority of statistical calculations on variability.

Stabilizing selection expresses the relations which have been formed over a long evolutionary period between structure and environmental requirements. If the direction and pressure of stabilizing selection with regard to variability of any trait is shown by vectors, then it is seen that the vectors with minimum value will be arranged on the curve against the modal group of variants (Figure 65), and the ones with maximum value will be arranged against the extreme classes of variants.

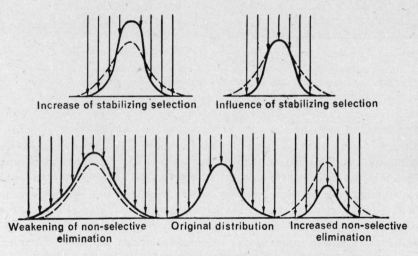

Increase of stabilizing selection   Influence of stabilizing selection

Weakening of non-selective   Original distribution   Increased non-selective
elimination   elimination

Figure 65.   Some variants of transformations of the original distribution of the variability of a trait.

It is easy to show that for the variability of the whole population, as determined by the sum of the variability of $(n \pm 1)$ traits, the resultant of its interaction with stabilizing selection appears as a "hill," the transverse section of which will give the variability of a practically unlimited number of traits (Figure 66).

During an increase in intensity of stabilizing selection, there is first a proportional and uniform reduction of variants in each of the classes, as a result of which the general variability is unchanged, but as the number

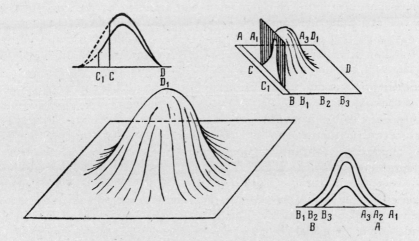

Figure 66.   Variant of the graphical representation of the "hill" of variability
and the effect of type of selection:

*AB, A_1B_1, A_2B_2, A_3B_3—some of the possible cross sections of the "hill" of variability
without pressure from the directional type of selection. CD, C_1D_1—some possible
cross sections with the influence of the directional type of selection.*

of individuals in the population decreases (Figure 65), then, through the
continuous action of selection, the frequency of variables begins to decrease
until they reach an equilibrium; with even stronger selection they can be
completely eliminated.

In a weakening of intensity of stabilizing selection, a proportional
increase in the frequency of variants takes place in the beginning in the classes
already available; then the appearance of extreme classes is possible, which
leads to a general increase in variability restricted perhaps only by genetical
limitations.   During the change in intensity of stabilizing selection, the
shape and disposition of the variability curve may remain constant.   This
means that the mean and the standard deviation and coefficient of variation
will remain constant.   It is possible to have a situation where the distribution would become changed in shape by changed intensity of stabilizing
selection, and then the standard deviation and coefficient of variation
would also change.   But, in all cases, the arithmetic mean of the population
would remain unchanged.

Directional Selection and Variability

The relations of this type of selection to variability are considerably
more complex.   Let us look at some examples.   In the first, as a result of
a sharp selective elimination by truncation, a large or small proportion of

the variants are destroyed from some part or other of the curve. This example is presented in a more or less general form in Figure 66, where some of the variants of the hypothetical "hill" of the general variability of the population, have been eliminated.[3] During the continuous influence of this form of selection in the given case, a mixing up of the whole curve of variability for specific traits takes place in the direction opposite to the one where elimination occurs. After a time, the curve should take up the normal shape, but the arithmetic mean will have moved. The same can be said with regard to the whole "hill" of variability. At various stages of this prolonged process different asymmetrical forms of the curve can be observed, always with a more elongate part away from the region of elimination.

The second example concerns the selective elimination of modal variants and has been worked out in detail by G. D. Polyakov (1961, 1962) on fish populations. During a sharp deterioration of feeding conditions in the water, the modal groups were in a worse state than those capable of feeding on several atypical types of food. The extreme variants, which were accustomed to food atypical for the whole population, appeared to be in a better position; they had a selective advantage in which was hidden the possibility of forming polymorphic groups or forms. This example, which to some extent can be taken as a model for some organisms, could hardly be true as such for mammals. But it should be remembered once again that not a single type of natural selection mentioned above and, correspondingly, not a single relation of variability with different types of selection, occurs in nature in pure form.

In observing these types of hypothetical and model examples, we are only making an attempt to penetrate the sort of phenomena for which the on-going processes in nature can be examined; but not one of these phenomena can occur individually in nature.

It would seem that other more complex cases of relations between directional selection and variability could exist, but all of them would be based on the two instances which we have seen.

Prolonged Variability and its importance in the Evolutionary Process

In nature the variability of a population is under constant control of natural selection in its different forms. However, in specific periods of population development (because of the environmental changes taking place), such control will be different in intensity and in direction. Simpson

---

[3] It can be seen in Figure 66 that the selection will always act only on some specific traits and not on all. Even those traits which it affects in a given situation, are not uniformly affected: Three cross sections (AB, CD, and EF) show different degrees of influence by eliminating effect of the given direction of selection.

(1948) observed that during periods of weak selection particularly, the role of other factors increases and becomes decisive in the evolution of a population. Here this proposition as applied to variability is examined in a general form.

During a weakening of selection on some trait, variability itself should act as an important evolutionary factor in determining those trends which, on the whole, will ultimately control the future of a population. The weakening of selection on a particular trait or group of traits (which very often happens in the evolution of a group) should be a main turning point capable of determining the future of an organ, or perhaps the future of an entire population for a long time to come.

When the selection weakens with regard to a given trait, genetic drift begins to play a greater role in the control of variability. With the lifting of all types of selection pressure, through the slowing down of the elimination of alleles, the hidden mobilized reserve of variability appears on a greater scale. The continued existence of the organ or trait (which has had an appreciable period of existence in the gene pool with its phenotypic expression) will be determined mainly by morphogenetic relations with other important structures by a selection. If the organism, as a part of a population, does not reconfirm the importance of the existence of the organ by means of an interaction with the biogeocenose (Schmalhausen, 1959, 1965) (because even the mere presence of a useless organ in an individual may act as an adverse trait from a selective viewpoint), these relations will start to be replaced by those which better conform to the present conditions. The structures and traits which have thereby become useless will morphogenetically drift more and more to earlier (and more general) developmental stages in the organism.

The disintegration of such relations, leading to the vanishing of a structure from the phenotype, is not a sudden but a very prolonged process. The phenotypic retention of a trait remains in an incomplete but variable stage during a long evolutionary period (the selection pressure has been reduced, the reserve variability has appeared); through this increased variability a breach of the morphogenetic relationship takes place, transforming its position, fixed by previous selection, into another. This process has been depicted in Figure 67, where the graphical expression of variability transformed on to a time scale should be helpful.

I would like to propose that the prolongation of a trait in a condition of elevated variability be named "prolonged" variability, taking into consideration the protracted nature of this stage in the evolution of an organ and structure. Some of the above-mentioned examples would surely permit one to examine the scope of such prolonged variability.

Certainly, the great variability of posterior limbs in cetaceans has been maintained for some tens of millions of years.

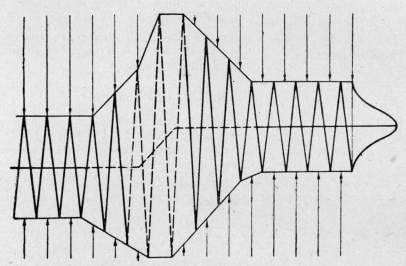

Figure 67.   Diagram of variability of a trait during a period of time:
Arrows—*selection pressure;* horizontal scale—*time;* vertical lines—
amplitude of variability.   See text.

Prolonged variability is of outstanding importance in the evolution of morphological aspects of animals.   The prolonged continuation of a vanishing organ in a condition of considerable variability may be taken as an important evolutionary property of a population.   For a period of many generations, a population seems to "test" or check whether a structure which became useless some time back, will again become useful and attain selective importance.   It is possible that the origin of structures in descendants which differ considerably from those of their ancestors, can be understood in this way.

Perhaps the proposed hypothesis of prolonged variability will considerably simplify our understanding of the processes going on in nature.   These processes are undoubtedly very complex because, due to the overall multi-functionality of an organism, an independent variability of structures occurs quite rarely before an appreciable reduction in size; and also, because environmental changes may occur to restore the selective value of a structure from time to time and frequently change the direction of its evolution.   An analysis of some developmental features of baleen and toothed whales shows the possibility of such complex organ development (Yablokov, 1964).

Here it would seem important to give only a general picture of the possible process to show the importance of the study of population variability for morphological structures from a purely phylogenetic aspect.   The collaborative work of paleontologists and morphologists on morphological variability will show how useful the proposed hypothesis is. In concluding this section, it would seem desirable to emphasize the fact that the mobilized reserve of variability is formed completely in higher animals (as shown by Schmalhausen, 1946), and hence the whole hypothesis of prolonged variability is applicable primarily to those animals.

Adaptive Importance of Variability

Because of the many examples of the relation of population variability to the processes of natural selection, the question naturally arises as to the adaptive significance of population variability and the fundamental nature of variability in general or, to express it in another way, the usefulness or uselessness of variability as observed in nature.

In looking at population variability as an important adaptive property of a population, an appreciable influence of it on evolutionary factors is implied. Now the question is posed from another point of view : Is the variability useful initially ? Is the observed end result—the coordination and adjustment of variability for all traits in a population in exact conformity to environmental requirements—true at the beginning ?

These views on the possible usefulness of specific changes in organisms have been advanced many times since Lamarck, and subjected to criticism by zoologists. However, recently these viewpoints have often been advocated (Raicu, 1960), which makes it necessary to examine this problem.

Recently, G. V. Nikol'skii (1963) re-emphasized that a population's reaction to any influence should be primarily adaptive and rapid. Such a reaction, in his opinion, is usual in all situations which arise during the group's development.

Let us examine a hypothetical example. Several changes occurred in a population of mice as a result of increased doses of radiation: deviations in the growth rate of young animals, disturbances of embryonic development, and disturbances of the characteristic indices of variability of other traits (number of vertebrae, number of hair per unit area of body, etc.). The reaction is clearly of an inadaptive nature, but the population continues to exist in the biogeocenose (as a result of changing some individuals to different food, others becoming less susceptible to predators, or a weakening of the different forms of the struggle for existence). There probably appear at this level of change in the population some individuals which, in the newly-created conditions, have a specific selective advantage. After some time, the population will come out of this difficult phase of development with some changed characteristics (because of the greater reproduction of some of these individuals).

Looking at this process more generally, it can be seen that there is a direct relationship between the environmental influence and the adaptive change.   But this seems to be only the external aspect of the process.   The imaginary usefulness of accidental and regular relations, and as a result of the constantly unbalanced relationship between the "micro-structure of the environment" (Verheyen, 1969) and the variability in a population, this forms a basis for self-development for the "population-biogeocenose" and is the main cause of the impossibility of direct adaptation.

If we study this example rather closely it can be seen that a typical process of "Darwinian" selection takes place through the elimination of non-adapted animals.   This very elimination confirms the presence of a typical picture of population variability.

In the majority of cases, the variability of a trait observed in nature is expressed by the curve of the normal distribution.   While accepting the statement about the initial usefulness of variability, it should be said that any environmental factors influencing the innumerable individual traits always give a normal distribution of values of the affected individuals, and the non-adaptive variants do not even appear in the world.

In the examination of population variability from the viewpoint of present controlling factors, it can be said that in fact the normal curve acts as the "stamp" which "separates" (leaves alive) only those variants out of the innumerable ones appearing in nature which appear to be capable of existing under the given conditions.   When these conditions continue, a preferential reproduction of the more efficient variants inevitably takes place over long periods (Berg, 1964; p. 5), which inevitably leads to the fact that fewer and fewer individuals in succeeding generations fall out beyond the border of the "stamp" and get lost.   In this way, a hereditarily fixed character for the norm of reaction takes shape in the nature of the curve, reflecting the variability for each trait.

A problem arises as to whether these are population traits whose variability would be the same for the whole population; this is directly related to the problem of the usefulness of variability.   Are there some individuals in a population who are carriers of traits which make no difference to the population ?

A sufficiently specific answer to these questions has been given in the previous chapter on vestigiality of organs.   There are such traits and, accordingly individuals in a population with such traits.   But if there are individuals in a population with traits which make no difference at a given moment of evolution to the life of the whole population, then we must admit that the variability of such traits should also make no difference to the population at that moment of its development.   Because of a progressive reduction in the pressure of controlling factors under the changed conditions of their existence, these traits cannot make any difference for the population. When selection pressure is reduced below a certain level, the variability ceases to be controlled by external factors, and its range can be determined only by hereditary mechanisms and genetic drift (Prout, 1964).

The Possibility of Studying Natural Selection through the Understanding of Variability

There is no doubt as to the importance of studying the properties of natural selection in a population, for the cognition of general evolutionary mechanisms (Gilyarov, 1959; Sokal, 1962; and others). By the study of variability, a specific contribution to the study of natural selection is possible. It is necessary to obtain data on the variability of the same organs and structures under different living conditions in order to understand the importance of natural selection, so that a comparison of the differences in variability under different living conditions will yield a key to determining the nature of the influence of natural selection. This is the first stage in studying the relationship between natural selection and variability. Then the second stage is inevitable, i.e., the functional analysis of different structures for determining the importance of the selective value of a given structure for the individual and the population as a whole. It is clear that in any case the answer obtained may only be indirect.

The study will initially yield then a good knowledge of those environmental conditions which are capable of influencing the variability of an organ or a trait. One of the main difficulties in solving this problem is obtaining a solid understanding of these conditions. We do not even know as yet how the variability of traits or the manifestation of an individual trait is determined in individual ontogeny and the successive changes in ontogeny (phylogeny). Molecular biology has just made an initial step toward an understanding of this process.

Strictly speaking, it is not possible at present to compare the environmental conditions of one population with those of another with any satisfactory degree of accuracy. That is why it is interesting to compare the features of variability in genetically similar populations placed in different environments. During such a comparison, at least there is one common denominator known—the identical initial genetical structure of the population and its general potentialities. As a result, the observed phenotypic variability can throw light on the differences in the influences of evolutionary factors.

One of the kinds of such an investigation is the comparison of the variability of wild and inbred populations. By completely taking off the pressure of natural selection in an inbred population, we can observe a somewhat "basic" variability, which has been deformed by the effects of selection (possibly, through reduction) in natural populations. But on the other hand, the inevitable genetical impoverishment of the inbred population decreases its potential variability as compared to natural populations.

Attempts to compare the variability of wild and inbred populations of mammals with regard to different traits have been made by different investigators. R. Bader (1956) made a serious attempt to compare the variability of a number of wild and inbred populations of rats, house mice, and guinea pigs through tens of thousands of individuals maintained in captivity. It was observed that on an average the variability of wild populations differed insignificantly from the variability of inbred populations, and the observable differences were more or less directed toward an increased variability in the wild populations. Looking at these data, it can be said that the removal of selection pressure, which was supposed to increase the variability of all traits, appeared to be less effective than the specific processes in the natural populations which increased the variability of the same traits.

V. N. Pavlinin (1962) presents data on the variability of skull measurements for wild Bashkir minks and minks from the Mramorsk ranch. The initial genetical material is the same : All the animals were transported from North America, apparently from a quite homogeneous group. Some were released into the new environment, where they had to fight for life in conditions differing greatly from those which existed in their motherland; others were placed in artificially-created favorable conditions where the eliminating factors were sharply reduced and all the animals having a normal quality of fur had a chance to live fully and reproduce.

An analysis of the variability values obtained (Table 90) leads to the conclusion that the variability of almost all traits in the females appeared

Table 90. Variability ($c. v. \pm s_{c.v.}$) **of skull measurements of wild and farmed minks (Calculated from the data of V. N. Pavlinin, 1962)**

Trait	Bashkir (wild)		Mramorsk ranch	
	Males	Females	Males	Females
Skull length	2.7±0.38	2.2±0.32	3.4±0.43	1.7±0.22
Condylobasal length	4.6±0.36	2.1±0.30	3.2±0.41	1.7±0.22
Zygomatic width	5.6±0.78	4.3±0.62	3.8±0.49	2.1±0.27
Height of skull	2.9±0.41	6.2±0.89	20.2±2.60	24.9±0.92
Mastoid width	4.3±0.60	3.0±0.43	3.8±0.49	1.9±0.24
Width of snout	6.2±0.88	4.0±0.58	41.1±5.30	33.7±4.34
Length of upper canines	3.5±0.49	3.5±0.46	24.5±3.50	33.6±4.33
Length of tympanic bone	5.0±0.70	5.3±0.77	4.2±0.54	3.4±0.44

to be somewhat increased in nature over the variability of animals in captivity; in the males, the situation was rather reversed. In both males and females in captivity, there were traits which showed a greater variability, such as height of skull and width of snout. Some problems arise, the answers to which are very problematic as yet. Why did the variability in males and females for skull length go in different directions ? Why did the variability value of some traits increase so much whereas the variability of other traits was maintained at a very low level ?

F. Sumner (1924) studied changes in the morphological characteristics of two subspecies of *Peromyscus maniculatus (P. m. sonoriensis* and *P. m. rubidus)* under the influence of the climatic environment of a third subspecies, *P. m. gambelli.* The animals of the first two subspecies, taken from natural populations, were transferred to the habitat (hills) of the third subspecies and raised in large open-air cages for several generations. The conclusions drawn by the author are very interesting when viewed with regard to the problems posed above. All the transferred groups considerably changed characteristics for a number of traits, but these changes were not closer to the characteristics of the subspecies which inhabited this region; instead, they deviated so much that the differences among the three natural subspecies, in the traits of color and body measurements, appeared to be less than those between the transferred populations and the local subspecies.

An analysis of the data presented by Sumner (1924) shows that in the transferred populations, the variability decreased in 12 out of 16 measurements, it remained practically unchanged in three measurements, and increased slightly in only one trait. It is still difficult to explain the phenomena observed. The possibility of the presence of some regularities, important in principle, and which could be brought to light by conducting a number of planned analogous experiments, cannot be excluded.

An interesting way to study the relationship of selection to the magnitude of variability is to examine the variability in animals of different ages. In Chapters III and IV, some examples of chronological variability were analyzed, bringing to light some specific trends in the changes of variability parameters for traits of animals of different ages which had been subject to abiotic influences that were inevitably different from year to year in the early stages of their development. The promise of such an approach in an analysis of selection under natural conditions was shown by the investigations of K. I. Kopein (1964) conducted on ermines in the Yamal-Nenetskii region.

Another way to study the relationship of variability and selection, with a view to understanding the regularities of selection, is to compare the variability of natural populations which have lived for a long time in similar and sufficiently dissimilar conditions. This last approach opens up the possibility of bringing to light the influence of specific environmental factors on the development of variability.

Here, the investigations must proceed in the direction of finding out "natural experiments," which in the wider perspective is the study of the influence of specific factors in nature. K. M. Lyutikov (1931) noted the importance of the detection and study of such "involuntary experiments." In recent years a large number of ecologists and evolutionists have been working in this field.

To set up an experiment in nature does not necessarily mean disturbing the flow of natural processes, but it is essential to separate the influencing factors, the object of the influences, and the result of such influences.

The transport of muskrats in the year 1929 to the Solovetskii Islands in the White Sea resulted in a strong and permanent population of these animals there. After some years, a number of them were transferred from these islands to the Arkhangelsk region, where they successfully reproduced. Thus a genuine opportunity arises for comparing the morphological characteristics of the initial and the transferred populations— both the characteristics of the environment and the characteristic action of natural selection. If data on the population of muskrats obtained from central and southern Europe, western Siberia, and Kazakhstan are included in such a comparison, then a real possibility exists for discussing not only the significance of the size of the population, the roles of temperature and ice cover, the features of water resources, the effect of particular food, but even more, the common regularities regarding the development of a population under the control of natural selection would come to light and thus, indirectly, provide an opportunity for understanding the process of selection itself, and the process of micro-evolution as a whole.

The number of such "natural experiments" representing a ready-made laboratory for a population-morphology study of mammals can be multiplied in our country: the squirrel in the hills of Crimea and the Caucasus compared with the original Altai type; the characteristics of the population morphology of the coypu in its natural habitat in the Trans-Caucasus compared with the same in central Asia; and of course, the island forms of mammals, beginning with the slightly isolated Ol'Khon Islands in Lake Baikal, to the more isolated Shantar Islands, the completely isolated Kuril Islands, etc. Here the researcher has an opportunity to select practically any degree of isolation, during quite a varied time period. It is significant that more and more investigators—both ecologists and morphologists—are attracted toward isolated natural populations (Blair, 1964; Berry, 1964; and many others), a tradition having its roots even in the work of Darwin and Wallace.

In the same context, it would be useful to study the distribution of variability of forms characterized by ring-like, looped, or ribbon-shaped areas. The regularities of changes of variability for traits in such regions are, perhaps, directly related to the general regularities of micro-evolution

(Timofeev-Ressovskii, personal communication).

It would be unjust to underestimate the difficulties involved in the interpretation of data obtained from such investigations, but nevertheless, only such studies of natural populations are capable of bringing something new to the solution of the general problems of micro-evolution.

The functional analysis of the organs and structures under investigation, which forms a necessary stage in the general study of the interrelation of selection and variability, also presents a number of major difficulties.

A thorough study of an organism allows only to understand the inherent functions of the organism in a unique way. Retrospectively, any functional analysis of any organ carried out 25 to 50 years ago must be outdated. And, 50 years hence, even the present functional analysis will similarly appear insufficient and outdated.

We can analyze with a high degree of accuracy the mechanical function of the digits of the hand in bats with respect to their function in flight, but recently it was found that the wings of bats are used not only for flight but also as a sort of net for catching insects. What fraction of variability, if that can be said, is controlled by selection for wings as an organ of flight, and what fraction for wings as an instrument for catching prey ? At the moment, this is entirely unclear, and only a critical ecological analysis of individual species and perhaps of individual populations, together with an analysis of the ecology of their food which is caught in this way, may solve the problem. And after conducting such a very difficult analysis, there arises the problem of determining the degree of importance and the role of the size of the digits and accordingly the size of the membrane in the production of vitamin D, or in the mechanism of thermoregulation, etc.

An ecological study of an animal will always bring about a closer understanding of its properties and its relation to its environment. A serious difficulty develops in such a study, namely, the necessity and inevitability of searching for newer methods and approaches for finding solutions to the problems posed by the investigation. It is generally apparent that these newer methods and other approaches lie hidden in the armory of the research techniques used by related natural sciences. One such method, perhaps, could be the "black box" which has been successfully developed by cybernetics. We know only the information entering and leaving the system, but it is not clear what processes take part in the analysis of the information which comes out. Models are being prepared, as if to strengthen the "black box," based on the knowledge of those aspects of objects which have been well-studied and have achieved, as far as possible, a full correspondence between the effect of the model and the effect of the modeled system. On the whole, understanding of structure appears to be possible through understanding of the model. In other words, the impossibility of knowing the processes and properties of the objects in the chain of related processes, is not a great obstacle to the study of these processes at this time.   It is very possible that experiments of ecologists with model populations (Odum, 1959; Nikol'skii, 1963a) will give a new impetus to the solution of the problems of micro-evolution.

The general aspects of the theory of variability mentioned in this chapter naturally cannot settle the innumerable vexing problems which arise during the study of variability in nature.   The majority of these difficulties have been examined in the past and hence their mention here is justified only because I think it necessary to draw attention to those general problems of population morphology which have not yet been seriously considered.

CHAPTER VIII

CONCLUSION

The aim of this investigation has been an attempt to systematize, summarize, and theoretically understand the data available on the variability of mammals, and to form specific working hypotheses for additional planned intensive studies of the phenomenon of population variability.

The data obtained in a morphological investigation of a population should only be analyzed against the background of ecology; the regularities of the appearance and disappearance of characteristics in a population cannot be made without the help of genetics. However, the relationship of population morphology to population ecology is not one-sided. Population morphology helps in planning ecological investigations of a specific group and in demarcating ecological questions which are not yet clear, and hence are awaiting solutions. The purpose of this analysis is as follows: to obtain information on the quantitative morphological characters of an organ, to bring to light particular trends in the variability of traits, to compare the trends which have appeared with the requirements of the elementary regularities of variability, and to bring out all the deviating cases which exhibit a typical difference from the usual relationships, and which accumulate in the evolution of groups with regard to these traits.

An animal population acts in different ways in different seasons and years. This means that the investigator cannot twice investigate absolutely identical populations; the response of a population to the changes in external conditions will be different at different times.

Finally, all the categories of within-population variability taken together have a direct relationship to the dynamics of the numbers of individuals in populations. For example, without calculating the variability of growth, our idea about the dynamics of a population seems to be fairly incomplete.   The role of growth variability appears to be different at different times, depending on when a new generation enters a population, characterizing each of the developmental stages of the variability itself, etc.

The study of population morphology may serve as one means of intensive ecological investigations of a group. By using an ecologic-morphological approach, a unified functional understanding of the organ and of a system of organs is obtained.   In a study of population morphology where an ecologic-morphological approach has been added in a unified way, a group emerges as a developing evolutionary unit.

In exploiting mammalian species which are important from a commercial point of view, it becomes essential to determine the optimum population catch from the group. During systematic, epidemiological, and geographic studies of mammals, questions about the real dimensions and the size of individual populations confront the investigators. It is necessary, as far as possible, to determine accurately the degree of independence (isolation) of individual populations, to decide these and many other questions.

Data on population variability are capable of specifically and convincingly contributing to the solution of this question. The values characterizing the variability of traits have a great importance in determining the independence of a population. Comparing populations in many traits of any dimensionality is obvious, and can be done by comparing standard deviations of relative values.

The study of a population by morphological methods should necessarily be carried out in conjunction with genetical and ecological methods. An elaboration of the best methods of mathematical analyses of biological material should be the important approach during these researches. But even the combination of population morphology with the genetics and ecology of a population, and the elaboration of the best mathematical methods of analyzing the material, are complex problems that are far from solved to this day. However, this should not stop investigations in the field of population morphology proper. These studies and among them, the study of population morphology is the foremost—are capable of making a substantial contribution to the study of the mechanism of the evolutionary process.

SUMMARY*

1. The work is devoted to a study of the characteristics of variability of mammalian organs, structures, and functions within a population ("variability" is meant as the presence of differences between individuals within a population). Original data of the author concern the morphological variability of Pinnipedia, Mystacoceti, and Odontoceti; apart from them, data on the variability of many characters of several hundred populations belonging to 10 other mammalian orders are used in the work.

The coefficient of variation $\left(c.v. = \dfrac{\sigma.100}{\bar{x}} \right)$ and standard deviation (σ), despite some disadvantages, were chosen as the main indices of quantitative variability; qualitative variability of the type of epigenetic polymorphism is estimated by means of the methods of x^2 and λ.

2. Whether a given genotype is preserved during evolution depends upon the fitness of the phenotype. That is why a study of any phenotypic variability in natural populations contributes to the understanding of the nature of micro-evolution. Unfortunately, the study of the population as an elementary unit of evolution receives but little attention from morphologists and comparative anatomists.

3. The "importance" of any character is relative, as all organs are multifunctional; they function at various degrees in various periods of ontogeny, being correlated, so that we can never say we know all the functions of the given organ. On the other hand, general regularities of variability must be the same for all characters (irrespective of whether this concerns the length of tail or the number of cells in the cerebral cortex). Because of this, general regularities of variability can be studied on any characters.

4. By the value of variability ($c. v.$), mammalian characters in samples

---

* Presented in English in the 1966 edition of the Russian work.

of the same sex, the same age, and the same time (i.e., in "pure samples") can be conditionally divided into three large groups (Chapter III):

  a.   variability is less than or near 10%, e.g., that of linear dimensions of the postcranial skeleton and the skull, the number of tracheal rings, the absolute weight of the brain, linear dimensions of hair and of the body, the number of vibrissae;

  b.   variability of 10 to 15%, e.g., linear dimensions of the intestine, the amount of hemoglobin, the number of elements in the postcranial skeleton and of the nervous system; and

  c.   variability over 15% is typical of the weight of the body, skeleton, skin, dimensions of the urogenital system, the number of hair and erythrocytes, the weight of the skull, musculature, heart, lungs, stomach, and of the majority of the glands.

These figures characterize the mean variability values of characters that may be higher or lower in specific cases. Such deviations from the mean values may show the trend of the action of the controlling evolutionary factors.

  5.   A comparison of variability of populations belonging to different species, genera, families, and orders (Chapter II), shows that the amount of variability does not depend on the taxonomic position of the populations compared: Variability of the same characters in populations within a species can differ more than that of populations of remote species.

Such a diversity in variability seems to reflect the difference in the trend of controlling factors, both ecological and genetic ones.

  6.   In previous classifications of the phenomena of phenotypic variability, different categories of variability were mixed up.   It is suggested that variability be regarded in at least three independent ways (Chapter IV). By type, variability can be morphological, physiological, biochemical, and ecological; by dimensionality, we may distinguish linear variability, that of volume, weight, area, color, angle, temperature, time, meristic variability, and epigenetic polymorphism; by form, variability may concern age, sex, generation, chronography, biotope; it may also be geographical and teratological.

Experiment shows that only the most "pure" samples (i.e., when taking into consideration the variability categories distinguished) provide a reliable comparison of populations as to their variability.

  7.   When studying the variability of many series of functionally related and similar characters, variability shows a trend to decrease with an increase in the absolute value of the character.   On the background of such elementary relationships, some characters can be found nearly always that are distinguished by a higher or lower variability in the general "flow."   These characters, deviating in the value of their variability, are individually related to the controlling genetic and ecological factors and may be the objects of special investigation.

Other elementary regularities determine the relationship of variability to the dimensionality of the character, and the relationship of the variability of absolute and relative indices.

8. If several different characters are arranged by their increasing or decreasing value of variability, it turns out that in many instances, despite considerable fluctuations of variability from season to season and year to year, the position of each character among others remains the same. Such a "comparative" variability shows that within a population, variability of all the characters at any moment of evolution is correlated.

9. The fact that an organ or a structure disappearing in phylogenesis undergoes a considerable variability (Figure 67), is an important adaptive property of the population. During many generations the population "checks" whether a structure that has become useless may again acquire selective importance. Such a "prolonged" variability permits adaptation to periodical environmental changes; it restores the selective value of the structures and permits a change in the function of organs and the direction of their evolution.

10. A study of variability may serve as an effective tool for insight into the regularities of micro-evolution when:

a. comparing variability of natural and experimental populations kept under strictly controlled conditions;

b. comparing variability of populations under the conditions of "natural experiments," i.e., different types of band-shaped ranges, island forms, and cases when it is possible to clearly distinguish the effect of environmental factors;

c. establishing relations of the variability of structures to their selective value.

11. A great amount of work still has to be done aimed toward the development of a general theory of variability and the understanding of the characteristics of variability in the main groups of animals and plants. A study of variability within a population gives a key to a deeper ecological investigation of the group. The ideas and methods of population morphology contribute to a solution of the problems of micro-evolution.

THE VARIABILITY OF BODY MEASUREMENTS AND INTERNAL ORGANS OF MAMMALS*

* The number of samples investigated are indicated in parantheses throughout

Table 1. Summarized data on coefficients of variation for some body measurements of some mammals

Species	Length of				Body Weight	Data
	Body	Tail	Feet	Ear		
1	2	3	4	5	6	7
Insectivora						
Sorex araneus	2.8-3.5(4)	5.6-6.5(4)	3.4-3.5(4)	—	7.5-9.7(4)	Dolgov, 1963
	2.0-8.4(46)	—	—	—	9.7-28.2(29)	Borowski, Dehnel, 1953
	11.8	0.8-6.9(2)	3.1-5.1(2)	—	9.5-21.6(2)	Schwartz, 1960, 1962
	3.1-7.4(4)	—	—	—	8.7-14.4(4)	Puček, 1956
	—	—	—	—	10.4	Il'enko, 1968
S. isodon	1.3-3.1	3.1-4.3	1.9-3.4	—	6.7(2)	Dolgov, 1963
S. minutus	2.3-3.2(4)	3.8-5.8(4)	1.7-2.7(4)	—	5.8-7.5(3)	Dolgov, 1963
	2.4-6.6(36)	—	—	—	8.4-12.2(12)	Borowski, Dehnel, 1953
	5.7	6.4	2.4	—	—	Schwartz, 1962
S. daphaenodon	2.6	9.4	4.0	—	11.0	Schwartz, 1962
S. arcticus	—	6.6	3.8	—	—	Schwartz, 1962
S. cinereus	4.7	—	—	—	—	Long, 1965
S. palustris	9.5	—	—	—	—	Long, 1965
Blarina brevicauda	3.7-4.7(2)	—	—	—	—	Long, 1965
Erinaceus rumanicus	6.5	11.1	8.0	9.6	—	Markov, 1957

(Contd.)

Table 1—*Continued*

	1	2	3	4	5	6	7
E. europaeus	· · ·	4.9-5.0	7.6-13.0	4.2-5.4	—	—	Markov, 1957
Sicista betulina	·	6.6-7.8	—	—	—	—	Kubik, 1953
Neomys fodiens	· · ·	—	—	—	—	9.6-16.6(6)	Bazan, 1956
		10.1	—	—	—	23.4	Borowski, Dehnel, 1953
		3.0-6.8(15)	—	—	—	8.9-14.9(17)	Schwartz, 1960
N. anomalurus	· · ·	4.5-18.8(8)	—	—	—	3.4	Borowski, Dehnel, 1953
Talpa europaea	· · ·	7.0-9.0(6)	—	—	—	5.7-23.8(6)	Fateev, 1962
Lagomorpha							
Sylvilagus auduboni	· ·	3.1-4.5(3)	—	—	—	—	Hoffmeister, Lee, 1963
Lepus californicus	· ·	4.2-4.5	8.4-12.8	11.8-12.7	13.8-15.1	9.8-11.3(2)	Bronson, 1958
L. flavigularis	· ·	5.2	—	—	—	—	Anderson, Gaunt, 1962
Oryctolagus cuniculus	· ·	3.0-6.8(11)	—	—	—	12.5-21.0(6)	Latimer, Sawin, 1955, 1959
			—	—	—	4.8-18.9(36)	Castle, 1931
		3.5	—	—	—	13.6-15.6(3)	Brown et al., 1926
			—	—	—	—	Long, 1968
Ochotona princeps	· · ·	5.5	—	—	—	—	Long, 1965
Rodentia							
Apodemus flavicollis	·	5.1-12.9(11)	4.2-14.4(11)	3.9-6.8(11)	—	—	Ursin, 1956

Species						Reference
A. sylvaticus	5.5-8.9(3)	6.1-9.2(3)	3.7-9.5(3)	4.3-6.7(3)	—	Saint Girons, van Bree, 1962
	6.6-11.9(12)	4.9-16.5(12)	2.7-5.8(12)	—	15.5	Schwartz, 1960
	5.7-9.0(8)	9.8-31.5(8)	3.9-7.1(12)	5.0-10.5(12)	15.1-24.6(8)	Ursin, 1956
						Adamczewska, 1959
			2.5-10.7(7)	4.1-7.0(8)	—	Peshev, Georgiev, 1961
Clethrionomys rutilus	5.0-9.9(5)	7.7-14.6(5)	3.4-11.4(5)	7.9-11.1(3)	—	Bol'shakov, Schwartz, 1962
	4.6-7.2(2)	—			7.5-12.2(2)	Il'enko, 1968
Cl. glareolus	3.7-8.7(7)	5.4-12.6(7)	3.5-6.9(7)	5.6-9.5(7)	—	Bol'shakov, Schwartz, 1962
Cl. gapperi	5.1	—	—	—	—	Long, 1965
Microtus agrestis	0.5	5.4	2.6	—	13.8	Haitlinger, 1963
	—	0.8-3.4(6)	—	—	—	Gebczynska, 1964
	—	—	—	—	4.1-9.7(14)	Newson and Chitty, 1962
					13.3-16.6(2)	
M. pennsylvanicus	8.6-10.5(2)	—	—	—	—	Goin, 1943
M. ochrogaster	4.3	—	—	—	—	Long, 1965
M. oeconomus	—	—	—	—	15.1	Schwartz, 1960
M. arvalis	—	—	—	—	10.5	Schwartz, 1960
Arvicola terrestris	—	—	—	—	18.2	Schwartz, 1960
Peromyscus leucopus	3.7-5.6(8)	5.4-7.4(8)	2.5-3.6(8)	—	/	Clark, 1941
P. eremicus	3.5-4.3(4)	4.8-6.0(4)	2.5-3.2(4)	—	—	Clark, 1941
P. merriami	3.7-5.2(3)	4.4-6.2(3)	1.9-4.0(3)	3.0-4.8(3)	—	Hoffmeister and Lee, 1963

(Contd.)

Table 1—Continued

1	2	3	4	5	6	7
P. maniculatus	3.1-5.2(9)	5.0-8.8(9)	2.2-3.9(9)	2.7-5.9(9)	—	Dice, 1938
	4.0-6.7(11)	4.8-6.6(11)*	2.5-4.1(22)	3.8-5.7(11)	—	Sumner, 1923
	4.2-5.4(4)	5.4-7.4(4)	1.9-3.5(8)	3.6-5.1(4)	—	Sumner, 1924
	3.1-5.6(30)	4.7-8.9(30)	2.5-4.0(30)	—	—	Clark, 1941
	—	3.9-5.2(16)	1.5-3.1(16)	2.7-3.8(16)	—	Sumner, 1920
	—	3.2-4.8(16)*	—	—	—	
P. polionotus	—	—	—	—	10.8-18.1(46)	Carmon et al., 1963
P. truei	3.3-7.6(14)	4.2-7.2(14)	3.0-5.9(14)	—	—	Hoffmeister, 1951
Citellus citellus	5.0-6.0(3)	8.2-12.1(3)	4.3-5.2(3)	9.3-9.7(3)	—	Straka, 1963
C. pygmaeus	7.9-8.5(2)	—	—	—	17.5-21.8(2)	Schwartz, 1960
Rattus rattus	6.7	—	—	—	8.9-28.2(84)	King, 1923
	—	—	—	—	—	Dhaliwal, 1962
Chinchilla laniger	—	—	—	—	6.0-11.9(3)	Roos and Shackelford, 1955
Ondatra zibethica	—	—	—	—	3.1-5.5(2)	Schwartz, 1962
Mus musculus	3.9-6.6(4)	3.4-11.3(4)	2.2-3.4(4)	2.7-4.4(4)	12.4-24.8(14)	Sumner, 1909
	—	5.3-7.5(2)*	6.2-6.6(2)*	4.9-6.1(2)*	—	
	1.7-2.6(8)	2.3-3.0(8)	—	—	6.3-8.5(8)	Castle, 1941
	—	4.1-5.6(18)	—	—	—	Castle et al., 1936
	7.9-21.0(24)	10.6-26.5(24)	—	—	5.6-22.7(24)	Law, 1938
	0.7-1.3(5)	1.9	—	—	3.2-5.3(5)	Castle, 1938
	2.9-3.8(8)	22.2-54.2*	—	—	9.8-12.0(8)	Castle et al., 1938
	6.9-10.0(6)	6.1-10.4(6)	2.9-4.0(6)	5.7-7.3(5)	15.9-30.9(6)	Dynowski, 1963

* Variability of relative length.

Lagurus lagurus	—	—	—	—	1.4-12.0(9)	Kryl'tsov'a, 1957
Baiomys musculus	3.5-5.9(2)	6.2-6.4(2)	3.0-4.1(2)	3.3-3.5(2)	—	Packard, 1960
B. taylori	2.8-5.0(2)	5.7-5.9(2)	3.4-3.7(2)	0.0(2)	—	Packard, 1960
Meriones unguiculatus	3.8-3.6(3)	3.9-5.7(2)	5.2-9.4(2)	—	16.1(2)	Kramer, 1964
Zapus hudsonicus	4.1	—	—	—	—	Whittaker, 1963
Thomomys talpoides	3.8-4.5(2)	—	—	—	—	Long, 1968
Spermophilus armatus	3.7-5.1(2)	—	—	—	—	Long, 1965
S. richardsoni	4.0	—	—	—	—	Long, 1965
Dipodomys merriami	2.9-5.3	3.1-5.3	2.1-3.4	4.2-5.0	—	Lidicker, 1960
D. insularis	2.6	—	—	—	—	Lidicker, 1960
D. ordi	4.7-8.3(8)	5.2-7.7(8)	3.8-5.5(8)	10.0-13.3(8)	—	Schmidly, 1971
Cavia porcellus	2.0-2.1(2)	—	—	—	—	Strandskov, 1942
Phyllotis darwini	8.4-10.1(3)	—	—	—	—	Pearson, 1958
Ph. osilae	5.0-6.3	—	—	—	—	Pearson, 1958
Ph. wolffsohni	7.0	—	—	—	—	Pearson, 1958
Ph. audium	6.7-7.9(3)	—	—	—	—	Pearson, 1958

(Contd.)

Table 1—*Continued*

Species	Body length	Nose-ear	Anus-navel	Anus-penis (between nipples)	Body weight	Data
			Pinnipedia			
Pagophilus groenlandicus · ·	3.1-7.4(15)	4.6-9.2(5)	6.6-12.8(7)	7.0-9.6(3)	9.0	Own data
	—		—	3.9-14.6(4)	—	Own data
Cystophora cristata · ·	4.3-9.2(20)	9.1-19.3(2)	8.4-10.9(2)	25.8	—	Own data
	—			16.3	—	Own data
Pusa caspica · ·	2.4-8.4(5)	—	6.4-7.2	11.6	—	Own data
Pusa sibirica · ·	8.1-18.7(1)	—	9.6-22.8	9.6	—	Own data
				22.5	—	Own data
Pusa hispida · · ·	7.5-9.3(4)	—	8.8-12.3(2)	8.9	—	Own data
				26.2	—	Own data
	1.4-7.6(19)	—	7.3-16.3(4)	11.9-18.3(2)	—	Own data
				15.2-11.8(2)	—	Own data
Histriophoca fasciata ·	3.3-7.4(14)	—	—	—	—	Own data
Phoca vitulina · ·	8.0	—	—	—	—	Plekhanov, 1940
Callorhinus ursinus · ·	3.2-13.4(20)	—	—	—	5.0-113.0(20)	Scheffer, 1962
Hydrurga leptonyx · ·	3.9-10.9(2)	—	—	—	—	Hamilton, 1939

Table 1—*Continued*

Species	Length of			Ear	Body Weight	Data
	Body	Tail	Feet			
Artiodactyla						
Ovis sp.	—	—	—	—	9.0-20.7(36)	Popova, 1941
Bos taurus	3.8-4.5(4)**	9.8-11.4(2)	5.6-7.1(3)*	—	8.8-11.4(3)	Sokolov, 1960
	2.4-4.0**		—		—	Tsalkin, 1964
Rangifer tarandus	3.3-5.9(4)	3.0-5.3(4)**	—	—	—	Segal', 1962
Odocoileus sp.	1.7	—	—	—	—	Klein, 1964
Hydropotes inermis	7.3	—	—	—	—	Allen, 1940
Carnivora						
Martes zibellina	1.7-3.8(10)	6.4-7.3(2)	—	—	—	Kuznetsov, 1941
Vulpes vulpes	2.3-7.9(6)	—	—	—	5.4-19.2(4)	Fateev et al., 1961
Mustela erminea	3.6-5.4(6)	—	—	—	13.0-15.7(6)	Kopein, 1967
Taxidea taxus	3.1-3.7	—	—	—	—	Long, 1968
Lutra lutra	4.1	—	—	—	—	Ognev, 1931
Enhydra lutris	2.9	—	—	—	—	Ognev, 1931
Felis catus	4.8-6.9(2)	—	—	—	—	Latimer, 1936

* Variability of relative length.
** Body height at withers.

(*Contd.*)

Table 1—Continued

1	2	3	4	5	6	7
Chiroptera						
Myotis lucifugus	5.1	—	—	—	—	Long, 1965
Eptesicus fuscus	3.8	—	—	—	—	Long, 1965
Plecotus townsendi	2.5	—	—	—	—	Long, 1965
Monotremata						
Ornithorhynchus anatinus	6.7	—	—	—	—	Long, 1965
Marsupialia						
Antechinus flavipes	5.0-7.1(2)	—	—	—	—	Long, 1965
Primates						
Macaca iris	—	—	—	—	14.8-17.4(2)	Kirisu et al., 1967
Cercopithecus aethiops	—	—	—	—	16.2	Kirisu et al., 1967
Cetacea						
Physeter macrocephalus	5.0-16.4(5)	—	—	—	—	Matthews, 1938a
Balaenoptera borealis	4.2-4.3(2)	—	—	—	—	Matthews, 1938b
Proboscidea						
Loxodonta africanus	9.1	—	—	—	—	Long, 1968

Table 2. Coefficients of variation for parameters of hair cover on some mammals

Species	Thickness			Length			Calculated from data of
	Directed	Medullated	Feathery	Directed	Medullated	Feathery	
Talpa europaea	0.6-1.7(4)	0.51-1.3(3)	1.6-3.1(4)	3.2-8.2(4)	2.1-7.0(4)	3.2-7.3	Kogteva, 1963
Lepus timidus	0.6-2.7(6)	0.8-5.9(24)	8.1-10.9(6)	2.3-7.2(6)	2.1-6.4(24)	0.2-6.2(6)	Kogteva, 1963
Nyctereutes procyonoides	0.8(2)	0.8-4.5(8)	2.3-11.6(4)	1.3-1.5(2)	1.9-9.8(8)	5.2-10.4(4)	Kogteva, 1963
Myocastor coypus	1.1-1.5(3)	1.3-10.5(15)	5.8-15.7(3)	3.8-12.6(3)	3.0-10.7(15)	7.3-12.0(3)	Fadeev, 1958
Martes zibellina	6.8-7.2(3)	7.1-40.0(20)	13.1-35.4(5)	2.1-6.6(3)	2.6-9.9(20)	6.8-10.3(5)	Gerasimova, 1958
Ovis sp.					13.0-23.3(8)	20.6-49.9(8)	Popova, 1941
Homo sapiens	5.8-19.8(40)						Banerjee, 1963
Homo sapiens	5.5-7.0(4)						Huestis, 1925

OTHER CHARACTERS : 1—Number of hair on unit body surface in *Mus musculus*, 11.7 to 17.7(2) (Sumner, 1909);

2—Weight of hair on *Mus musculus*, 23.6 to 26.8(2) (Sumner, 1909); on *Ovis sp.* 10.6 to 23.4(8) (Popova, 1941).

Table 3.   Coefficients of variation for

Species	Lip vibrissae (rows)					
	1st	2nd	3rd	4th	5th	6th
Erignathus barbatus . .	—	—	—	—	—	—
Phoca vitulina . . .	0.0	3.8	5.6	2.0	5.3	6.5
Histriophoca fasciata .	17.1	8.0	6.7	7.9	13.7	14.2
Pagophilus groenlandicus	4.2-10.6 (17)	3.7-7.1 (17)	5.3-7.7 (17)	6.5-16.7 (17)	8.4-13.2 (17)	13.2-24.7 (17)
Cystophora cristata . .	8.5-9.8 (6)	7.7-11.1 (6)	5.9-9.7 (6)	6.8-9.0 (6)	8.3-16.3 (6)	12.3-38.6 (6)
Pusa caspica . . .	5.4-8.8 (8)	4.6-5.6 (8)	5.4-7.7 (8)	5.8-8.2 (8)	4.9-11.3 (8)	14.2-21.9 (8)
Pusa sibirica . . .	4.2-5.2 (6)	5.2-7.8 (6)	5.5-6.8 (6)	3.9-6.4 (6)	6.6-11.1 (6)	11.0-17.4 (6)
Pusa hispida . . .	6.3-13.7 (6)	5.6-10.0 (6)	5.4-6.6 (6)	6.3-12.9 (6)	8.7-14.1 (6)	15.4-20.0 (6)
Pinnipedia . . .	0-17.1	3.7-11.1	5.3-9.7	2.0-16.7	4.9-16.3	6.5-38.6

number of vibrissae in some mammals

7th	8th	9th	Total lip vibrissae	Eye vibrissae	Nose vibrissae	
—	—	—	10.1	37.8	—	♀♀ *ad*, Okhotsk Sea
11.0	266.7	—	2.7	—	—	♂♂ + ♀♀ *ad*, Okhotsk Sea
67.5	32.0	—	10.0	30.5	—	♂♂ *ad*, Okhotsk Sea
30.1-47.8 (17)	130-594.0 (17)	0-980.0 (17)	3.8-7.8 (17)	25.8-37.2 (17)	13.5-35.3 (15)	All sexually mature groups, 1961-1963, North Atlantic
15.6-136.8 (6)	—	—	5.4-6.9 (6)	16.6-19.6 (4)	13.7-78.7 (4)	Different sexually mature groups, Greenland Sea, 1962
20.8-28.8 (8)	38.5-74.2 (8)	214-342 (8)	4.4-6.0 (8)	11.3-22.6 (8)	26.6-53.0 (8)	Different sexually mature groups, 1962
21.0-29.4 (6)	43.1-101.0 (6)	150-600 (6)	3.2-6.8 (6)	1.6-35.8 (9)	30.8(1)	Different sexually mature groups, 1962
3.5-46.0 (6)	65-1189 (6)	—	4.1-8.6 (18)	9.3-36.2 (5)	20.8-31.0 (2)	Pechora, Okhotsk, Bering, and Chukchi Seas
3.5-136.8	32-1189	0-980	2.7-10.1	1.6-37.8	13.5-78.7	

Table 4.   **Summarized data on coefficients of**

Species	Condylobasal length	Mastoid width	Inter-orbital width	Width of the snout	Length of toothrow in upper jaw
1	2	3	4	5	6
					Rodentia
Dipodomys nitratoides .	2.4-3.1(3)	—	—	—	—
Apodemus sylvaticus . .	6.2-15.2(3)	7.8-13.1(3)	—	—	—
	2.5-5.5(10)	—	—	—	—
	2.7-4.9(3)	1.0-2.7(3)	3.7-4.3(3)	—	3.3-5.0(3)
	2.2-5.7(10)	—	—	—	2.7-4.6(10)
A. flavicollis . . .	2.0-6.8(8)	—	—	—	1.4-4.0(13)
	2.9-3.4(4)	—	3.7-4.2(4)	—	—
Microtus agrestis . .	2.6	—	2.4	—	16.6
	—	—	—	—	—
	0.4-3.6(6)	—	—	—	—
M. pennsylvanicus . .	4.7-5.0(2)	—	5.7-6.1(2)	—	4.3-5.8(2)
M. ochrogaster . . .	2.6	—	—	—	5.2
Peromyscus maniculatus .	1.8-2.7(8)	—	—	—	—
	1.3-2.3(12)	—	—	—	—
	2.50(30)	—	—	—	—
P. leucopus	2.3(8)	—	—	—	—
P. eremicus	2.0(4)	—	—	—	—
P. merriami	1.9-2.6(3)	2.0-3.1(3)	2.6-4.2(3)	—	2.6-3.1(3)
P. truei	1.3-2.2(7)	—	2.5	—	3.3
Clethrionomys glareolus .	2.2-3.6(7)	—	2.4-7.0(0)	—	1.8-6.1(7)
	2.6-6.2(4)	—	—	—	—
Cl. rutilus	3.2-7.3(5)	—	3.2-5.4(5)	—	2.7-5.4(5)
	1.1-2.2(2)	—	2.4-5.3(2)	—	3.0-3.4(2)
	2.2-2.8(2)	—	—	—	3.0-3.2(2)
Cl. gapperi	3.0	—	4.0	—	3.5
Mus musculus . . .	2.6-5.1(6)	—	2.3-3.7(6)	—	—

variation for skull measurements in some mammals

Length of lower jaw	Height of skull	Zygo-matic width	Length of the palate	Data
7	8	9	10	11
—	—	—	—	Boolootian, 1954
—	—	—	—	Pelt, van Bree, 1962
—	—	1.8-4.9(10)	—	Peshev and Georgiev, 1961
3.8-5.6(3)	—	3.6-5.2(3)	—	Saint Girons, van Bree, 1962
—	—	—	—	Ursin, 1956
—	—	—	—	Ursin, 1956
—	2.9-3.9(4)	—	3.5-5.6(4)	Adamczewska, 1959
—	9.6	2.9	10.0	Haitlinger, 1963
—	2.7-3.9(6)	3.2-3.6(2)	—	Wasilewski, 1956
—	—	0.4-1.4(6)	—	Gebczynska, 1964
—	5.6-6.5(2)	—	—	Goin, 1943
—	4.1	—	—	Long, 1965
—	—	—	—	Sumner, 1920
—	—	—	—	Sumner, 1923
2.7(30)	—	2.4(30)	—	Clark, 1941
2.6(8)	—	2.3(8)	—	Clark, 1941
2.3(4)	—	1.8(4)	—	Clark, 1941
—	—	—	—	Hoffmeister and Lee, 1963
—	—	—	—	Hoffmeister, 1951
—	2.2-4.0(7)	2.0-3.9(7)	—	Bol'shakov, Schwartz, 1962
—	—	—	—	Wasilewski, 1956
—	2.5-3.8(5)	4.8-6.3(5)	—	Bol'shakov, Schwartz, 1962
—	1.3-3.3(2)	—	—	Il'enko, 1968
—	3.5-4.0(2)	—	—	Manning, 1956
	3.4	—	—	Long, 1965
—	—	2.7-4.4(6)	—	Dynowski, 1963

Table 4

	1	2	3	4	5	6
Castor fiber	— 1.7-2.2(2)	— 2.6-5.3(2)	—	—	3.9-5.0(4) —
Ondatra zibethica . .	4.3 4.5 1.2-2.1(2)	2.8 — —	6.1 6.8 —	— — —	4.2 4.0 —
Lagurus lagurus . . .	1.2-5.3(10)	—	6.2-10.6(8)	—	4.5-6.2(8)
Baiomys musculus . .	1.8-2.3(2)	2.2-2.7(2)	2.2-2.9(2)	—	2.8-3.2(2)
B. taylori	2.2-2.7(2)	3.3-3.6(2)	3.2-3.3(2)	—	2.6-2.7(2)
Spermophilus armatus .	3.1-3.2(2)	—	—	—	2.2-3.2(2)
S. richardsoni . . .	3.0	—	—	—	4.0
Rattus rattus . . .	5.9	3.6	4.9	—	4.9
Zapus hudsonius . . .	2.7	3.6	5.8	—	3.6
Cavia porcellus . . .	3.0-3.2(2)	6.5-7.5(2)	—	—	—
Thomomys talpoides . .	3.1	—	6.5	—	6.3
Dipodomys ordi . . .	2.3-2.5(2)	2.6-3.0(2)	3.4(2)	5.7-6.7(2)	4.6-5.0(2)
D. merriami	1.5-1.7(2)	1.1-2.3(2)	2.7-3.2(2)	—	5.4-6.1(2)
D. insularis	1.8	2.3	2.1	—	1.9
Sicista betulina . . .	2.3-3.0(2)	2.5-3.2(2)	—	—	—
Phyllotis darwini . .	2.9-4.5(3)	—	3.8(3)	—	3.7-4.6(3)
Ph. osilae	3.2-4.0(2)	—	3.7(2)	—	3.6-3.9(2)
Ph. wolffsohni . . .	4.0	—	4.6	—	4.0
Ph. andium	3.4-4.2(3)	2.3-3.2(3)	—	—	4.2-4.6(3)
Monotremata					
Ornithorhynchus anatinus	6.0	—	6.8	—	—
Marsupialia					
Didelphis marsupialis .	6.3	—	—	—	4.0

—*Continued*

7	8	9	10	11
—	—	—	—	Paaver, 1964
—	—	—	—	Hinze, 1950
4.1	—	4.9	10.0	Latimer and Riley, 1934
—	—	4.5	—	Long, 1965
—	—	2.1-2.4(2)	—	Schwartz, 1962
—	3.3-6.6(8)	2.1-5.4(10)	—	Schwartz, 1962
—	2.5(2)	—	—	Packard, 1960
—	2.5-3.6(2)	—	—	Packard, 1960
—	2.8-3.3(2)	—	—	Long, 1965
—	3.3	—	—	Long, 1965
—	4.9	—	—	Dhaliwal, 1962
—	4.0	—	—	Whitaker, 1963
—	—	2.3-3.1(2)	—	Strandskov 1942
—	5.9	—	—	Long, 1968
2.9-3.2(2)	1.9-2.2(2)	3.0-3.1(2)	—	Desha, 1967
—	—	—	—	Lidicker, 1960
—	—	—	—	Lidicker, 1960
—	2.2-2.7(2)	—	—	Kubik, 1953
—	—	—	—	Pearson, 1958
—	—	—	—	Pearson, 1958
—	3.8	—	—	Pearson, 1958
—	—	—	—	Pearson, 1958
—	—	5.4	—	Long, 1968
		5.6	—	Long, 1968

(Contd.)

Table 4

	1	2	3	4	5	6
Antechinus flavipes . .	2.4-4.9(2)	—	2.6-4.5(2)	—	1.5-5.1(2)	

Insectivora

	1	2	3	4	5	6
Sorex araneus . . .	1.5-1.7(4)	1.8-1.9(4)	3.0-3.8(4)	—	1.9(4)	
	2.3-3.0(2)	—	—	—	—	
	1.9	3.2	3.1	—	2.7	
S. minutus	1.6-1.3(4)	1.6-2.6(4)	1.5-3.0(4)	—	1.3-1.9(4)	
	1.3	3.3	3.9	—	2.9	
	1.4	3.2	4.4	—	3.6	
S. daphaenodon . . .	2.1	—	6.6	—	2.8	
S. palustris	2.5	2.1	3.9	—	3.2	
S. cinereus	2.0	3.4	6.0	—	3.3	
S. vagrans	1.4	2.8	3.3	—	3.8	
S. nanus	2.6	3.7	4.5	—	5.1	
S. raddei	1.6	2.3	2.9	—	2.1	
S. arcticus	2.9	3.4	4.1	—	5.1	
S. isodon	1.7-1.8(2)	1.6-1.9(2)	3.4-3.7(2)	—	1.7-2.0(2)	
Crocidura suaveolens . .	2.3	2.5	3.9	—	3.8	
C. leucodon	2.2	4.2	5.0	—	2.3	
Talpa europaea . . .	2.0-5.2(12)	—	—	—	—	
	1.5-2.9(3)	—	—	—	—	
Erinaceus europaeus . .	1.3-5.9(8)	3.1-3.9(2)	3.1-3.8(2)	3.9-4.1(2)	1.0-2.2(2)	
E. romanicus . . .	2.5-13.1(3)	3.1	3.6	5.3	2.5	

Chiroptera

	1	2	3	4	5	6
Tadarida brasiliensis .	1.7	—	—	—	—	
T. sp.	0.6-2.5(2)	—	—	—	1.7-5.4(2)	
T. fossilis	2.8	—	—	—	2.8	
Myotis sodalis . . .	1.7	2.0	—	—	—	

—*Continued*

7	8	9	10	11
—	—	4.5-19.2(2)	—	Long, 1968
—	2.4-2.6(4)	—	—	Dolgov, 1963
—	1.8-4.0(11)	—	—	Puček, 1956
—	4.6	—	—	Schwartz, 1962
—	—	—	—	Dolgov, 1963
—	4.3	—	—	Lavrova, Zazhigin, 1966
—	5.2	—	—	Schwartz, 1962
—	—	—	—	Schwartz, 1962
—	—	—	—	Long, 1965
—	—	—	—	Long, 1965
—	—	—	—	Long, 1965
—	—	—	—	Long, 1965
—	4.7	—	—	Lavrova, Zazhigin, 1966
—	6.3	—	—	Schwartz, 1962
—	2.0(2)	—	—	Dolgov, 1963
—	3.6	—	—	Lavrova, Zazhigin, 1966
—	3.2	—	—	Lavrova, Zazhigin, 1966
—	—	—	—	Stein, 1963
—	—	—	—	Skoczeń, 1962
2.6-2.9(2)	—	—	—	Markov, 1957
3.4	—	—	—	Markov, 1957
—	—	—	—	Long, Jones, 1966
1.5-1.4(2)	—	—	—	Jegla, Hall, 1962
0.0	—	—	—	Jegla, Hall, 1962
—	—	—	—	Bader, Hall, 1960

(*Contd.*)

Table 4

1	2	3	4	5	6
M. lucifugus . . .	2.6	2.1	—	—	—
Macrotus waterhousii .	1.5-2.0(4)	2.0-2.9(4)	2.9-4.3(4)	—	—
Eptesicus fuscus . . .	1.9	2.7	3.5	—	—
Plecotus townsendi . .	2.5	3.6	1.8	—	—
					Perissodactyla
Equus hemionus . . .	4.1	—	—	—	3.3
	5.8	2.2	—	—	—
E. asinus	2.4	2.5	—	—	—
E. quagga	3.2	2.4	—	—	—
E. przewalskii . . .	3.7	3.8	—	—	—
E. caballus	10.6	18.4	—	—	8.3
					Artiodactyla
Rangifer tarandus . .	1.5-5.0(9)	—	—	—	4.0-5.9(9)
Hydropotes inermis . .	0.6-3.8(2)	—	—	—	3.4-30.5(2)
Muntiacus reevesi . .	1.9-3.4(2)	—	—	—	3.8-7.4(2)
Sus scrofa	3.2	3.7	—	—	—
Odocoileus hemionus . .	—	—	—	—	—
O. virginianus . . .	4.6	5.1	—	—	5.4
Merycochoerinae . . .	3.49(5)	—	9.68(5)	6.23(5)	—
Merychyinae	4.93(5)	—	8.06(5)	7.15(5)	—
Capra caucasica . . .	2.9-3.5(2)	—	—	—	—
C. cylindicornis . . .	2.6-3.3(2)	—	—	—	—
Cervus elaphus . . .	3.6-4.0(2)	—	3.3-5.6(6)	4.2-4.7(2)	3.6-5.3(2)

—Continued

7	8	9	10	11
—	—	—	—	Bader, Hall, 1960
—	—	—	—	Anderson, Nelson, 1965
—	3.3	—	—	Long, 1965
—	3.0	—	—	Long, 1965
—	—	4.0	—	Allen, 1940
—	—	—	—	Hay, 1915
—	—	—	—	Hay, 1915
—	—	—	—	Hay, 1915
—	—	—	—	Hay, 1915
—	—	—	—	Nehring, 1884
—	—	—	—	Banfield, 1961
—	—	0.7-6.5(2)	—	Allen, 1940
—	—	4.0-4.8(2)	—	Allen, 1940
—	3.1	—	—	Schultz, 1926
0.2-3.9(10)	—	—	—	Bergerud, 1964
—	—	—	—	Phillips, 1920
6.01(5)	—	6.45(5)	7.28(5)	Bader, 1955
6.21(5)	—	7.21(5)	9.37(5)	Bader, 1955
—	11.7*	8.6**	—	Tsalkin, 1956
—	9.3*	6.7**	—	Tsalkin, 1956
—	—	—	—	Brna, 1964

(*Contd.*)

Table 4

1	2	3	4	5	6
					Primates
Papio sp.	2.0-3.5(2)	3.0-4(2)	—	—	—
Alouatta palliata . .	2.4-3.2(2)	3.4-3.8(2)	—	—	—
Ateles geoffroyi	3.2.3.8(3)	3.9-5.2(2)	—	—	—
Macaca iris	—	—	—	—	5.7-6.8(2)
Tupaia clarensis . .	2.2	—	3.9	—	3.4
Homo sapiens (Ancient Egypt) .	2.7-3.2(4)	4.1-5.3(4)	—	—	—
(England) . . .	3.3-3.5(2)	4.3-4.6(2)	—	—	—
Cercopithecus aethiops .	—	—	—	—	4.0
					Lagomorpha
Lepus europaeus . . .	3.7	—	—	—	4.8
L. mandschuricus . .	2.3	—	—	—	3.1
L. timidus	2.7	—	—	—	3.8
	3.0-3.9	—	—	—	4.8
L. europaeus	4.0-4.7	—	—	—	4.5
L. flavigularis . . .	2.2	2.6	—	—	—
Oryctolagus cuniculus .	5.8	—	—	—	—
	2.9-5.0(5)	—	—	—	—
Sylvilagus auduboni . .	1.5-3.2(3)	2.7-3.7(3)	—	—	2.6-4.1(3)
Ochotona princeps . .	4.1	—	5.4	—	—
					Proboscidea
Loxodonta africanus . .	—	—	—	—	—
					Cetacea
Physeter macrocephalus .	18.8	—	—	—	—
Balaenoptera borealis .	5.6-7.8(4)	7.0-9.0(2)	—	—	—

—*Continued*

7	8	9	10	11
5-6.0(2)	—	—	5.0(2)	Freedman, 1963
—	—	—	—	Schultz, 1926
—	—	—	—	Schultz, 1926
—	—	—	6.2-8.0(2)	Kirisu *et al.*, 1967
—	—	13.7	—	Long, 1968
—	—	3.6-4.8(4)	—	Pearson, Davin, 1924
—	—	4.1-4.3(2)	—	McDonell, 1907
—	—	—	4.0	Kirisu *et al.*, 1967
—	—	—	10.4	Lebedkina, 1957
—	—	—	6.5	Lebedkina, 1957
—	—	—	9.1	Lebedkina, 1957
—	—	—	6.9	Filipchenko, 1916
—	—	—	10.7	Filipchenko, 1916
—	—	—	—	Anderson, Gaunt, 1962
—	—	—	—	Long, 1968
—	—	—	—	Latimer, Sawin, 1959
—	2.1-3.1(3)	—	—	Hoffmeister, Lee, 1963
—	3.9	—	—	Long, 1965
—	—	10.4	—	Long, 1968
—				Matthews, 1938a
—	—	—	—	Matthews, 1938b

(*Contd.*)

Table 4

1	2	3	4	5	6
Delphinus delphis . .	2.9-3.7(2)	2.0-2.9(2)	3.0-3.8(2)	3.1-4.4(2)	5.6-4.7(2)
Tursiops truncatus . . .	1.0-4.8(2)	3.3-6.1(2)	4.0-5.8(2)	3.9-7.8(2)	3.2-5.8(2)
					Carnivora
Gulo gulo	0.8-3.6(7)	—	4.9	—	1.6-3.0(3)
Lynx lynx	2.3-5.6(6)	—	—	—	—
L. rufus	3.5	—	—	—	3.8
Martes zibellina . .	1.7-2.9(11)	—	3.7-6.0(11)	2.7-4.8(11)	1.8-2.6(2)
	1.5-3.4(10)	—	—	—	—
M. foina	1.2-3.3(3)	—	3.6-4.4(3)	2.5-5.0(3)	1.5-3.7(3)
M. martes . . .	2.3-4.4(4)	—	2.2-6.5(4)	2.7-6.0(4)	1.9-6.3(4)
M. americana . . .	1.4-4.1(10)	—	—	—	—
Vulpes vulpes . . .	2.7-3.4(3)	2.8-3.4(8)	—	—	—
	2.7-3.1(2)	—	6.2-8.0(2)	—	3.3-3.7(2)
Canis familiaris . . .	1.8-3.9(2)	—	6.1-6.9(2)	—	3.0-4.7(2)
(boxer)	4.2-6.6(3)	—	12.4-13.6(3)	—	7.6-11.6(3)
("Rassenhunde ingesamt", N=503)	37.8	—	29.5	—	40.5
C. lupus	3.6-6.0(6)	—	6.6-11.6(6)	—	2.4-7.6(6)
Taxidea taxus . . .	2.4-2.6(2)	—	—	—	2.9-3.3(2)
Mephitis mephitis . .	3.6-3.8(2)	3.8-4.5(2)	—	—	—
Enhydra lutris . . .	2.5	—	4.5	—	2.9
Felis catus	2.4-5.0(3)	—	—	—	—
Mustela vison . . .	1.7-4.4(8)	1.9-4.3(4)	6.5-7.9(4)	4.0-8.6(6)	3.5(2)
M. erminea	2.3-3.5(6)	—	—	—	—
Alopex lagopus . . .	1.4-3.7(12)	—	—	—	—
Ursus americanus . .	2.9-5.5(4)	6.0-8.3(4)	4.3-5.7(4)	4.1-5.7(4)	—

—*Continued*

7	8	9	10	11
4.9-5.1(2)	2.5-3.7(2)	—	—	Kleinenberg, 1956
3.2-4.9(2)	1.5-5.0(2)	—	—	Kleinenberg, 1956
—	—	3.3	3.5	Kurtén and Rausch, 1959
—	—	—	—	Rausch, 1963
—	—	4.5	—	Long, 1965
—	2.6-4.3(8)	2.3-5.9(11)	—	Pavlinin, 1962
—	—	2.2-6.8(10)	3.3-5.9(10)	Kuznetsov, 1941
—	1.0-1.6(3)	2.9-4.4(3)	—	Kuznetsov, 1941
—	2.7-5.8(4)	2.4-6.5(4)	—	Kuznetsov, 1941
—	—	—	—	Hagmeier, 1961
2.8-3.4(3)	—	2.0-3.6(3)	—	Churcher, 1960
—	—	2.9-4.4(2)	3.2-4.6(2)	Rausch, 1953
—	—	2.1-7.1(2)	3.4-4.6(2)	Rausch, 1953
—	—	4.0-6.3(3)	—	Stockhaus, 1965
—	—	24.2	—	Stockhaus, 1965
—	—	5.0-10.2(6)	—	Stockhaus, 1965
—	—	—	—	Long, 1968
—	—	4.1-4.3(2)	—	Latimer, 1937
—	—	2.6	—	Ognev, 1931
—	—	5.8-8.3(2)	—	Latimer, 1936
2.5-6.2(3)	2.1-12.0(8)	—	—	Pavlinin, 1962
—	—	—	—	Kopein, 1967
—	—	—	—	Smirnov, 1962
—	4.1-8.3(4)	5.6-8.4(4)	3.3-5.5(4)	Harlow, 1962

(*Contd.*)

Table 4

	1	2	3	4	5	6
U. arctos	2.1-5.2(26)	—	—	—	—
	4.4	—	6.5	—	—
U. maritimus . . .	2.2-2.6(2)	3.3-3.5(2)	5.2(2)	3.8-4.2(2)	2.1-2.7(2)
Lutra lutra	2.3-5.3(5)	3.2-6.2(6)	1.4-7.5(6)	0.9-6.2(4)	3.0-4.7(4)
					Pinnipedia
Pusa hispida . . .	1.2-5.1(9)	2.6-5.1(9)	5.1-24.8(9)	5.7-10.1(9)	3.9-10.6(9)
Callorhinus ursinus . .	2.5-4.7(5)	2.5-5.6(5)	—	—	3.0-6.1(5)
Cystophora cristata . .	3.8-4.9(2)	2.4-5.0(2)	7.7-9.6(2)	9.4-10.6(2)	6.1-9.2(2)
Pagophilus groenlandicus	2.2-3.6(6)	2.7-5.0(6)	12.4-31.3	5.3-8.6(6)	4.6-5.1(6)
Hydrurga leptonyx . .	2.6	—	3.7	—	3.9
Eumetopias jabata . .	2.4-4.3(2)	5.5-6.6(2)	5.8	—	8.5
Odobenus rosmarus . .	9.3-10.5(2)	11.7	—	—	—

* Length of 2nd to 5th segments of horns of males.
** Circumference of horns at base.

—*Continued*

7	8	9	10	11
—	—	—	—	Rausch, 1963
—	—	4.1	—	Long, 1965
2.3-3.0(2)	2.6-4.0(2)	3.9-4.8(2)	—	Chernyavskii, 1969
3.6-9.2(4)	—	2.2-6.3(6)	2.9-6.0(5)	Hysing-Dahl, 1959
2.9-5.9(9)	—	4.3-7.1(9)	—	Own data
1.2-3.4(5)	2.3-4.3(5)	5.0-9.6(5)	—	Muzhzhinkin (*in litt.*)
4.2-3.2(2)	—	5.4-5.9(2)	—	Own data
3.0-5.3(4)	—	3.5-4.8(4)	—	Own data
—	—	3.8	—	Hamilton, 1939
—	—	5.3	—	Allen, 1880
—	—	—	11.0	Ognev, 1931

Table 5. Summarized data on variability ($Lim_{c.v.}$) of linear measurements of the mammalian skull

Order	Condylo-basal length	Mastoid width	Inter-orbital width	Width of the snout	Length of tooth row: upper jaw	Length of lower jaw	Height of skull	Zygomatic width	Length of the palate
Monotremata	6.0	—	6.8	—	—	—	—	5.4	—
Marsupialia	2.4-6.3	—	2.6-4.5	—	1.5-5.1	—	—	4.5 (19.2*)	—
Insectivora	1.3-5.9 (13.1*)	1.6-3.9	1.5-6.6	3.9-5.3	1.0-5.1	2.6-3.4	1.8-6.3	—	—
Chiroptera	0.6-2.8	2.0-3.6	1.8-3.2	—	1.7-5.4	0.8-1.4	3.0	—	—
Perissodactyla	2.4-5.8 (10.6*)	2.2-3.8 (18.4*)	—	—	3.3-8.3	—	—	4.0	—
Artiodactyla	0.6-4.9	3.7-5.1	8.1-9.7	6.2-7.2	—	—	3.1	0.7-7.2	—
Primates	2.0-3.8	3.0-5.3	3.9	—	3.4-6.8	5.0-6.0	—	3.6-13.7	4.0-8.0
Proboscidea	—	—	—	—	—	—	—	10.4	—
Lagomorpha	1.5-5.0	2.6-3.7	5.4	—	2.6-4.8	—	2.1-3.9	—	6.5-10.7
Cetacea	1.0-7.8 (18.8*)	2.0-9.0	3.0-5.8	3.1-7.8	3.2-5.8	3.2-5.1	1.5-5.0	—	—
Carnivora	0.8-6.6 (37.8*)	1.9-8.3	1.4-13.6 (29.5*)	0.9-0.5 (41.0*)	1.5-11.6 (40.5*)	2.3-9.2	2.1-12.0	2.0-10.2 (24.2*)	2.6-6.0
Pinnipedia	2.2-5.1 (10.5*)	2.4-6.6 (11.7*)	3.7-9.6 (31.3*)	5.3-10.6	3.0-10.6	2.9-5.9	2.3-4.3	3.8-9.6	11.0
Rodentia	0.4-6.8 (15.2*)	1.0-7.8 (13.1*)	2.1-10.6	5.7-6.7	1.4-6.2 (16.6*)	2.6-5.6	1.3-9.6	0.4-6.3	10.0
All Mammalia	0.4-6.8	1.0-8.3	1.5-10.6	0.9-10.6	1.0-11.6	0.2-9.2	1.3-12.0	0.4-13.7	2.6-11.0

* Uncharacteristic datum; possible error in the calculations, or insufficiently "clean" sample.

Table 6. Coefficients of variation ($Lim_{c.v.}$) for linear and meristic traits of the postcranial skeleton of some mammals (From my data and those of other authors)

Linear Measurements

Vertebrae	2.0 – 14.9	(27)
Humerus	2.2 – 7.4	(15)
Radius and ulna	2.2 – 6.6	(18)
Metacarpals and metatarsals	3.0 – 9.4	(39)
Femur	2.3 – 8.3	(68)
Tibia	2.7 – 11.7	(47)
Foot	2.4 – 11.1	(48)
Phalanges	3.0 – 9.0	(90)*

Meristic Traits

Number of ribs		
Sternal	0.0 – 8.7	(30)
Asternal	0.0 – 21.4	(27)
Number of vertebrae		
Thoracic and lumbar	1.2 – 3.2	(4)
Caudal	1.5 – 11.7	(49)

* *Tadarida brasiliensis,* 10.8 and 18.5 (Long *et al.*, 1967); *Myotis sodalis,* 17.5 and 20.3 (Bader and Hall, 1960).

Table 7.   Coefficients of variation for absolute weight of some glands in mammals

	Liver	Spleen	Pancreas	Adrenals	Hypophysis	Ovary	Testis	Thyroid	Salivary gland	Remarks
Histriophoca fasciata ..	27.9	76.0	—	—	—	—	—	—	—	Own data
Pagophilus groenlandicus	15.6-41.9 (3)	58.9-84.2 (3)	—	—	—	—	—	—	—	Own data
Cystophora cristata ..	23.4-24.3 (2)	33.9-43.0 (2)	—	—	—	—	—	—	—	Own data
Pusa caspica ..	29.3±6.5	47.0±11.7	26.1±6.52	—	—	—	—	—	—	Own data
Pusa sibirica ..	10.4-19.9 (2)	28.1-47.0 (2)	—	—	—	—	—	—	—	Own data
Delphinapterus leucas ..	29.4±5.5	43.1±7.9	1.7±1.4	45.9	—	—	—	—	—	Own data
Ondatra zibethica ..	21.2-27.3 (2)	—	—	—	—	—	—	—	—	Calculated from data of Schwartz, 1962
Chinchilla laniger ..	—	—	—	24.7-22.7 (2)	24.6-40.9 (2)	38.2±4.16	29.5±2.44	—	—	Roos and Shackelford, 1955
Microtus agrestis	—	50.5-80.3 (4)	—	—	—	—	—	—	—	Newson and Chitty, 1961
Cavia porcellus ..	—	—	—	29.4	17.2	—	21.0	29.9	—	Latimer, 1951

	1	2	3	4	5	6	7	8	9	Reference
Arvicola terrestris	—	—	—	25.0-25.5 (2)	—	—	—	—	—	Krotova, 1962
Talpa europaea	13.7-32.5 (6)	18.2-43.2 (4)	—	—	—	—	—	—	—	Fateev, 1963
Neomys fodiens	—	—	—	—	—	—	—	50.2-71.0 (6)	—	Bazan, 1956
Macropus sp. ..	—	—	—	—	—	—	—	21.2±4.16	24.1±4.72	Tribe and Peel, 1964
Vulpes vulpes ..	5.0-24.2 (4)	—	10.4-34.3 (4)	—	—	—	—	22.3-70.3 (9)	—	Fateev et al., 1926
Oryctolagus cuniculus ..	22.1-31.8 (9)	30.8-51.5 (9)	22.1-30 (6)	29.6-43.3 (9)	18.5-34.1 (9)	31.4-38.7 (6)	56.8-62.7 (3)	—	—	Latimer and Sawin, 1955; Brown et al., 1926
Meriones unguiculatus	28.8-32.3 (2)	58.7-65.5 (2)	27.4-29.1 (2)	18.3-22.9 (2)	23.4-29.4 (2)	29.5±5.9	9.3±0.95	23.8-24.8 (2)	11.2-12.5 (2)	Kramer, 1964

Table 8. Coefficients of variation ($c.v. \pm s_{c.v.}$; in case of two or more samples, $Lim_{c.v.}$) of length and weight of gut for some mammals

Species	Length whole gut	Weight whole gut	Stomach weight	Length small intestine	Length large intestine	Stomach volume	Intestine volume	Length esophagus	Stomach length	Remarks
Talpa europaea	8.1-18.7 (6)	45.3-46.1 (2)	18.2-51.8 (6)	—	—	—	—	—	—	Fateev, 1963 (Weight with full stomach)
Oryctolagus cuniculus	6.0-11.8 (6)	11.8-21.3 (6)	—	—	—	—	16.1-32.3 (9)	—	—	Latimer, 1955; Brown et al., 1926
Rattus norvegicus	12.8±3.4	—	—	—	—	—	—	—	—	Calculated from data by Astanin, 1962
Rattus rattus	11.6±3.1	—	—	—	—	—	—	—	—	Calculated from data by Astanin, 1962
Delphinapterus leucas	4.2±1.1	19.7±3.9	24.8±5.9	—	—	—	—	—	—	Own data
Vulpes vulpes	5.4-27.8 (6)	—	—	9.4-6.7 (2)	9.3-9.7 (2)	9.1-16.6 (2)	12.5-12.6 (2)	—	—	Fateev et al., 1941; Sokolov, 1941
Mustela vison	11.2-13.6 (2)	—	—	—	—	6.1-12.9	9.7-10.5 (2)	—	—	Sokolov, 1941
Macropus sp.	—	—	—	25.8±4.4	29.0±6.8	56.8±11.1	26.8±46.0 (3)	—	—	Tribe and Peel, 1963

Species									Source
Cystophora cristata	10.6-16.0 (4)	—	10.5-16.4 (4)	18.9-58.0 (4)	—	—	12.3-13.1 (2)	8.3-13.6 (2)	Own data
Pagophilus groenlandicus	10.7-12.0 (2)	—	11.1-12.2 (2)	15.3-17.2 (2)	—	—	11.0-12.1 (2)	11.3-15.7 (2)	Own data
Pusa sibirica	5.3±1.3	—	4.5±1.1	15.0±3.8	—	—	4.4±1.1	13.2±3.3	Own data
Pusa caspica	8.2±2.6	—	—	—	—	—	—	—	Own data
Pusa hispida	12.1±3.0	—	—	—	—	—	—	—	Own data
Histriophoca fasciata	—	23.1±5.8	33.3±8.3	—	—	—	—	—	Own data
Meriones unguiculatus	8.3-7.7 (2)	—	9.8-10.5 (2)	10.1-22.2 (2)	—	—	—	—	Kramer, 1964

Table 9.   Variability ($Lim_{c.v.}$) of some characters of the respiratory system

Species	Lung weight	Number of tracheal rings	Author
Vulpes vulpes	16.1-34.0(3)	—	Fateev *et al.*, 1961; Bogolyubskii, 1933
Oryctolagus cuniculus .	15.5-50.6(4)	—	Latimer and Sawin, 1955
Talpa europaea . . .	15.7-23.6(6)	—	Fateev, 1963
Delphinapterus leucas . .	19.1-23.3(3)	—	Own data
Pagophilus groenlandicus .	17.2-35.7(3)	6.7-10.4(15)	Own data
Cystophora cristata . .	24.4-37.1(2)	9.1-10.1(8)	Own data
Pusa hispida	—	5.7- 6.3(4)	Own data
Pusa caspica	62.5-63.7(2)	3.2- 5.8(3)	Own data
Pusa sibirica	19.4-27.0(2)	4.4-10.0(2)	Own data
Histriophoca fasciata . .	25.0	5.0- 5.3(2)	Own data
Phoca vitulina	—	3.8- 6.7(2)	Own data
Meriones unguiculatus . .	25.1-27.1(2)	—	Kramer, 1964

Table 10.   Coefficients of variation ($Lim_{c.v.}$) for absolute weight of heart, kidneys, and skin of some mammals

Species	Heart	Kidneys	Skin	Author
Histriophoca fasciata . .	18.1	44.4	—	Own data
Pagophilus groenlandicus .	10.9-70.9(3)	15.9-26.0(5)	—	Own data
Cystophora cristata . .	22.8-25.3(2)	11.9-22.2(5)	—	Own data
Pusa caspica	14.6	25.9-26.3(2)	—	Own data
Pusa sibirica	13.0-16.2(2)	18.5-19.7(3)	—	Own data
Callorhinus ursinus . .	—	—	6.5—13.6 (13)	Scheffer, 1962
Delphinapterus leucas . .	11.1	12.7-39.9(6)	14.8	Own data
Ondatra zibethica . . .	16.1-17.0(2)	24.2-43.1	—	Calculated from data of Schwartz, 1962 Latimer, 1961
Canis familiaris . . .	24.9	—	—	Fateev, 1962
Talpa europaea . . .	16.7-44.3(6)	13.3-34.0	—	
Oryctolagus cuniculus . .	7.8-19.4(9)	10.9-22.1(9)	—	Latimer, Sawin, 1955 ; Brown *et al.*, 1926
Meriones unguiculatus . .	15.9-21.7(2)	14.8-17.3(2)	—	Kramer, 1962

BIBLIOGRAPHY*

ADAMCZEWSKA K. A., 1959. "Untersuchungen über die Variabilität der Gelbhausmaus *Apodemus flavicollis flavicollis* (Melchior, 1834)," *Acta Theriol.*, 3 : 141-190.

ALEXANDER, M. M., 1960. "Shrinkage of Muskrat Skulls in Relation to Aging," *J. Wildlife Manag.*, 24 : 326-329.

ALLEN, G. M., 1940. *The Mammals of China and Mongolia.* Pt. II, 1350 pp. [Cited from Long (1968).]

ALLEN, J. A., 1880. *History of North American Pinnipeds . . . U. S. Geol. & Geogr. Surv. Terr. Misc. Publ.* 12 : 1-785. [Cited from Long (1968).]

ALPATOV, V., 1924. "Izmenchivost' i nizhnie sistematecheskie kategorii" ("Variability and Lower Taxonomic Categories"), *Zool. Zh.*, 4 : 240-244.

ALPATOV, V., 1956. "Po povodu statii G. V. Nikol'skovo 'Ob izmenchivosti Organizmov' " ("The Article of G. V. Nikol'skii 'On the Variability of Organisms' "), *Zool. Zh.*, 35 : 373-375.

ALPATOV, W. W., and A. M. BOSCHKO-STEPANENKO, 1928. "Variation and Correlation in Serially Situated Organs in Insects, Fishes, and Birds," *Amer. Naturalist*, 62 : 409-424.

ANDERSON, A. E., L. G. FRARY, and R. H. STEWART, 1964. "A Comparison of Three Morphological Attributes of Mule Deer from the Guadalupe and Sacramento Mountains, New Mexico," *J. Mammal.*, 45 : 48-53.

ANDERSON, S., and A. S. GAUNT, 1962. "A Classification of the White-sided Jack Rabbits of Mexico," *Amer. Mus. Nov.*, 2088 : 1-16.

ANDERSON, S., and C. E. NELSON, 1965. "A Systematic Revision of *Macrotus* (Chiroptera)," *Amer. Mus. Nov.*, 2212 : 1-39.

ANDREEV, I. F., 1954. "K voprosu O putyakh formoobrazovatel'nogo protsesa na primere izmenchivosti zheltogorlii myshi v stepyakh Moldavii" ("The Problem of the Action of Developmental Processes from the Example of Variability of Yellow-necked Mice in the Steppes of Moldavia"), III *Ekol. kon. v Kiev. Tez. Dokl.* III.

* Some works have been listed in the bibliography that have not been referred to in the text. This has been done because the factual data presented in these works on variability agrees well with that discussed already. Secondly, I came to know these works after the final draft and after handing over the manuscript for printing. (Some of these works were published in 1964 and a majority in 1965.) Hence this section of the book may be seen as of independent importance for reviewing variability of mammals from contemporary literature—Author.

ANDREEVA, T. V., and A. V. YABLOKOV, 1965. "Novoe v razrabotke metodiki opredelemiya voprosa usatykh kitov" ("New Method of Age Determination of Whales"), *Zool. zh.*, 44 : 145-146.

ARATA, A. A., 1964. "A Comment on the Utility of the Testicular Blood Supply in Taxonomic Studies," *J. Mammal.*, 45 : 493-494.

ARGIROPULA, A. I., 1946. "K voprosu ob individual'noi i geograficheskoi izmenchivosti u nekotorikh vidov roda *Apodemus* Kaup (Mammalia)" ("The Problem of Individual and Geographical Variability in Certain Species of the Genus *Apodemus* Kaup"), *Trudy Zool. Inst.* Akad. Nauk SSSR, 8 : 195-220.

ARTEM'EV YU. T., 1946. "K sravnitel'noi morfologii suslikov volzhako-kamskovo kraya" ("Comparative Morphology of Susliks of the Volga and Kamskii Regions"), *Tez. Dok. Itogovoi Nauch. Aspirant. Konf.* 1964, *Kazansk. Univ.*, pp. 83-85.

ASHOU, M. R., J. D. BIGGERS, A. McLAREN, and D. MICHIE, 1958. "The Effect of the Environment on Phenotypic Variability," *Proc. Roy. Soc. London*, ser. B, 149 : 192-204.

ASHTON, E. H., and C. E. OXNARD, 1964. "Functional Adaptations in the Primate Shoulder Girdle," *Proc. Zool. Soc. London*, 142 : 49-66.

ASHTON, E. H., C. E. OXNARD, and T. F. SPENCE, 1965. "Scapular Shape and Primate Classification," *Proc. Zool. Soc. London*, 145 : 125-142.

ASTANIN, L. P., 1960. "Sootnositel'naya izmenchivost' cherepa i mozga nekotorykh mlekopitayushchikh" ("Correlated Variability of Skull and Brain in Certain Mammals"), *Arkhiv Anatomii, Gistol. i Embryol.*, 39 : 39-45.

ASTANIN, L. P., 1962. "Materialy k izucheniyu tserebralizatsii blizkikh vidov mlekopitayushchikh" ("Materials for the Study of the Cerebralization in Related Species of Mammals"), *Uch. Zap. Stavr. Med. Inst.*, No. 5.

BADAMSHIN, B. I., 1949. "Nekatorye novye dannye o biologii kaspiiskogo tyulenya vo l'dakh" ("Some New Data on the Biology of the Caspian Seal on Ice"), *Rybnoe khoz.*, 3 : 39-44.

BADAMSHIN, B. I., 1963. "Biologicheskie i tekhnicheskie predposil'ki k uvelicheniyu dobychi kaspiiskogo tyulenya na ostrovnykh lezhbishchkh" ("Biological and Technical Prerequisites for Increasing the Catch of Caspian Seals from Island Colonies"), *Tez. dokl. Vtorogo Vsesoyuz. Soveshch o Izuch. Morskikh Mlekopitayushchikh.*

BADAMSHIN, B. I., 1965. "Osobennosti lin'ki kaspiiskovo tyulenya" ("Characteristics of Moulting of Caspian Seals"), in Sb. *Morskie mlekopitayushchie.* Moscow : Izdatelstvo 'Nauka'.

BADER, R. S., 1955. "Variability and Evolutionary Rate in the Oreodonts," *Evolution*, 9 : 119-140.

BADER, R. S., 1956. "Variability in Wild and Inbred Mammalian Population," *Quart. J. Florida Acad. Sci.*, 19 : 14-34.

BADER, R. S. and J. S. HALL, 1960. "Osteometric Variation and Function in Bats," *Evolution*, 14 : 8-17.

BANERJEE, A. R., 1963. "Variations in the Medullary Structure of Human Head Hair," *Proc. Nat. Inst. Sci. India*, Part B, 29 : 306-316.

BANFIELD, A. W., 1961. "A Revision of the Reindeer and Caribou, Genus *Rangifer*," *Canada Nat. Mus. Bull.*, 177 : 1-137.

BARABASH-NIKIFOROV, I. I., 1940. *Fauna kitoobraznykh chernogo morya* (Cetaceans of the Black Sea). Voronezh : Izdatelstvo Voronezhskii Gos. Univ.

BASHENINA, N. V., 1962. *Ekologiya obyknovennoi polevki i nekotorye cherty ee geograficheskoi izmenchivosti* (Ecology of the Common Field Vole and Certain Aspects of Its Geographical Variability). Moscow : Izdatelstvo Moskovskii Gos. Univ.

BASU, S. S., and S. HASARY, 1960. "Variations of the Lumbrical Muscles of the Hand," *Anat. Rec.*, 136 : 501-503.

BATESON, W., 1894. *Materials for the Study of Variation, Treated with Special Regard to Discontinuity in the Origin of Species*. London : MacMillan Company.

BAUR, E., 1925. "Die Bedeutung der Mutationen für das Evolutions Problem," *Z. indukt. Abstammungs- und Vererbungslehre*, 37 : 107-115.

BAZAN, I., 1953. "Zmiany morfohistologiczne grasicy u *Sorex araneus* L. w cyklu zycoiwym," *Ann. Univ. M. Curie-Slodowska*, Sect. C, 7 : 253-297.

BAZAN, I., , 1956. "Untersuchungen über die Veränderlichkeit des Geschlechtsapparatus und des Thymus der Wasserspitzmaus (*Neomys fodiens fodiens* Schreb.)," Ibid., Sect. C, 9 : 213-258.

BEDDARD, F. E., 1900. *A Book of Whales*. London : J. Murray.

BEI-BIENKO, G. YA., 1959. "Printsip smeny statsii i problema nachal'noi divergentsii vidov" ("Principle of Change of Habitat and the Problem of the Initial Divergence of Species"), *Zhur. Obsch. Biol.*, 20 : 351-358.

BEILI, N., 1964. *Statisticheskie metody v biologii* (Statistical Methods in Biology). Moscow : Izdatelstvo 'Mir'.

BEKLEMISHEV, V. N., 1960. "Prostranstvennaya i funktsional'naya struktura populyatsii" ("Spatial and Functional Structure of a Population"), *Bull. Mosk. Obshch. Ispyt. Prirody* (Biol.), 65 : 41-50.

BEKLEMISHEV, V. N., 1964. "Ob obshchikh printsipakh organizatsii zhizni" ("General Principles of Organization of Life"), *Bull. Mosk. Obshch. Ispyt. Prirody* (Biol.), 69 : 22-38.

BEL'KOVICH, V. M. and A. V. YABLOKOV, 1960. "Osobennosti stroeniya zubnoi sistemy morzha" ("Characteristics of the Structure of the Dental System of the Walrus"), IV *Molodezhn. Nauchn. Konf. Inst. Morfol. Zhivotnykh* Akad. Nauk SSSR, Moscow, 3-7.

BEL'KOVICH, V. M. and A. V. YABLOKOV, 1961. "Sredi morzhei" ("Among Walruses"), *Priroda*, 1961 (3) : 50-56.

BEL'KOVICH, V. M. and A. V. YABLOKOV, 1962. "Nablyudeniya morzhei na lezhbishakh v Anadirskom zalive i Chukotskom morye" (Observations on Walruses of the Colonies of Anadir Bay and the Chukchi Sea"), *Kraevedcheskie zap. Magadansk. obl. kraeved, Muzeya*, 4 : 156-174.

BEL'KOVICH, V. M. and A. V. YABLOKOV, 1963. "Obitateli morya delyatsa opytom s konstruktorami" ("Inhabitants of the Sea Shore : Their Experience in Construction"), *Nauka i zhizn*, 1963 (5) : 61-64.

BEL'KOVICH, V. M. and A. V. YABLOKOV, 1963a. "Molodost' drevnei nauki: Morfologia zakluchaet soyuz s tekhnikoi" ("Youth of an Old Science : Morphology Establishes a Relationship with Technique"), *Priroda*, 1963 (8) : 20-30.

BEL'KOVICH, V. M. and A. V. YABLOKOV, 1965. "O strukture stada zubatykh kitobraznykh" ("On the Composition of a Group of Toothed Whales"), in Sb. *Morskie mlekopitayushchie*, pp. 25-29. Moscow: Izdatelstvo 'Nauka'.

BELYAEV, D. K., 1962. "O nekotorykh problemakh korrelyativnoi izmenchivosti i ikh znachenie dlya teorii evolyutsii i selektsii zhivotnykh" ("Certain Problems of Correlated Variability and Their Significance for the Theory of Evolution and Animal Breeding"), *Izv. Sibirsk. Otd. Akad. Nauk SSSR*, 10 : 11-124.

BERG, L. S., 1910. "Fauna Baikala i ee proiskhozhdenie" ("Fauna of the Baikal and Its Origin"), *Biol. zh.*, 1 : 10-45.

BERG, R. L., 1957. "Tipy polimorfizma" ("Types of Polymorphism"), *Vestnik Leningradskii Gos. Univ.*, 1957 (21) : 115-139.

BERG, R. L., 1959. "Ekologicheskaya interpretatsiya korrelyatsionnykh pleyad" ("Ecological Interpretation of Correlation Pleiads"), *Vestnik Leningradskii Gos. Univ.*, 1959 (9) : 142-152.

BERG, R. L., 1959. "A General Evolutionary Principle Underlying the Origin of Developmental Homeostasis," *Amer. Naturalist*, 93 : 103-105.

BERG, R. L., 1964a. "Korrelyatsionnye pleyadi i stabiliziruyushchii otbor" ("Correlation Pleiads and Stabilizing Selection"), *Primenenie matematicheskikh metodov v biologii*, (3) : 23-60.

BERG, R. L., 1964b. Stabiliziruyushchii otbor, v evolyutsii razmerov tsevtov i semyan travyanistykh rastenii (Stabilizing Selection in the Evolution of Size of Flowers and Seeds of Grasses). *Avtoref. Diss. na Soisk. Uch. Step. Doktora Biol. Nauk*. Leningrad. Biologicheskii Institut, Akad. Nauk SSSR.

BERGERUD, A. T., 1964. "Relationship of Mandible Length to Sex in Newfoundland Caribou," *J. Wildlife Manag.*, 28 : 54-56.

BERNSHTEIN, N. A., 1962. "Puti razvitiya fiziologii i svyazannye s nimi zadachi kibernetiki" ("The Ways of Development of Physiology and the Problems of Cybernetics Related to Them"), in Sb. *Biologicheskie aspekty kibernetiki*, Moscow : Izdatelstvo Akad. Nauk SSSR, 52-65.

BERRY, R. J., 1963. "Epigenetic Polymorphism in Wild Populations of *Mus musculus," Genet. Res.* 4 : 193-220.

BERRY, R. J., 1964. "The Evolution of an Island Population of the House Mouse," *Evolution,* 18 : 468-483.

BERRY, R. J., and A. G. SEARLE. "Epigenetic Polymorphism of the Rodent Skeleton," *Proc. Zool. Soc. London,* 140 : 577-615.

BETESHEVA, E. I., 1961. *Pitanie promyslovikh kitov Kuril'skogo raiona* (The Feeding of Whales in the Kuril Region). *Trudy Soveshch. Ikhtiol. Komis. Akad. Nauk SSSR,* 12.

BHATNAGAR, D. S., and G. S. TANEJA, 1960. "Variation in the Performance of Hariyans Cattle," *Sci. and Culture,* 25 : 595.

BIANCHI, N. O., and MOLINA OMAR, 1966. "Autosomal Polymorphism in a Laboratory Strain of Rat," *J. Heredity,* 57 : 231-232.

BIGGERS, J. D., 1958. "Biometrical Analysis of Variance," *Proc. Roy. Soc. London,* 148 : 199-202.

BILLI, K., 1959. *Biologiya (Biology).* Moscow: Izdatelstvo Inostrannoi Literatury.

BLAIR, W. F., 1964. "The Case for Ecology," *Biol. Sci.,* 14 : 17-19.

BOGOLYUBSKII, S. N., 1941. *Sootnoshenie massy razmerov organov u razvodimykh Mustelidae* (Correlation of a Number of Organ Measurements in Farm-bred Mustelidae). *Trudy Morsk. Zootekhn. Inst.,* 1.

BOL'SHAKOV, V. N., 1962. *Individual'naya izmenchivost' okraski dvukh vidov lesnykh polevok (Clethrionomys rutilus* Pall i *Cl. glareolus* Schreb) [Individual Variability of Coloration of Two Species (*Clethrionomys rutilus* Pall and *Cl. glareolus)* of Field Voles], *Trudy Inst. Biol. Schreb. Uralsk. Fil. Akad. Nauk SSSR,* 29.

BOL'SHAKOV, V. N., 1964a. "O vidospetsifichnosti geograficheskoi izmenchivosti" ("The Species Specificity of Geographical Variability"), in Sb. *Voprosy vnutrividovoi izmenchivosti. . . . i mikroevolyutsii,* Sverdlovsk, 17-18.

BOL'SHAKOV, V. N., 1964b. "O taksonomicheskom polozhenii lemmingovidnoi polevki v svyazi s nekotorymi problemami nadvidovoi sistematiki" ("The Taxonomic Position of the Lemming-like Field Vole with Reference to Certain Supraspecific Taxonomy"), in Sb. *Voprosy vnutrividovoi izmenchivosti. . . . i mikroevolyutsii,* Sverdlovsk, 19-21.

BOL'SHAKOV, V. N., 1965. "Materialy po sravnitel'nomu izucheniyu geograficheskoi izmenchivosti inter'ernykh priznakov blizkikh vidov polevok" ("Data on a Comparative Study of Geographical Variability of Internal Traits of Related Species of Field Voles"), *Trudy Inst. Biol. Uralsk Fil. Akad. Nauk SSSR,* 38 · 53-60.

BOL'SHAKOV, V. N. and S. S. SCHWARTZ, 1962. Nekotorye zakonomernosti geograficheskoi izmenchivosti gryzunov na sploshnom uchaske ikh areala (na primere roda *Clethrionomys)* [Some Regularities of Geographical

Variability of Rodents in a Continuous Part of Their Range (an Example from *Clethrionomys*)], Ibid., 29.

BOL'SHAKOV, V. N., and S. S. SCHWARTZ 1965. "Novoi podvid krasnoi polevki (*Clethrionomys rutilus tundrensis*)" ["A New Subspecies of the Red Field Vole (*Clethrionomys rutilus tundrensis*)"], Ibid., 38 : 63-65.

BOOLOOTIAN, R. A., 1954. "An Analysis of Sub-specific Variations in *Dipodomys nitratoides*," *J. Mammal.*, 35 : 570-577.

BOREL', E., 1964. *Veroyatnosti' i dostovernost'* (Probability and Significance). Moscow : Izdatelstvo 'Nauka'.

BOROWSKI, ST., 1964. "Moult of Shrews (*Sorex* L.) Under Laboratory Conditions," *Acta Theriol.*, 8 : 125-135.

BOROWSKI, ST., 1964. "Studies on the European Hare : I. Moulting and Coloration," *Acta Theriol.*, 9 : 217-231.

BOROWSKI, ST., and A. DEHNEL, 1953. "Materialy do biologii Soricidae," *Ann. Univ. M. Curie-Slodowska*, 7: 305-436.

BOTHMA, J. DU P., 1966. "Color Variation in Hyracoidea from Southern Africa," *J. Mammal.*, 47 : 687-693.

BRNA, J., 1964. "Prilog poznavanju beljskog jelena," *Jelen :* 19-31.

BROADHURST, P. L., and J. L. JINKS, 1965. "Parity, as a Determinant of Birth Weight in the Rhesus Monkey," *Folia Primatol.*, 3 : 201-210.

BROADHURST, P. L. and J. L. JINKS, 1966. "Stability and Change in the Inheritance of Behavior in Rats : A Further Analysis of Statistics from a Diallel Cross," *Proc. Roy. Soc. London* (B) 165 : 450-472.

BRONSON, F. H., 1958. "Notes on Body Size of Blacktailed Jack-rabbits," *Trans. Kansas Acad. Sci.*, 61 : 109.

BROWN, S. G., 1965. "The Color of the Baleen Plates in Southern Hemisphere Sei Whales," *Norsk Hvalfangst-tidende*, 54 : 131-135.

BROWN, W. H., L. PEARCE, and C. M. VAN ALLEN, 1926. "Organ Weights of Normal Rabbits," *J. Exper. Med.*, 43 : 733-741.

BROWNELL, R. L., JR., 1964. "Observation of Odontocetes in Central Californian Waters," *Norsk Hvalfangst-tidende*, 53 : 60-62, 64-66.

BUCHALCZYK, A., 1961. "Variation of Weight of the Internal Organs of *Sorex araneus* Linnaeus, 1758 : I. Salivary Glands," *Acta Theriol.*, 5 : 229-252.

BUJALSKA, G., 1964. "Studies on the European Hare : IV. Variations in the Pelvis and Sacrum," *Acta Theriol.*, 9 : 287-304.

BYCHKOV, V. A., 1965. "O polovoi i vozrostnoi izmenchivosti cherepa kuril'skogo morskogo komika" ("Sex and Growth Variabilities of the Skull of the Kuril Fur Seal"), in Sb. *Morskie mlekopitayushchie*. Moscow : Izdatelstvo 'Nauka,' 183-188.

BYUNNING, E., 1964. *Biologicheskie chasy* (Biological Clocks). Moscow : Izdatelstvo 'Mir'.

CABON, K., 1958. "Untersuchungen über die Schädelvariabilität des

Wildschweines *Sus scrofa* L. aus Nordostopolen," *Acta Theriol.*, 11 : 195-266.

CABON-RACZYNSKA, K., 1964a. "Studies on the European Hare : II. Variations in the Weight and Dimensions of the Body and Weight of Certain Internal Organs," *Acta Theriol.*, 9 : 233-248.

CANNON, H. G., 1959. *Lamarck and Modern Genetics.* Manchester : Manchester Univ. Press.

CARMON, J. L., F. B. GOLLEY, and R. G. WILLIAMS, 1963. "An Analysis of Growth and Variability in *Peromyscus polionotus*," *Growth*, 27 : 247-254.

CASTLE, W. E., 1931. "Size Inheritance in Rabbits : the Backcross to the Large Parent Race," *J. Exper. Zool.*, 60 : 325-338.

CASTLE, W. E., 1938. "The Relation of Albinism to Body Size in Mice," *Genetics*, 23 : 269-274.

CASTLE, W. E., 1941. "Influence of Certain Color Mutations on Body Size in Mice, Rats and Rabbits," *Genetics*, 26 : 177-191.

CASTLE, W. E., and S. C. REED, 1936. "Studies of Inheritance in Lop-eared Rabbits," *Genetics*, 21 : 297-323.

CASTLE, W. E., S. C. REED, and W. H. GATES, 1936. "Studies of a Size Cross in Mice," *Genetics*, 21 : 66-78.

CASTLE, W. E., S. C. REED, W. H. GATES, and L. W. LAW, 1936. "Studies of a Size Cross in Mice: II," *Genetics*, 21 : 310-323.

CAVE, A. J., 1930. "On Fusion of the Atlas and Axis Vertebrae," *J. Anat.*, 64 : 337.

CAVE, A. J. and F. L. D. STEEL, 1964. "Craniometric Sex Determination in the Colobus Skull," *Proc. Zool. Soc. London*, 143 : 503-510.

CEZARIUSZ, WILAND, 1967. "Krag totniczy i tetnica podstawowa mozgu u lisow," *Prace Komis. Nauk Roln. Komis. Nauk Lesn. Poznan. Towarz. Przyiacio Nauk.*, 23 : 305-324.

CHAI, C. K., 1957. "Developmental Homeostasis of Body Growth in Mice," *Amer. Naturalist*, 91 : 49-56.

CHAI, C. K., 1966. "Selection for Leukocyte Counts in Mice," *Genet. Res.*, 8 : 125-142.

CHAPSKII, K. K., 1938. "Morskoi zayats (*Erignathus barbatus* Pall.) Karskogo i Barentsova morei" ["The Bearded Seal (*Erignathus barbatus* Pall.) of the Kara and Barents Seas"], *Trudy Arkticheskovo Nauch.-Issled. Inst.*, 123 : 7-70.

CHAPSKII, K. K., 1952. "Opredelenie vozrosta nekotorykh mlekopitayushchikh po microstrukture kosti" ("Age Determination of Some Mammals by Microstructure of Bones"), *Izv. Istestv. Nauch. Inst. im P. F. Lesgaft, Moscow*, 25 : 47-66.

CHAPSKII, K. K., 1952a. "Vozrostno-polovaya izmenchivost' kraniologicheskikh priznakov i ee vliyanie na diagnostiku nekotorykh lastonogikh" ("Age-sex Variability of Cranial Traits and Its Effect on the Diagnosis of Some Pinnipeds"), Ibid., 25 : 47-66.

CHAPSKII, K. K., 1955. "K voprosu ob istorii formirovaniya kaspiiskogo i baikal'skogo tyulenei" ("On the Problem of the History of the Formation of the Caspian and Baikal Seals"), *Trudy Zool. Inst. Akad. Nauk SSSR*, 17 : 200-215.

CHAPSKII, K. K., 1955a. "Opyt peresmotra sistemy i diagnostiki tyulenei podsemeistva *Phocinae*" ("An Attempt to Revise the Taxonomy and Diagnosis of Seals of the Subfamily *Phocinae*"), *Ibid.*, 160-199.

CHAPSKII, K. K., 1961. "Nekotorye ekologicheskie obosnovaniya sezonnoi diagnostiki a reala belomorskoi popyulyatsii grenlandskogo tyulenya (*Pogophoca groenlandica*)" ["Some Ecological Bases for Seasonal Distinctions of the Habitat of the White Sea Population of the Greenland Seal (*Pogophoca groenlandica*)"], *Trudy Vsesoyuzn. Soveshch. po Izucheniyu Morskikh Mlekopitayushchikh*, 150-163.

CHAPSKII, K. K., 1963. *VII. Otryad Pinnipedia : Lakstonogie.* (Order Pinnipedia : Seals), Mlekopitayushchie Fauny SSR, 2 : 895-964.

CHAPSKII, K. K., 1963a. "Resursy zveroboinogo promysla, ikh sostoyanie ispolzovanie i izuchenie" ("Resources of the Whale Industry : Their Condition, Use and Study"), *Tezizy Dokladov Vtorogo Vsesoyuznogo Soveshchaniya po Izucheniyu Morskikh Mlekopitayushchikh*, pp. 43-47.

CHERNYAVSKII, F. B., 1969. "Kraniometricheskaya kharakteristika belogo medvedya (*Ursus maritimus* Phipps, 1774) Sovetskoi Arktiki" ["Craniometric Characters of the Polar Bear (*Ursus maritimus* Phipps, 1774) of the Soviet Arctic"], in Sbornik *Belyi Medved' i Ego Okhrana v Sovetskoi Arktike*, pp. 54-67. Leningrad : Gidrometeoizdat.

CHETVERIKOV, S. S., 1926 (1965). "O nekotorykh momentakh evolyutsionnogo protsesa s tochki zreniya sovremennoi genetiki" ("On Certain Aspects of the Evolutionary Process from the Standpoint of Modern Genetics"), *Bull. Moskov. Obshch. Inst. Prir. (Biol.)* 70 : 33-74. (Translated 1961, *Proc. Amer. Philos. Soc.*, 105: 167-195).

CHURCHER, C. S., 1960. "Cranial Variation in the North American Red Fox," *J. Mammal.*, 41 : 349-360.

CLARK, F. H., 1940. "Correlation and Body Proportions in Mature Mice of the Genus *Peromyscus*," *Genetics*, 26 : 283-306.

COLLIN, R., 1960. *Evolution : Hypotheses and Problems.* London : Burns and Oates.

CORBET, G. B., 1963. "The Frequency of Albinism of the Tail-tip in British Mammals," *Proc. Zool. Soc. London*, 140 : 327-330.

CRUSAFONT-PAIRO, M., and I. TRUYOLS-SANTONJA, 1956. "A Biometric Study of the Evolution of Fissiped Carnivores," *Evolution*, 10 : 314-332.

DALMIER, R., 1952. "Remarque au sujet du polymorphism du mulot en Belgique," *Bull. Inst. Sci. Natur. Belg.*, 28 : 1-11.

DANFORTH, C. H., 1930. "Numerical variation and Homologies in

Vertebrae," *Amer. J. Phys. Anthropol.*, 14 : 463.

DARWIN, C., 1868. *The Variation of Animals and Plants under Domestication.* London : J. Murray.

DARWIN, C., 1877. *The Different Forms of Flowers on Plants of the Same Species.* London : J. Murray.

DARWIN, C., 1939. *Sobranie sochinenii* (Collected Works). Vol. III, Moscow.

DECABAN, A., and J. E. LIEBERMAN, 1964. "Calculation of Cranial Capacity from Linear Dimensions," *Anat. Rec.*, 150 : 215-219.

DEHNEL, A., 1949. "Studies on the Genus *Sorex* L.," *Ann. Univ. M. Curie-Slodowska*, Sect. C, 4 : 17-102.

DEHNEL, A., 1950. "Studies on the Genus *Neomys Kaup*," *Ibid.*, 5 : 1-63.

DEMEREC, M., 1937. "A Mutability Stimulating Factor in the Florida stock of *Drosophila melanogaster*," *Genetics*, 22: 190-195.

DEMIDOVA, Z. A., 1941. Zavisimost' mezhdu dlitel'nostyu embryonal' nogo razvitia, rostom i nastrigom shersti u ovets (Relation between the Length of Embryonic Growth, Development, and Wool Clippings in Sheep). *Trudy Mosk. Zootekhn. Inst.*, vol. 1.

DENISOVA, I. A., 1966. "Elektroforeticheskoe issledovanie vozrostnykh izmenenii v otnoshenii belko'vykh fraktsii sivorotki krovi malogo suslika" ("Electrophoretic Investigations on Protein Fractions of Blood Plasma of Pigmy Ground Squirrels of Different Ages"), *Trudy Vsesoyuzn. Soveshchaniya "Vnutrivid. Izmenchivost Nazemnykh Pozvonochnykh Zhivotnykh i Mikroevolyutsiya."* Sverdlovsk, pp. 237-241.

DEOL, M. S., 1955. "Genetical Studies on the Skeleton of the Mouse : XIV. Minor Variation of the Skull," *J. Genet.*, 53 : 498-514.

DERUMS, V. YA., 1964. "Nekotorye paleoantropologicheskie dannye o zhitelyakh Pribaltiki" ("Some Paleoanthropological Data on Inhabitants of the East Baltic Area"), *Arkhiv Anat. Gistol. Embryol.* 16 : 80-90.

DESHA, P. G., 1967. "Variation in a Population of Kangaroo Rats," *Dipodomys ordii medius* (Rodentia : *Heteromyidae*) from the High Plains of Texas," *Southwestern Nat.*, 12 : 275-290.

DHALIWAL, S. S., 1962. "Studies on the Body Measurements and Skeletal Variations of Two Taxa of *Rattus rattus* in Malaya," *J. Mammal.*, 43 : 249-261.

DICE, L. R., 1938. "Variation in Nine Stocks of the Deer Mouse, *Peromyscus maniculatus* from Arizona," Univ. Mich. Occasion. Paper, Mus. Zool., 375 : 1-19.

DICE, L. R., and H. L. LERAAS, 1940. "Ecologic and Genetic Variability within Species of *Peromyscus*," *Amer. Naturalist*, 74 : 212-221.

DOBZHANSKY, TH., 1937. *Genetics and the Origin of Species.* New York : Columbia Univ. Press.

DODSON, E. O., 1960. *Evolution, Process and Product.* New York : Reinhold.

DOLGOV, V. A., 1961. "Ob izmenchivosti nekotorykh kostei postkranial'-

nogo skeleta zemleroek (*Mammalia, Soricidae*)" ["Variability of Some Postcranial Skeletal Bones of Rodents (*Mammalia, Soricidae*)"], *Acta Theriol.*, 5 : 203-227.

DOLGOV, V. A., 1963. "Ob izmenchivosti burozubok poimy r. Oki. (*Mammalia, Soricidae*)" ["Variability of Shrews in the Flood Plains of the Oka River (*Mammalia, Soricidae*)"], *Bull. Mosk. Obshch. Ispyt. Prirody*, (Biol.), 68: 135-140.

DORN, A., 1936. *Printsip smeny funktsii* (Principles of Change of Function). Moscow : Biomedgiz.

DORNESCO, G. T., and G. MACROCI, 1961. "Étude Comparative du Crane des Cervidés," *Rev. Biol.*, 6: 261-294.

DUBININ, N. P., 1931. "Genetiko-avtomaticheskie protsessy i ikh znachenie dlya mekhanizma organicheskoi evolutsii" ("Genetic-automatic Processes and Their Significance for the Mechanism of Organic Evolution"), *Zh. Eksperim. Biol.*, 7 : 463-479.

DUBININ, N. P., 1932. "O nekotorykh osnovnykh problemakh genetiki" ("Some Basic Problems of Genetics"), *Biol. Zh.*, 1(1-2) : 112-146.

DUBININ, N. P., 1940. "Genetika i 'Proiskhozhdenie vidov' Ch. Darvina" ("Genetics and the 'Origin of Species' by Charles Darwin"), *Zh. Obshch. Biol.*, 1 : 37-74.

DUBININ, N. P., and D. D. ROMASHOV, 1932. "Geneticheskoe stroenie vida i ego evolyutsiya" ("Genetical Build-up of a Species and Its Evolution"), *Biol. Zh.*, 1(5-6) : 52-95.

DUBININ, N. P., N. N. SOKOLOV and G. G. TINYAKOV, 1937. "Vnutrivido-vaya khromozomnaya izmenchivost'" ("Intra-species Chromosomal Variability"), *Biol. Zh.*, 6: 1007-1054.

DUNN, L. C., A. B. BEASLEY, and H. TINKER, 1960. "Polymorphism in Populations of Wild House Mice," *J. Mammal.*, 41 : 220-229.

DUNN, L. C., and D. C. CHARLES, 1937. "Studies of Spotting Patterns : I. Analysis of Quantitative Variations in the Pied Spotting of the House Mouse," *Genetics*, 22 : 14-42.

DWYER, P. D., 1962. "Studies on the Two New Zealand Bats," *Zool. Publ. Victoria Univ.*, Wellington, 28 : 1-28.

DYNOWSKI, J., 1963. "Morphological Variability in the Vialowieza Population of *Mus musculus* Linnaeus, 1758," *Acta Theriol.*, 7 : 51-67.

EHRLICH, P. R. and P. W. HOLM, 1962. "Patterns and Populations," *Science*, 137 : 652-657.

ELTON, C., 1927. *Animal Ecology*. London : Sidgwick and Jackson.

EMERSON, A. E., 1961. "Vestigial Characters of Termites and Processes of Regressive Evolution," *Evolution*, 15 : 115-131.

FADEEV, E. V., 1958. "Vozrostnye izmeneniya mekha nutrii" ("Age Variations of Fur of Nutria"), *Trudy Vsesoyuzn. Nauch.-Issled. Inst. Zhivotn. Syriya Pushniny*, 17 : 161-179.

FALCONER, D. S., and M. LATYSZEWSKI, 1952. "Selection for Size in Mice on High and Low Planes of Nutrition," *Quantitative Inheritance*, London : Agricultural Research Council, pp. 145-151.

FATEEV, K. Ya., 1961. "Morfobiologicheskie izmeneniya krolikov v raznykh usloviyakh sredy" ("Morpho-biological Changes in Rabbits under Different Environmental Conditions") *Zh. Obshch. Biol.*, 22 : 388-392.

FATEEV, K. Ya., 1962. "Izamenchivost' vnutrennykh orgonov evropeiskogo krota (*Talpa europaea*)" ["Variability of Internal Organs of the European Mole (*Talpa europaea*)"], *Zool. Zh.*, 41: 1700-1705.

FATEEV, K. Ya., M. V. KHROMOVA and L. S. GUZOVA, 1961. "Izmenchivost' vnutrennykh organov u serebristo chernykh lisets (*Vulpes fulves* Docm.)" ["Variability of Internal Organs of Silver-black Foxes (*Vulpes fulves Docm.*)"], *Zool. Zh.*, 40: 1090-1098.

FEDOSEEV, G. A., 1964. "Ob embrional'nom, post-embrional'nom roste i polovom sozrevanii okhotskoi kol'chatoi nerpy" ("On the Embryonic and Post-embryonic Growth and Sexual Maturity of the Ringed Seal of the Okhotsk Sea"), *Zool. Zh.*, 43 : 1228-1235.

FEDOSEEV, G. A., 1965. "Sravnitel'naya kharakteristika populyatsii kolchatoi nerpy pribrezhnykh vod Chukotskogo poluostrova" ("Comparative Characters of Populations of the Ringed Seal in the Coastal Waters of the Chukchi Peninsula"), *Izv. Tikh Nauchno-Issled. Inst. Ryb. Khoz. i Okeanogi* (Vladivostok), 59: 194-212.

FEDOSEEV, G. A., and A. V. YABLOKOV, 1965. "Morfologicheskaya kharakteristika okhotskogo kol'chatoi nerpy (*Pusa hispida, Pinnipedia*) okhotskogo morya" ["Morphology of the Ringed Seal (*Pusa hispida, Pinnipédia*) of the Okhotsk Sea"], *Zool. Zh.*, 44 : 759-765.

FEDOTOV, D. M., 1959. "Filogeniya zhivotnykh kak kompleksnaya problema" ("Phylogeny of Animals as a Complex Problem"), *Vestnik Akad. Nauk SSSR*, 1959(9) : 9-12.

FELTEN, H., 1952. "Untersuchungen zur Ökologie und Morphologie der Waldmaus (*Apodemus sylvaticus* L.) und der Gelbhalmaus (*Apodemus flavicollis* Melchior) im Rhein-Main-Gebiet," *Bonn. Zool. Beitr.*, 3 : 187-206.

FILIPCHENKO, YR. A., 1916. "Izmenchivost' i nassledstvennost' cherepa mlekopitayushchikh" ("Variability and Heredity of the Mammalian Skull"), *Russk. Arkhiv. Anat. Gistol. Embriol.*, 1 : 311-403.

FILIPCHENKO, YR. A., 1926. *Izmenchivost' i metody ee izucheniya* (Variability and Methods of Its Study). Leningrad.

FISHER, R. A., 1930. *The Genetical Theory of Natural Selection.* Oxford : Clarendon Press.

FORD, E. B., 1955. "Rapid Evolution and the Conditions Which Make It Possible," *Cold Spring Harbor Sympos. Quant. Biol.*, 20 : 230-238.

FORD, E. B., 1958. "Darwinism and the Study of Evolution in Natural Populations," *J. Linnean Soc. London*, 44 : 41-48.

FORD, E. B., 1964. *Ecological Genetics*. London : Methuen.

FORD, E. B., and H. O. BULL, 1926. "Abnormal Vertebrae in Herrings," *J. Marine Blol. Assoc. United Kingdom*, 14 : 509-517.

FRANKEL, O. H., 1959. "Variation under Domestication," *Austral. J. Sci.*, 22 : 27-32.

FREEDMAN, L., 1963. "A Biometric Study of *Papio cynocephalus* Skulls from Northern Rhodesia and Nyasaland," *J. Mammal.*, 44 : 24-43.

FREEMAN, V. A., 1939. "Variation in the Number of Vertebrae in Swine," *J. Heredity*, 30 : 61-64.

FREIMAN, S. YU., 1935. "Rasspredelenie lastonogikh v moryakh Dal'nego vostoka" ("Distribution of Pinnipeds in the Far East Seas"), *Trudy Vses. Nauch-Issled. Inst. Ryb. Khoz. i Okeanogr.*, 3 : 195-198.

FREYE, H. A., 1964. "Variabilität und Fehlbildungen in der Occipital Region von *Ondatra zibethica* (L. 1766)," *Z. Säugetierkunde*, 29: 331-336.

FRICK, H., 1957. "Quantitative Untersuchungen an äthiopischen Säugetieren : I. Absolute und Relative Gewichte von Herz, Leber, Milz und Nieren," *Anat. Anz.*, 104 : 305-333.

GALBRAITH, D. B., 1964. "The Agouti Pigment Pattern of the Mouse ; a Quantitative and Experimental Study," *J. Exper. Zool.*, 155 : 71-89.

GEBCZYNSKA, Z., 1964. "Morphological Changes Occurring in Laboratory *Microtus agrestis* with Age," *Acta Theriol.*, 9 : 67-76.

GEGENBAUR, C., 1898-1901. *Vergleichende Anatomie der Wirbeltiere*. 2 vols. Leipzig : W. Engelmann.

GENTILE, J., 1952. "A Craniometric Study of the Norway Rat," *J. Mammal.*, 33 : 190-197.

GERASIMOVA, M. A., 1958. Kachestvo mekha Barguzinskogo sobolya, akklimatizirovannogo v Tomskoi oblasti (Quality of Fur of Barguzins Sable Acclimatized to the Tomsk Region). *Trudy Vsesoyuzn. Nauch.-Issled. Inst. Zhivotn. Syrya i Pushniny.* 17.

GERSHENZON, S. M., 1941. " 'Mobilizatsionnyi rezerv' vnutrividovoi izmenchivosti" (" 'Mobilized Reserve' of Intra-species Variability"), *Zh. Obshch. Biol.*, 2 : 85-108.

GERSHENZON, S. M., 1946. "Rol' estestvennogo otbora vrasprostranenii i dinamike melanisma u khomyachkov (*Cricetus cricetus* L.)" ["Role of Natural Selection in the Spread and Dynamics of Melanism in Hamsters (*Cricetus cricetus* L.)"], *Zh. Obshch. Biol.*, 7: 97-130.

GILYAROV, M. S. (GHILAROV), 1959. "Problemy sovremennoi ekologii i teoria estestvennogo otbora" ("Problems of Modern Ecology and the Theory of Natural Selection"), *Usp. Sovrem. Biol.*, 48 : 267-278.

GILYAROV, M. S. (GHILAROV), 1960. "Nekotorie obshchie zadachi evolyutsionnoi morfologii bezpozvonochnykh" ("Some General Problems of

Evolutionary Morphology of Invertebrates"), *Usp. Sovrem. Biol.*, 49 : 214-224.

GILYAROV, M. S. (GHILAROV), 1964. "Sovremennye predstavleniya o gomologii" ("Modern Concepts of Homology"), *Usp. Sovrem. Biol.*, 57 : 300-316.

GIMMEL'REIKH, G. A., 1962. "*M. palatopharyngeus* v svete evolyutsii bronkhiel'noi muskulatory mlekopitayushchikh" ("*M. palatopharyngeus* in the Light of the Evolution of the Bronchial Musculature of Mammals"), *Arkhiv Anat. Gistol, Embriol.*, 43 : 76-82.

GLADKINA, T. S., M. N. MEIER and T. M. MOKEEVA, 1963. "O vnutrividovoi izmenchivosti melkikh gryzunov" ("Intra-species Variability of Small Rodents"), *Dokl. Akad. Nauk SSSR*, 148 : 962-965.

GOIN, O. B., 1943. "A Study of Individual Variation in *Microtus p. pennsylvanicus*," *J. Mammal.*, 24 : 212-220. [Cited from Long (1968)].

GOLDSCHMIDT, R., 1935. "Geographische Variation und Artbildung," *Naturwissenschaften*, 23 : 169-176.

GOWEN, J. W., 1936. "Inheritance as It Affects Survival of Rats Fed on a Diet Deficient in Vitamin D.," *Genetics*, 21 : 1-23.

GREEN, E. L., 1939. "The Inheritance of a Rib Variation in the Rabbit," *Anat. Rec.*, 74 : 47-60.

GREEN, E. L., 1941. "Genetic and Non-genetic Factors which Influence the Type of the Skeleton in an Inbred Strain of Mice," *Genetics*, 26 : 192-222.

GROVES, C. P., 1963. "Results of a Multivariate Analysis of the Skulls of Asiatic Wild Asses; with a Note on the Status of *Microhoppus hemionus blanfordi* Pocock," *Ann. and Mag. Natur. History*, 6 : 329-336.

GRÜNEBERG, H., 1950. "Genetical Studies on the Skeleton of the Mouse : I. Minor Variation of the Vertebral Column," *J. Genet.*, 50 : 112-141.

GRÜNEBERG, H., 1955. "Genetical Studies on the Skeleton of the Mouse : XV. Relations between Major and Minor Variations," *J. Genet.*, 53 : 515-535.

GRÜNEBERG, H., 1961. "Evidence for Genetic Drift in Indian Rats (*Rattus rattus* L.)," *Evolution*, 15 : 335-338.

GRÜNEBERG, H., 1963. *The Pathology of Development*. Oxford : Oxford University Press.

GUILDAY, J. E., 1957. "Individual and Geographic Variation in *Blarina brevicauda* from Pennsylvania," *Ann. Carnegie Mus.*, 35 : 41-68.

GUTHRIE, R. D., 1965. "Variability in Characters Undergoing Rapid Evolution : an Analysis of *Microtus* Molars," *Evolution*, 19 : 214-233.

HAECKEL, E., 1894-1896 *Systematische Phylogenie*, Ed. 1-3. Berlin : G. Reimer.

HAGMEIER, E. M., 1961. "Variation and Relationships in North American Marten," *Canadian Field Nat.*, 75 : 122-138.

HAITLINGER, R., 1962. "Morphological Variability in *Apodemus agrarius* (Pallas, 1771)," *Acta Theriol.*, 6 : 239-258.

HAJEK, K., 1962. "Vedecka hodnota teoretickeho odkazu Ch. Darwina," *Biologia* (Czechoslovakia), 17 : 546-551.

HALDANE, J. B. S., 1949. "Suggestions as to Quantitative Measurements of Rates of Evolution," *Evolution*, 3 : 51-56.

HALDANE, J. B. S., 1955. "The Measurement of Variation," *Evolution*, 9 : 484.

HALL, K. R. L., and G. B. SCHALLER, 1964. "Tool-using Behavior of the California Sea Otter," *J. Mammal.*, 45 : 287-298.

HAMAJIMA, FUSANORI, 1964. "The Life History of the Japanese Mouse, *Mus molossinus* Temminck and Schlegel : XI. Measurements of External Characters, Skull, and Reproductive Organs in Adult Mice," *Sci. Bull. Fac. Agric. Kyushi Univ.*, Fukuoka, 21 : 73-82 (English Summary).

HAMBURGH, M. and E. LYNN, 1964. "The Influence of Temperature on Skeletal Maturation of Hypothyroid Rats," *Anat. Rec.*, 150 : 163-168.

HAMBURGH, M., E. LYNN, and E. WEISS, 1964. "Analysis of the Influence of Thyroid Hormone on the Prenatal and Postnatal Maturation of the Rat," *Anat. Rec.*, 150 : 147-161.

HAMILTON, J. E., 1939. "The Leopard Seal *Hydrurga leptonyx* (de Blainville)," *Discov. Rep.*, 18 : 239-264. [Cited from Long (1968)].

HAY, O. P., 1915. "Contributions to the Knowledge of the Mammals of the Pleistocene of North America," *Proc. U. S. Nat. Mus.*, 48 : 515-575. [Cited from Long (1968)].

HAYNE, D. W., 1950. "Reliability of Laboratory-bred Stocks as Samples of Wild Populations, as Shown in a Study of the Variation of *Peromyscus polionotus* in Parts of Florida and Alabama," *Contribs. Lab. Vert. Gen. Univ. Mich.*, 46 : 1-56.

HARLOW, R. F., 1962. "Osteometric Data for the Florida Black Bear," *Quart. J. Florida Acad. Sci.*, 25 : 257-274.

HELSOP-HARRISON, J., 1959. "Variability and Environment," *Evolution*, 13 : 145-147.

HIGHTON, R., 1960. "Heritability of Geographic Variation in Trunk Segmentation in the Red-backed Salamander, *Plethodon cinereus*," *Evolution*, 14 : 351-360.

HINZE, G., 1950. *Der Biber*. Berlin : Akademie-Verlag.

HOFFMEISTER, D. F., 1951. "A Taxonomic and Evolutionary Study of the Pinon Mouse, *Peromyscus truei*," *Illinois Biol. Monogrs.*, 21 : 1-104.

HOFFMEISTER, D. F., and M. R. LEE, 1963. "The Status of the Sibling Species *Peromyscus merriami* and *Peromyscus eremicus*," *J. Mammal.*, 49 : 201-213.

HOWELL, A. B., 1924. "Individual and Age Variation in *Microtus montanus* of Yosemite," *J. Agric. Res.*, 28 : 974-1016.

HOWELL, J. M., and P. B. SPIEGEL, 1966. "Morphological Effects of the Manx-factor in Cats," *J. Heredity*, 57 : 100-104.

HROMADA, J., and L. STRNAD, 1962. "Prispevek ke kraniologii makaku," *Ceskosl.. Morfol.*, 10 : 341-351.

HROMADA, J., and L. STRNAD, 1964. "Beitrag zur Kenntnis der Austritt-stellan des Nervus trigeminus und des Foramen symphyseos mandibulae an den Schädeln des *Macaca mulatta* und *Macaca irus* (*cynomologus*)," *Z. Morphol. und Anthropol.*, 55 : 368-379.

HUESTIS, R. R., 1925. "A Description of Microscopic Hair Characters and of Their Inheritance in *Peromyscus*," *J. Exper. Zool.*, 41 : 429-270.

HUGHES, R. L., 1964. "Sexual Development and Spermatozoan Morpho-logy in the Male Macropod Marsupial *Potorous tridactylus* (Kerr)," *Austral. J. Zool.*, 12 : 42-81.

HUXLEY, J. S., 1942. *Evolution, the Modern Synthesis*. London : G. Allen and Unwin.

HUXLEY, J. S., 1957. "The Three Types of Evolutionary Process," *Nature*, 180 : 454-455.

HUXLEY, J. S. (ed.), 1940. *The New Systematics*. Oxford : Clarendon Press.

HUXLEY, T. H., 1858. "On the Theory of the Vertebrate Skull," *Proc. Roy. Soc. London*, 9 : 381-457.

HYSING-DAHL, CHR., 1954. "Den Norske Greyling, *Meles meles* (L.)," *Arbok Univ. Bergen, Naturvit. rekke*, 16 : 1-57.

HYSING-DAHL, CHR., 1959. "The Norwegian Otter *Lutra lutra* (L.) : A Craniometric Investigation," Ibid., 5 : 1-44.

ICHIHARA, T., 1963. "Identification of the Pigmy Blue Whale in the Antarctic," *Norsk. Hvalfangst-tidende*, 5: 128-130.

IL'ENKO, A. I., 1968. "Vliyanie zagryazneniya uchastka mestnosti strontsiem-90 na izmenchivost' v populyatsiyakh melkikh mlekopitayush-chikh" ("The Influence of Pollution by Strontium-90 in Different Geographical Regions on Variability of Populations of Small Mammals"), *Zool. Zh.*, 47: 1370-1377.

IVANOVA, E. I., 1961a. "Morfologicheskaya kharakteristika kashalota (*Physeter catodon* L.) raiona kuril'skikh ostrovov" ("Morphological Characteristics of *Physeter catodon* L. in the Region of the Kuril Island"), *Trudy Inst. Morf. Zhivot. Akad. Nauk SSSR*, 34 : 151-173.

IVANOVA, E. I., 1961b. "Proportsii tela i rost finvala (*Balaenoptera physalus* L.) dobyvaemogo u kuril'skikh ostrovov" ["Proportions of the Body and Growth of the Finwhale (*Balaenoptera physalus* L.) Found Near the Kuril Islands"], Ibid., 34 : 174-194.

IVANOVA, E. I., 1961c. "Proportsii tela Seivala (*Balaenoptera borealis* L.) dobyvaemogo u kuril'skikh obstrovov" ["Body Proportions of the Sei Whale (*Balaenoptera borealis* L.) Found Near the Kuril Islands"], Ibid., 34 : 195-204.

JACKSON, C. M., 1913-14. "Postnatal Growth and Variability of the Body and the Various Organs in the Albino Rat," *Amer. J. Anat.*, 15 : 1-68.

JAFFE, F. A., 1951. "A Quantitative Study of the Islets of Langerhans in the Rabbit," *Anat. Rec.*, 111 : 109-122.

JAFHA, A., 1910. "Die Haare der Waltiere," *Zool. Jahrb., Abt. Anat.*, 32 : 1-32.

JAMES, TH. N., 1960. "The Arteries of the Free Ventricular Walls in Man," *Anat. Rec.*, 136 : 371-376.

JEGLA, TH. C., 1963. "A Recent Deposit of *Myotis lucifugus* in Mammoth Cave," *J. Mammal.*, 44 : 121-122.

JEGLA, TH. C., and J. S. HALL, 1962. "A Pleistocene Deposit of the Free Tailed Bat in Mammoth Cave, Kentucky," *J. Mammal.*, 43 : 474-481.

JEWELL, P. A., and P. J. FULLAGAR, 1966. "Body Measurements of Small Mammals : Sources of Error and Anatomical Changes," *J. Zool.*, 150 : 401-409.

KALELA, OLAVI, 1957. "Regulation of Reproduction Rate in Subarctic Population of the Vole *Clethrionomys rufocanus* (Suud)," *Suom. Tied. Toimit*, Ser. A, IV, No. 34 : 7-60.

KALKOWSKI, W., 1966. "Preferential Temperatures in the White Mouse under Age Differentiation," *Folia Biolog.*, 14 : 273-289.

KAMSHILOV, M. M., 1939. "Otbor kak faktor menyayushchii zavisimost' priznaka ot izmenenii vneshnykh uslovii" ("Selection as a Means of Changing the Relations of a Trait from the Changes in Environmental Conditions"), *Dokl. Akad. Nauk SSSR*, 23 : 361-364.

KAMSHILOV, M. M., 1959. "Vzaimnye otnosheniya mezhdu organismami i ikh rol' v evolyutsii" ("Mutual Relations between Organisms and Their Role in Evolution"), *Zh. Obshch. Biol.*, 20 : 370-378.

KASUYA, TOSHIO, and T. ICHIHARA, 1965. "Some Information on Mink Whales from the Antarctic," *Sci. Rept. Whales Res. Inst., Tokyo*, 19 : 37-43.

KAUL, D. K., 1966. "An Instance of Congenital Right Renal Agenesia in the Indian Desert Gerbil, *Meriones hurrianae* Jerdon," *Proc. Zoolog. Soc. India*, 19 : 121-125.

KEIN, A., 1958. *Vid i evo evolyutsis* (The Species and Its Evolution) Moscow: Izdatelstvo Inostrannoi Literatury.

KHUZIN, R. SH., 1963. "K voprosu o somostoyatel'nosti trekh stad grenlandskogo tyulenya" ("On the Problem of the Independence of Three Groups of Greenland Seals"), in *Sb. Rabot. Sev. Otd. Polyarnogo Inst. Ryb. Khoz. i Okeanogr.* (Arkhangelsk, 1962), pp. 130-136.

KHUZIN, R. SH., 1964. "Morfo-ekologicheskaya kharakteristika grenlandskogo tyulenya Yan-Maienskogo stada" ("Morpho-ecological Characters of Greenland Seals of the Yan-Maien Group"), *Materialy Sessii Uch. Soveta Polyarnogo Inst. Ryb. Khoz. i Okeanogr. po Rezul'tatem Issledovanii*, 1962-1963 ; Murmansk, pp. 226-234.

Khuzin, R. Sh., and A. V. Yablokov, 1963. "O nekotorykh chertakh funktsionirovaniya pishchevaritel'nogo trakta khokhlacha (*Cystophora cristata*) v period molochnogo pitaniya" ["On Certain Aspects of the Function of the Digestive Tract of the Hooded Seal (*Cystophora cristata*) During the Period of Milk Feeding"] *Zool. Zh.*, 18 : 1273-1275.

Khuzin, R. Sh., and M. Ya. Yakovenko, 1964. "O rasspredelenii i biologii khokhlacha grenlandskogo morya" ("On the Distribution and Biology of the Hooded Seal of the Greenland Sea"), *Trudy Polyarnogo Inst. Ryb. Khoz. i Okeanogr.* (Murmansk), No. 4.

Kibler, H. H., 1943. "Relation of Certain Endocrine Glands to Body Weight in Growing and Mature New Zealand White Rabbits," *Endocrinology*, 33 : 250-256.

King, H. D., 1923. "The Growth and Variability in the Body Weight of the Norway Rat," *Anat. Rec.*, 25 : 79-94.

King, J. A., 1965. "Body, Brain and Lens Weight of *Peromyscus*," *Zool. Jahrb.*, Abt II, 32: 177-188.

King, J. A., D. Mass, and R. G. Weismann, 1964. "Geographic Variation in Nest Size among Species of *Peromyscus*," *Evolution*, 18: 230-234.

Kirisu, K., S. Kanda, and T. Kanazawa, 1967. "A Metrical Study on the Bony Palate of *Macaca irus* and *Cercopithecus aethiops*," *Med. J. Osaka Univ.*, 18 : 11-18.

Kirpichnikov, A. A., 1964. "O proiskhozhdenii Kaspiiskogo tyulenya" ("Origin of the Caspian Seal"), *Bull. Mosk. Obshch. Ispyt. Prir. (Biol.)*, 69 : 136-139.

Kirpichnikov, V. A., 1935. "Rol'nasledstvennoi izmenchivosti v protsesse estestvennogo otbora (gipoteza o kosvennom otbore)" ["The role of Hereditary Variability in the Process of Natural Selection (Hypothesis of Indirect Selection)"] *Biol. Zh.*, 4 : 775-801.

Kirpichnikov, V. A., 1940. "Znachenie prisposobitel'nykh modifikatsii v evolyutsii" ("The Significance of Adaptive Modifications in Evolution") *Zh. Obshch. Biol.*, 1 : 121-151.

Kitchen, H., F. M. Putnam, and W. J. Taylor, 1964. "Hemoglobin Polymorphism : Its Relationship to Sickling of Erythrocytes in White-tailed Deer," *Science*, 144 : 1237-1239.

Klein, D. R., 1964. "Range-related Differences in Growth of Deer Reflected in Skeletal Ratios," *J. Mammal.*, 45 : 226-235.

Kleinenberg, S. E., 1956. *Mlekopitayushchie Chernogo i Azovskogo morei* (Mammals of the Black and Azov Seas). Moscow : Izdatelstvo Akad. Nauk SSSR.

Kleinenberg, S. E., 1958. "K voprosu o proiskhozhdenii kitoobraznykh" ("On the Question of the Origin of Cetaceans"), *Dokl. Akad. Nauk SSSR*, 122 : 950-952.

KLEINENBERG, S. E., 1961. "Izuchenie morskikh mlekopitayushchikh v SSSR i osnovnoe napravlenie semiletnego plana issledovanii" ("Studies on the Marine Mammals of the USSR and the Basic Direction of the Seven-Year Plan of Researches"), *Trudy Soveshch. Ikhtiol. Komissii,* 12 : 5-16.

KLEINENBERG, S. E., V. M. BEL'KOVICH and A. V. YABLOKOV, 1965. "O vyrobotke edinoi metodiki izucheniya morskikh mlekopitayushchikh" ("On the Development of a Unified Method of Study of Marine Mammals"), in Sb. *Morskie mlekopitayushchie,* pp. 242-249. Moscow : Izdatelstvo 'Nauka'.

KLEINENBERG, S. E., A. V. YABLOKOV, V. M. BEL'KOVICH, and M. N. TARASEVICH, 1964. *Belukha. Opyt monograficheskogo issledovaniya vida.* Moscow : Izdatelstvo 'Nauka'. [Translated 1969, Beluga (*Delphinapterus leucas*) : Investigation of the Species. Jerusalem : Israel Program for Scientific Translations].

KLEINENBERG, S. E., and A. V. YABLOKOV, 1964a. "Morfologicheskaya izmenchivost' mlekopitayushchikh i ee znachenie dlya ponimaniya strukturi i dinamiki chislennosti populyatsii" ("Morphological Variability of Mammals and Its Significance for the Understanding of the Structure and Dynamics of Population Numbers"), *Materialy Soveshch. po Sovrem. probl. Dinamiki Chislennosti,* pp. 50-51. Moscow.

KLEINENBERG, S. E., A. V. YABLOKOV, G. A. KLEVEZAL', V. M. BEL'KOVICH, and V. YA. ETIN, 1965. "Spravochnye pokazateli po kharakteristike nekotorykh lastonogikh u kitoobraznykh" ("Handbook of Indices for Characteristics of Some Pinnipeds and Cetaceans"), *Sbornik Morskie mlekopitayushchie,* pp. 252-257. Moscow : Izdatelstvo 'Nauka'.

KLEMMT, L., 1960. "Quantitative Untersuchungen an *Apodemus sylvaticus* (Linnaeus, 1758)," *Zool. Anz.,* 165 : 249-275.

KLEVEZAL', G. A. and S. E. KLEINENBERG, 1967. *Opredelenie vozrosta mlekopitayushchikh po sloistym strukturam zubov i kosti* (Determination of the Age of Mammals by the Layered Structure of Teeth and Bones). Moscow : Izdatelstvo 'Nauka'.

KLUMOV, S. K. and E. S. CHUZHAKINA, 1955. "Akiba : kol'chataya nerpa (*Phoca hispida ochotensis* Pallas, *Phoca hispida krascheninikovi*)" ["Akiba : the Ringed Seal (*Phoca hispida ochotensis* Pallas, *Phoca hispida krascheninikovi*)"], *Trudy Inst. Okeanol.,* 14 : 104-107.

KOGTEVA, E. Z., 1963. "Sezonnaya izmenchivost' i vozrostnie osobennosti stroeniya kozhi i volosyannogo pokrova krota, zaitsabelyaka ien otovidnoi sobaki" ("Seasonal Variability and Age Characteristics of Skin Structure and Hair of Moles, White Hares, and Raccoon Dogs"), in *Sb. Nauchn. Statei Zap. Otd. Vses. Nauch.-Issled. Inst. Zhiv. Syr. Push.,* 2 : 213-271.

KOL'TSOVA-SADOVNIKOVA, M. P., 1931. "Geneticheskii analiz psikhicheskikh sposobnostei krys" ("Genetical Analysis of Psychological Characters of Rats"), *Zh. Eksperim. Biol.*, 7 : 265-283.

Konstantinov, K. G., 1956. "Napravlennaya izmenchivost' ili estestven-
nyi otbor ?" ("Directed Variability or Natural Selection ?"), *Zool. Zh.*,
35 : 972-977.

Kopein, K. I., 1964. "Opyt izucheniya estestvennogo otbora v prirodnykh
usloviyakh" ("An Experiment to Study Natural Selection under Natural
Conditions"), Sb. *Voprosy Vnutrividovoi Izmenchivosti Nazemnykh Pozvonochnykh Zhivotnykh i Mikroevolyutsiya*, pp. 61-62, Sverdlovsk.

Kopein, K. I., 1967. "Morfo-fiziologicheskie osobennosti severnykh
populyatsii gornostaya" ("Morpho-physiological Characteristics of
Northern Populations of Weasels"), *Trudy Moskovskogo Obshch. Ispyt.
Prir.*, 25 : 40-48.

Korotova, L. G., 1962. "Izmeneniya nadpochechnikov i uglevodmogo
obmena u vodyanoi polevki (*Arvicola terrestris*) v vesene-letnyi period"
["Changes in Adrenals and Carbon Dioxide Metabolism in Water Voles
(*Arvicola terrestris*) in the Autumn-summer Period"], *Trudy Inst. Biol.
Uralsk Fil. Akad. Nauk SSSR*, 29 : 129-140.

Korzhuev, P. A., 1964. *Gemoglobin : Sravnitel'naya fiziologiya i biokhimiya*
(Hemoglobin : Comparative Physiology and Biochemistry). Moscow :
Izdatelstvo 'Nauka'.

Koshkina, T. V., 1964. "Mezhvidovaya konkurentsia lesnykh polevok
i regulyatsiya ikh chislennosti" ("Intra-species Competition of Field
Voles and the Regulation of Their Numbers"), *Materialy Soveshch.
Sovremennye Problemy Izucheniya Dinamiki Chislennosti Populyatsii Zhivotnikh.*
Inst. Morf. Zhivotnykh Akad. Nauk SSSR, pp. 51-53.

Kostelecka-Myrcha, A., and A. Myrcha, 1964. "The Rate of Passage
of Foodstuffs through the Alimentary Tracts of Certain *Microtidae*
under Laboratory Conditions," *Acta Theriol.*, 9 : 37-53.

Kostelecka-Myrcha, A., and A. Myrcha, 1964a. "Choice of Indicator
in the Investigation of the Passage of Foodstuffs through the Alimentary
Tract of Rodents," *Acta Theriol.*, 9 : 55-65.

Kostelecka-Myrcha, A., and A. Myrcha, 1964b. "Rate of Passage of
Foodstuffs through the Alimentary Tract of *Neomys Fodiens* (Pennant,
1770-1771) under Laboratory Conditions," *Acta Theriol.*, 9 : 371-373.

Kozakevich, V. P., 1967. "Soderzhanie askorbinovoi kisloty v nadpoche-
chnikakh i nekotorye ekologo-fisiologicheskie osobennosti malykh
Suslikov" ("Ascorbic Acid Content in the Adrenals and Some Ecologo-
physiological Characteristics of Small Susliks"), *Bull. Mosk. Obshch.
Ispyt. Prir. (Biol.)* 72: 107-113.

Kramer, A. W., Jr., 1964. "Body and Organ Weights and Linear Measurements of the Adult Mongolian Gerbil," *Anat. Rec.*, 150 : 343 348.

Krivosheev, V. G., and O. L. Rossolimo, 1964. "Vnutrividovaya
izmenchivost' sibirskogo lemminga" ("Intra-species Variability of the

Siberian Lemming"), Sb. *Vopr. Vnutrivid Izmenchivosti Nazemnykh Pozvonochnykh Zhivotnykh i Mikroevolyutsiya,* pp. 65-66. Sverdlovsk.

KRUSHINSKII, L. V., 1946. "Polovoe razlichie v povedenii sobak" ("Sex Differences in the Behavior of the Dog"), *Zh. Obshch. Biol.,* 7 : 131-146.

KRYZHANOVSKII, S. G., 1950. "Teoroticheskie osnovy embriologii" ("Theoretical Basis of Embryology"), *Usp. Sovrem. Biol.,* 30 : 382-413.

KRYL'TSOV'A, A. I., 1957. "Izmenenie vesa stepnykh pestrushek (*Lagurus lagurus*) v zavisimosti ot ikh pola i vozrosta" ("Changes in the Weights of *Lagurus lagurus* Due to Their Sex and Growth"), *Zool. Zh.,* 36 : 1239-1250.

KUBIK, J., 1951. "Analysis of the Pulawg Population of *Sorex araneus* and *Sorex minutus minutus* L.," *Ann. Univ. M. Curie-Slodowska,* Sect. C, 5 : 194-215.

KUBIK, J., 1953a. "Badania nad morfologia i biologia smuzki (*Sicista betulina* Pall.) z Bialowieskiego Parku Narodowego," *Ibid.,* 7 : 1-64.

KUBIK, J., 1953b. "*Micromys minutus* Pall. w Bialowieskim Parku Narodowym," *Ibid.,* 7 : 449-527.

KUBOTA, KINZIRO, 1967. "Comparative Anatomical and Neurohistological Observations on the Tongue of Elephants (*Elephas indicus* and *Loxodonta africana*)," *Anat. Res.,* 157 : 505-515.

KÜKENTHAL, W., 1890. "Über die Hand der Cetacean," *Anat. Anz.,* 5 : 44-52.

KÜKENTHAL, W., 1909. "Untersuchungen an Walen," *Z. Naturwiss,* 45 : 454-588.

KUNZE, A., 1912. "Über die Brustflosse der Wale," *Zool. Jahr., Abt. Anat. Ontog.,* 32 : 577-651.

KURTÉN, B., 1964. "The Evolution of the Polar Bear (*Ursus maritimus* Phipps)," *Acta Zool. Fennica,* 108 : 1-30.

KURTÉN, B., 1965. "On the Evolution of the European Wild Cat (*Felis silvestris* Schreber)," *Acta Zool. Fennica,* 111 : 1-29.

KURTÉN, B., 1965a. "The Carnivora of the Palestine Caves," *Acta Zool. Fennica,* 107 : 1-74.

KURTÉN, B., 1965b. "The Pleistocene Felidae of Florida," *Bull. Florida State Mus., Biol. Sci.,* 9 : 215-273.

KURTÉN, B., and R. RAUSCH, 1959. "Biometric Comparison between North American and European Mammals," *Acta Artica,* 11 : 1-44.

KUSHNER, KH. F., 1941. "O geneticheskoi i fiziologicheskoi prirode geterozisa i intsukht depressii" ("The Genetical and Physiological Nature of Heterosis and Inbreeding Depression"), *Zh. Obshch. Biol.,* 2 : 259-271.

KUZNETSOV, B. A., 1941a. "Geograficheskaya izmenchivost' sobolei i kunits fauny SSSR" ("Geographical Variability of the Sable and Marten of the USSR"), *Trudy Moskovskovo Zootekhn. Inst.,* 1 : 113-133.

Kuznetsov, B. A., 1941b. "Aberrativnaya izmenchivost' okraski pushnykh zverei" ("Abnormal Variability of Colors of Fur Animals"), *Trudy Mosk. Zootekhn. Inst.*, 1 : 134-140.

Kuznetsov, V. V., 1956. "Nekotorye zakonomernosti vidovoi morfologicheskoi i biologicheskoi raznokachestvennosti na primere morskikh bezpozvonochnykh" ("Some Regularities of Morphological and Biological Species Differentiation with Examples from Marine Invertebrates"), *Zool. Zh.*, 35 : 1118-1130.

Larina, N. I., 1958. "K voprosu o diagnostike blizkikh vidov lesnoi i zheltogorloi myshi" ("On the Question of the Diagnosis of the Close Species of Field and Yellow-necked Mice"), *Zool. Zh.*, 37 : 1719-1732.

Larina, N. I., 1962. "Individial'naya vozrostnaya u geograficheskaya izmenchivost' shukhovykh kostochek u gryzunov (Na primere blizkikh vidov rodov *Apodemus* i *Citellus*)" ["Individual Age and Geographical Variability of Ear Bones in Rodents (with Examples from Related Species of the Genera *Apodemus* and *Citellus*)"]. *Zool. Zh.*, 41 : 1536-1547.

Larina, N. I., 1964. "Vnutrividovaya izmenchivost' yader mezoteliya u lesnoi i zheltogorloi myshi" ("Intra-species Variability of Nuclei of Mesothelium in Field and Yellow-necked Mice"), Sb. *Vopr. Vnutrivid Izmenchivosti i Mikroevolyutsiya,* pp. 69-71. Sverdlovsk.

Larina, N. I., 1966. "Vnutrividovaya izmenchivost' razmerov yader mezoteliya bryzhzheiki u lesnoi (*Apodemus sylvaticus* L.) i zheltogorloi (*A. tauricus* Pall.) myshi" ["Intra-species Variability of Measurements of Nuclei of Mesothelium of Mesentery in Wild (*Apodemus sylvaticus* L.) and Yellow-necked (*A. tauricus* Pall.) Mice"], *Trudy Vsesoyuzn. Soveshchaniya Vnutrivid. Izmenchivost' Nazemnykh Zhivotnykh i Mikroevolyutsiya,* pp. 255-258. Sverdlovsk.

Latimer, H. B., 1936. "Weight and Linear Measurements of the Adult Cat," *Amer. J. Anat.*, 58 : 329-347.

Latimer, H. B., 1937. "Weights and Linear Dimensions of the Skull and Some of the Long Bones of the Skunk (*Mephitis mesomelas avia*)," *J. Morphol.*, 60 : 379-391.

Latimer, H. B., 1944. "The Prenatal Growth of the Cat : XIV. The Weight of the Skeleton in the Fetal and in the Adult Cat," *Growth*, 8 : 149-158.

Latimer, H. B., 1944a. "The Prenatal Growth of the Cat : XV," *Growth*, 8 : 205-219.

Latimer, H. B., 1951. "The Weight of the Eyeballs in the Guinea Pig," *Anat. Rec.*, 110 : 349-358.

Latimer, H. B., 1951a. "Weights, Percentage of Weights, and Correlations of the Endocrine Glands of the Adult Male Guinea Pig," *Anat. Rec.*, 111 : 299-315.

Latimer, H. B., 1961. "Weights of the Ventricular Walls of the Heart in the Adult Dog," *Univ. Kansas Sci. Bull.*, 62 : 3-12.

LATIMER, H. B., and R. B. RILEY, 1934. "Measurements of the Skull and of Some of the Long Bones of the Muskrat (*Ondatra zibethica cinnamomina*)," *J. Morphol.*, 56 : 203-212.

LATIMER, H. B., and P. B. SAWIN, 1955. "Morphological Studies of Rabbits : XII. Organ Size in Relation to Body Weights in Adults of Small-sized Race X," *Anat. Rec.*, 143 : 81-97.

LATIMER, H. B., and P. B. SAWIN, 1955a. "Morphological Studies of Rabbits : XIII. The Influence of the Dwarf Gene upon Organ Size and Variability in Race X," *Anat. Rec.*, 143 : 447-466.

LATIMER, H. B., and P. B. SAWIN, 1959. "Morphogenetic Studies of the Rabbit, XXII : Linear Measurements of Large Race III and Small Race X," *Anat. Rec.*, 134 : 69-86.

LAVROV, N. P., 1953. "Sistematicheskoe polozhenie ondatri akklimatizirovannoi v SSSR, i vliyaniya uslovii sredi na izmenenie priznakov" ("Taxonomic Position of *Ondatra* acclimatized in the USSR, and the Effect of Environmental Conditions on the Changes in Traits"), *Zool. Zh.*, 32 : 745-747.

LAVROVA, M. YA., and V. S. ZAZHIGIN, 1965. "O sistematike i biologii zemleroik Krasnodarskovo kraya s otsenkoi ikh roli v leptospiroznykh ochagakh" ("Taxonomy and Biology of Shrews of the Krasnodar Region, with an Evaluation of Their Role in the Leptospira Breeding Grounds"), *Zool. Zh.*, 44 : 101-105.

LAW, L. W., 1938. "Studies of Size Inheritance in Mice," *Genetics*, 23 : 399-422.

LAWRENCE, B., 1960. "Fossil *Tadarida* from New Mexico," *J. Mammal.*, 41 : 320-322.

LEBEDKINA, N. S., 1957. "Morfofunktsional'nyi analiz chelyustnogo apparata zaitsev" ("Morpho-functional Analysis of the Jaw Apparatus in Hares"), *Zool. Zh.*, 36 : 1539-1555.

LEE, A. K., 1963. "The Adaptation to Arid Environment in Wood Rats of the Genus *Neotoma*," *Univ. Calif. Publ. Zool.*, 64 : 57-96.

LEHMAN, E., 1961 (1962). "Langschwanzmäuse der Gattung *Apodemus* in Hohe Venn," *Decheniana*, 114 : 177-185.

LEVINE, C. J., W. MANN, H. C. HODGE, J. ARIEL, and O. DuPONT, 1941. "Distribution of Body Weight in the Organs and Tissues of the Rabbit," *Proc. Soc. Exper. Biol. and Med.*, 47 : 318-321.

LEWENZ, M. A., and M. A. WHITELEY, 1902. "A Second Study of the Variability and Correlation of the Hand," *Biometrics*, 1 : 345-350.

LEWONTIN, R. C., 1957. "The Adaptations of Populations to Varying Environments," *Cold Spring Harbor Sympos. Quart. Biol.*, 22 : 395-408.

LEWONTIN, R. C., 1961. "Evolution and the Theory of Games," *J. Theoret. Biol.*, 1 : 382-403.

LIDICKER, JR., 1960. "An Analysis of Intra-specific Variation in the Kangaroo Rat, *Dipodomys merriami," Univ. Calif. Publ. Zool.,* 67 : 125-218.

LITTLEPAGE, J. L., 1963. "Diving Behavior of a Weddell Seal Wintering in McMurdo Sound, Antarctica," *Ecology,* 44 : 775-777.

LIVANOV, N. A., 1960. "O zakonomernostyakh zhivoi prirody" ("On the Regularities of the Living World"), *Uch. Zp. Kazan' Univ.,* 120 : 3-32.

LONG, C. A., 1965. "The Mammals of Wyoming," *Univ. Kansas Publ. Mus. Nat. Hist.,* 14 : 266 pp.

LONG, C. A., 1968. "An Analysis of Patterns of Variation in Some Representative Mammalia : Pt. I. A Review of Estimates of Variability in Selected Measurements," *Trans. Kansas Acad. Sci.,* 71 : 201-227.

LONG, C. A., 1969. "An Analysis of Patterns of Variation in Some Representative Mammalia : Pt. II. Studies on the Nature and Correlation of Measures of Variation," in *Contr. in Mammalogy : A Volume Honoring Prof. E. R. Hall.* Univ. Kansas Mus. Nat. Hist. Publ., 51 : 289-302.

LONG, C. A., 1970. "An Analysis of Patterns of Variation in Some Representative Mammalia : Pt. III. Some Equations on the Nature of Frequency Distributions of Estimated Variabilities," *Acta Theriol.,* 15 : 517-528.

LONG, C. A., and C. J. JONES, 1966. "Variation and Frequency of Occurrence of the Baculum in a Population of Mexican Free-tailed Bats," *Southern Nat.,* 11 : 290-295.

LONG, C. A., C. J. JONES, and P. KAMENSKY, 1967. "Osteometric Variation and Function of the High-speed Wing of the Free-tailed Bat," *Amer. Midland Natur.,* 77 : 452-461.

LOWRANCE, E. O., and H. B. LATIMER, 1957. "Weights and Linear Measurements of 105 Human Skeletons from Asia," *Amer. J. Anat.,* 101 : 445-459.

LUKIN, E. E., 1936. "O parallelizme nasledstvennoi i nenasledstvennoi izmenchivosti" ("On the Parallelism of Hereditary and Non-Hereditary Variability"), *Uch. Zap. Khar'k. Univ.,* Vols. 6-7.

LUKIN, E. E., 1940. *Darvinizm i geograficheskie zakonomernosti v izmenenii organismov* (Darwinism and Geographical Regularities in the Variation of Organisms). Moscow, Leningrad : Izdatelstvo Akad. Nauk, SSSR.

LYNE, A. G., G. S. MOLYNEUX, R. MYKYTOWYCZ, and P. F. PARAKKAL, 1964. "The Development, Structure, and Function of the Submandibular Cutaneous (Chin) Glands in the Rabbit," *Austral. J. Zool.,* 12 : 340-348.

LYUBISHCHEV, A. A., 1923. "O kriterii izmenchivosti organizmov" ("On the Criteria of Variability of Organisms"), *Izv. Biol. Nauch.-Issled Inst Permsk. Gos. Univ.,* Vol. I, No. 7-8.

LYUBISHCHEV, A. A., 1959. "O primenenii biometrii v sistematike" ("On the Use of Biometry in Taxonomy"), *Vestnik Leningradskii Gos. Univ.*, 1959 (3) : 128-136.

LYUTIKOV, K. M., 1931. "Geneticheskii analiz v otnoshenii medlinno plodyashchikhsya, zhivotnykh" ("Genetical Analysis of Slowly Maturing Animals"), *Trudy* IV *Vses. S'ezda Zoologov. Anatomov i Gistologov.*, Kiev, pp. 142-145.

MALINOVSKII, A. A., 1939. "Rol' geneticheskikh i fenogeneticheskikh yavlenii v evolyutsii vida : Chast' I. Pleiotropia" ("The Role of Genetical and Phenogenetical Phenomena in the Evolution of Species : Part I. Pleiotropy"), *Izvest. Akad. Nauk SSSR, Seria Biol.*, 1939 : 575-614.

MALINOVSKII, A. A., 1948. "Elementarnye korrelyatsii i izmenchivost' chelovecheskogo organizma" ("Elementary Correlations and Variability of the Human Organism"), *Trudy Inst. Tsitol. Gistol. i Embriol.*, 2 : 136-198.

MALM, A. V., 1866. *Einiges von den Walfischen im Allgemeinen und Balanoptera carolinae im Besonderen.* Berlin.

MANNING, T. H., 1956. "The Northern Red-backed Mouse, *Clethrionomys rutilus* (Pallas) in Canada," *Nat. Mus. Canada Bull.*, 144 : 1-67. [Cited from Long (1968)].

MANVILLE, R. H., 1959. "Bregmatic Bones in North American Lynx," *Science*, 130 : 1245.

MANVILLE, R. H., 1961. "The Entepicondylar Foramen in *Ochrotomys*," *J. Mammal.*, 42 : 103-104.

MARKOV, G., 1957. *Nasekomyadnite bozainitsi v Bulgariya. Fauna Bulgariya*, Vol. 3, Sophia.

MATSUI, TAKAYASU, 1964. "The Medio-ventral Muscles of the Abdomen in *Macacus cyclopsis* (*M. rectus abdominis* and *M. pyramidalis*)," *Acta Med. Nagasakiensia*, 8 : 63-80.

MATTHEWS, L. H., 1938a. "The Sperm Whale, *Physeter catodon*," *Discov. Reports*, 42 : 93-168. [Cited from Long (1968)].

MATTHEWS, L. H., 1938b. "The Sei Whale, *Balaenoptera borealis*," *Discov. Repts.*, 42 : 183-290. [Cited from Long (1968)].

MATTHEY, R., 1949. *Les Chromosomes des Vertébrés.* Lausanne : F. Rouge.

MATVEEV, B. S., 1936. "Sovremennye zadachi evolyutsionnoi morfologii" ("Modern Problems of Evolutionary Morphology"), *Izv. Akad. Nauk SSSR, Seriya Biol.*, 1936 : 863-893.

MATVEEV, B. S., 1954. "Rol' morfologii v razreshennii ocherednykh problem biologii" ("The Role of Morphology in the Solution of Major Problems in Biology"), *Zool. Zh.*, 33 : 743.

MAYR, E., 1942. *Systematics and the Origin of Species.* New York : Columbia Univ. Press.

MAYR, E., 1947. *Sistematika i proiskhozhdenie vidov* (Systematics and the Origin of Species). Moscow : Izdatelstvo Inostrannoi Literatury.

MAYR, E., 1962. *Animal Species and Evolution.* Cambridge : Harvard University Press.

MAYR, E., E. LINSLEY and R. USINGER, 1956. *Metody i printsipy zoologicheskoi sistematiki* (Methods and Principles of Zoological Taxonomy). Moscow : Izdatelstvo Inostrannoi Literatury.

McDONELL, W. R., 1907. "A Second Study of the English Skull, with Special Reference to Moorfields Crania," *Biometrika,* 5 : 86-104. [Cited from Long (1968)].

McKEEVER, ST., 1963. "Seasonal Changes in Body Weight, Reproductive Organs, Pituitary, Adrenal Glands, Thyroid Gland and Spleen of the Belding Ground Squirrel (*Citellus beldingi*)", *Amer. J. Anat.,* 113 : 153-173.

McKEEVER, ST., 1964. "Variation in Weight of the Adrenal, Pituitary and Thyroid Glands of the White-footed Mouse (*Peromyscus maniculatus*)," *Amer. J. Anat.,* 114 : 1-16.

McKEEVER, ST., and T. P. QUENTIN, 1963. "Observations on the Adrenal Glands of the Mongoose," *Anat. Rec.,* 147: 163-169.

McLAREN, J. A., 1960. "On the Origin of the Caspian and Baikal Seals, the Paleoclimatological Implication," *Amer. J. Sci.,* 258 : 47-65.

McMEEKAN, C. P., 1940. "Growth and Development in the Pig with Special Reference to Carcass Quality Characters," *J. Agric. Sci.,* 30 : 276-311.

MEIER, M. N., 1957. "O vozrostnoi izmenchivosti malogo suslika (*Citellus pigmaeus* Pall.)" ["On the Growth and Variability of the Small Suslik (*Citellus pigmaeus* Pall.)"], *Zool. Zh.,* 36 : 1392-1402.

MEZHZHERIN, V. A., 1964a. "Yavlenie denelya i ego vozmozhnoe ob'yasnenie" ("The Denel Phenomenon and Its Possible Explanation"), *Acta Theriol.,* 8 : 95-114.

MEZHZHERIN, V. A., 1964b. "Osobennosti sezonnoi i geograficheskoi izmenchivosti zemleroek-burozubok i ikh znachenie v evolyutsii dannoi gruppy" ("Characteristics of Seasonal and Geographical Variability of Shrews and Their Significance in the Evolution of this Group"), Sb. *Voprosy Vnutrividovoi Izmenchivosti Mikroevolyutsiya,* pp. 76-77. Sverdlovsk.

MEZHZHERIN, V. A., 1965. "O smene adaptatsii v protsesse evolyutsii (na primere roda *Sorex, Insectivora, Mammalia*)" ["On Changes in Adaptation in the Process of Evolution (with an Example from the Genus *Sorex, Insectivora, Mammalia*)"], *Materialy Zool. Soveshch. po Probleme Biologicheskie Osnovy Rekonstruktsii-Fauny Yuzhnoi Zoni Evropecheskoi Chasti SSSR,* pp. 76-78. Kishimev.

MICHURIN, L. N., 1965. "O nekotorykh morfologicheskikh osbennostyakh dikikh sovernykh olenei poluostrova Taimyr" ("On Certain Morphological Characters of Northern Wild Deer of the Taimyr Island"), *Zool. Zh.,* 44 : 1396-1404.

MOMENT, G. B., 1962. "Reflexive Selection : A Possible Answer to an Old Puzzle," *Science,* 136 : 263-272.

MUKHAMEDGALIEV, F. M., 1953. "O biodinamike legkikh" ("On the Bio-dynamics of Lungs"), *Trudy Alma-Atinskogo Zoovetinstituta,* 7 : 159-169.

MURRAY, K. F., 1965. "Population Changes during the 1957-1958 Vole (*Microtus*) Outbreak in California," *Ecology,* 46 : 163-171.

NAEVDAL, GUNNAR, 1966. "Protein Polymorphism Used for Identification of Harp Seal Populations," *Bergen Univ. Aarbok, Mat. Naturvit. Ser.*

NAKAI, J., and T. SHIDA, 1948. "Sinus Hairs of the Sei Whale (*Balaenopteris borealis*)," *Sci. Repts. Whales Res. Inst.,* Tokyo, 1 : 41-49.

NAUMOV, N. P., 1941. "Lastonogie okhotskogo morya" (Pinnipeds of the Okhotsk Sea"), *Uch. zap. Mosk. Gos. Ped. Inst.,* 24 : 19-72.

NAUMOV, N. P., 1945. "Geograficheskaya izmenchivost', dinamika chislennosti i evolyutsii zhivotnykh" ("Geographical Variability, Dynamics of Number and Evolution of Animals"); *Zh. Obshch. Biol.,* 6 : 37-52.

NAUMOV, N. P., 1958. "Vzaimodeistvie so sredoi edinichnykh organizmov i populyatsii zhivotnykh" ("Interaction of Individual Organisms and Populations with the Environment"), *Filosof. Vopr. Estestv.,* 1 : 289-308.

NAUMOV, N. P., 1963. "Biologicheskie makrosistemy" ("Biological Macro-systems"), *Priroda,* 1963 (5) : 22-29.

NAUMOV, N. P. and G. V. NIKOL'SKII, 1962. "O nekotorykh obshchikh zakonomernostyakh dinamiki populyatsii zhivotnykh" ("Some General Patterns of Population Dynamics of Animals"), *Zool. Zh.,* 41 : 1132-1141.

NAZARENKO, YU. I., and A. V. YABLOKOV, 1962. "Otsenka metoda ucheta chislennosti belomorskogo lysuna i soobrazheniya o sostoyanii ego zapasov" ("Evaluation of a Method of Calculation of the Numbers of the White Sea Lisun and a Consideration of the State of the Population"), *Zool. Zh.,* 41 : 1864-1871.

NEHRING, A., 1884. "Fossile Pferde aus Deutschen Diluvial-Ablagerungen . . . ," *Landwirtshaft Jahrb.,* 13 : 81-160. [Cited from Long (1968)].

NEMOTO, T., 1959. "Food of Baleen Whales with Reference to Whale Movements," *Sci. Repts. Whales Res. Inst.,* Tokyo, 14 : 149-205.

NEWMAN, H. H., 1913. "The Modes of Inheritance of Aggregates of Meristic (Integral) Variates in the Polyembryonic Offspring of the Nine-banded Armadillo," *J. Exper. Zool.,* 15 : 145-192.

NEWSON, J., and D. CHITTY, 1962. "Hemoglobin Levels, Growth and Survival in Two *Microtus* Populations," *Ecology,* 53: 733-738.

NIKOL'SKII, G. V., 1955. "Ob izmenchivosti organizmov" ("On the Vari-ability of Organisms"), *Zool. Zh.,* 34 : 723-733.

NIKOL'SKII, G. V., 1961. "O prichinakh fluktatsii chislennosti ryb" ("On the Reasons of Fluctuations of Numbers of Fish"), *Vopr. Ikhtiol.,* Vol. 1, 4(21): 659-665.

Nikol'skii, G. V., 1963a. *Vid i vidoobrazovanie* (Species and Speciation). Moscow, 'Znanie'.

Nikol'skii, G. V., 1963b. "O biologicheskikh osnovakh matematicheskogo modelirovaniya dinamiki populyatsii ryb" ("On the Biological Basis of a Mathematical Model for the Dynamics of a Fish Population"), *Vopr. Ikhtiol.*, 3 : 591-609.

Nikol'skii, G. V., and V. A. Pikuleva, 1958. "O prisposobitel'nom znachenii amptitudy izmenchivosti vidovykh priznakov i svoistv organizma" ("On the Adaptive Significance of the Amount of Variability of Traits of Species and the Nature of an Organism"), *Zool. Zh.*, 37 : 972-988.

Nikoro, Z. S., 1964. "Izmenenie stroeniya populyatsii nad deistviem otbora v sluchae sverkhdominirovaniya" ("Change in Population Structure under the Influence of Selection in Case of Overdominance"), *Bull. Mosk. Obshch. Ispyt. Prir. (Biol.)*, 19 : 5-21.

Nikulin, P. G., 1937. "Nablyudeniya nad lastonogimi Okhotskogo i Yaponskogo morei" ("Observation on Pinnipeds of the Okhotsk and Japan Seas"), *Izv. Tikh. Nauchno-Issled. Inst. Ryb. Khoz. i Okeanogr.* (Vladivostok), 10 : 49-59.

Nishiwaki, M., Toshio Kasuya, T. Kamia, T. Tobayama, and M. Nakajima, 1965. *Sci. Rept. Whales Res. Inst.*, Tokyo, 19 : 65-90.

Nissen, H. W., and A. H. Riesen, 1964. "The Eruption of the Permanent Dentition of the Chimpanzee," *Amer. J. Phys. Anthropol.*, 22 : 285-294.

Nord, H. J., 1963. "Quantitative Untersuchungen am *Mus musculus domesticus* Rutty, 1772," *Zool. Anz.*, 170 : 311-335.

Nuzhdin, N. I., 1956. "Vozglyadi Darvina i Michurina na rol' sredi v izmenchivosti organizmov" ("The Views of Darwin and Michurin on the Role of Environment in the Variability of Organisms"), *Izv. Akad. Nauk SSSR, Ser. Biol.*, 1956 (2) : 18-28.

Odum, E., 1959. *Fundamentals of Ecology.* Philadelphia : Saunders.

Oetteking, B., 1923. "On the Morphological Significance of Certain Cranio-vertebral Variations," *Anat. Rec.*, 25 : 339-353.

Ogawa, T., and T. Kamia, 1957. "A Case of the Cachalot with Protruded Rudimentary Hind Limbs," *Sci. Repts. Whales Res. Inst.*, Tokyo, 12: 197-208.

Ognev, S. I., 1931. *Zveri Vostochnoi Evropy i Severnoi Azii* (Mammals of Eastern Europe and Northern Asia). Vol. 2, *Khishchnye* (Carnivores). Moscow : Glavnauka-Gosudarstvennoe Izdatelstvo. (Translated 1962, Jerusalem: Israel Program for Scientific Translations).

Ognev, S. I., 1935. *Zveri SSSR i prilezhashchikh stran : III. Khishchnye i lustunugie* (Mammals of the USSR and Adjacent Countries: III. Carnivores and Seals). Moscow : Izdatelstvo Akad. Nauk SSSR.

Ognev, S. I., 1942. "Problemy sistematiki : I. Znachenie Morfologii dlya sistematicheskikh issledovanii" ("Problems of Taxonomy : I. Significance of Morphology for Taxonomic Research"), *Zool. Zh.*, 21 : 281-283.

OLENOV, YU. M., 1941. "O vliyanii predshestvuyushie istorii vida na ego dalneishee razvitie" ("On the Influence of the Present History of the Species on Its Future Development"), *Dokl. Akad. Nauk SSSR*, 31 : 157-160.

OLENOV, YU. M., 1961. "Nekotorye problemy evolyutsionnoi genetiki i Darvinizma" ("Some Problems of Evolutionary Genetics and Darwinism"), Moscow and Leningrad: Izdatelstvo Akad. Nauk SSSR.

OLENOV, YU. M., and I. S. KHRMATS, 1939. "Transformatsiya genotipa v prirodnykh popyulyatsiyakh *D. melanogaster*" ("Transformation of the Genotype in Natural Populations of *D. melanogaster*"), *Dokl. Akad. Nauk SSSR*, 24 : 972-975.

OMURA, H., 1964. "A Systematic Study of the Hyoid Bones in the Baleen Whale," *Sci. Repts. Whales Res. Inst.*, Tokyo, 18 : 149-170.

ORLOV, V. N., 1961. "Vozrostnaya izmenchivost' cherepa kulana (*Equus hemionus* Pall.)" ["Growth Variability of the Skull of the Kulan (*Equus hemionus* Pall.)"], *Zool. Zh.*, 40 : 592-601.

OSBORN, D. J., 1964. "Notes on the Moles of Turkey," *J. Mammal.*, 45 : 127-129.

OSBORN, H. F., 1915. "Origin of Single Characters as Observed in Fossil and Living Animals and Plants," *Amer. Natur.*, 49 : 193-240.

OVCHINIKOVA, N. A., 1962. "Izmenenie otnositel'nogo vesa nadpochechnikov u mlekopitayushchikh v eksperimental'nykh usloviyakh" ("Change in the Relative Weights of Adrenals of Mammals under Experimental Conditions"), *Dokl. II Nauchnoi Konf. Molodykh Spetsialistov-biologov*, pp. 79-85. Sverdlovsk.

OVCHINIKOVA, N. A., 1964. "Biologicheskie osobennosti nominal'nogo i severnogo podvidov polevki ekonomiki i ikh gibridov" ("Biological Characteristics of the Nominal and Northern Subspecies of Field Voles and Their Hybrids"), Sb. *Vopr. Vnutrividovoi Izmenchivosti i Mikroevolutsiya*, pp. 89-90. Sverdlovsk.

OVCHINIKOVA, N. A., 1966 "O nekotorykh morfologicheskikh izmeneniyakh gryzunov v zrelom vozroste" ("On Some Morphological Changes in Adult Rodents"), *Trudy Vsesoyuzn. Soveshchnii Vnutrivid Izmenchivost Nazemnykh Pozvonochnykh Zhivotnykh i Mikroevolyutsiya*, pp. 199-201. Sverdlovsk.

PAAVER, K. L., 1964. "O vekovoi izmenchivosti subfossilnykh popyulyatsii mlekopitayushchikh v pribaltike" ("On the Temporal Variability of Subfossil Mammal Populations in the Baltic Region"), *Bull. Mosk. Obshch. Ispyt. Prir. (Biol.)*, 19 : 83-95.

PAAVER, K. L., 1965. *Formirovanie teriofauny i izmenchivost' mlekopitayush-chikh pribaltiki v Golotsene* (The Formation of the Mammal Fauna and Mammalian Variability in the East Baltic Region in the Holocene). Tartu : Akad. Nauk Estonskoi SSR. 497 pp.

PACKARD, R. L., 1960. "Speciation and Evolution of the Pigmy Mice, Genus *Baiomys*," *Univ. Kansas Publ. Mus. Nat. Hist.*, 9 : 579-670.

PACKARD, R. L., and H. GARNER, 1964. "Arboreal Nests on the Golden Mouse in Eastern Texas," *J. Mammal.*, 45 : 369-374.

PAULUS, M., 1964. "Étude ostéographique et ostéométrique sur deux *Grampus griseus* G. Cuvier 1812, echoues au brusc (var.) en 1887 et 1895," *Bull. Mus. Histoire Nat. Marseille*, 24 : 81-122.

PAVLININ, V. N., 1962. "O morphologicheskoi opredelennosti popyulyatsii khishchnykh mlekopitayushchikh" ("On the Morphological Identifica-tion of Populations of Carnivorous Mammals"), *Trudy Isnt. Biol. Uralsk Fil. Akad. Nauk SSSR*, 29 : 93-119.

PAVLININ, V. N., 1963. *Tobol'skii sobol'* (The Sable of Tobol). Ibid., Vol. 34.

PAVLININ, V. N., 1964. "Vnutrividovaya izmenchivost' zhivotnykh i okhotniche khozyaistvo" ("Intra-population Variability of Animals and the Hunting Industry"), Sb. *Vopr. Vnutrividovoi Izmenchivosti . . . i Mikroevolyutsiya*, pp. 102-105. Sverdlovsk.

PAVLININ, V. N., 1965. "Ob areale i morfologii lesnykh kunits Tyumenskoi oblasti" ("On the Habitat and Morphology of Wild Martens of the Tyumensk Region"), *Trudy Inst. Biol., Uralsk Fil. Akad. Nauk SSSR*, 38 : 41-52.

PAWLIK, M., 1967. "Über die Variabilität der präbasialen Kyphose bei der Gattung *Cercopithecus*," *Folia Primatol.*, 5 : 201-212.

PEARL, R., 1939. *The Natural History of Populations.* London : Oxford Univ. Press.

PEARSON, K., and A. G. DAVIN, 1924. "On the Biometric Constants of the Human Skull," *Biometrika*, 16 : 328-363. [Cited from Long (1968)].

PEARSON, O. P., 1958. "A Taxonomic Revision of the Rodent Genus *Phyllotis*," *Univ. California Publ. Zool.*, 56 : 391-496.

PECK, E. D., and P. B. SAWIN, 1950. "Morphogenetic Studies of the Rabbit : VIII. Genetic Variations in the Sternum as Determined by the Interaction of General and of Regionally Specific Growth Factors," *J. Exper. Zool.*, 114 : 335-357.

PELT, F. L. VON, and P. J. H. BREE, 1962. "Notizen über die Waldmaus, *Apodemus sylvaticus* (Linnaeus, 1758) von der niederlandischen Insel Terschelling," *Z. Säugetierkunde*, 27 : 222-228.

PESHEV, T., and G. GROROMY, 1961. "Studien in the Taxonomy of Some Populations of *Apodemus sylvaticus* (Linnaeus, 1758) in Bulgaria," *Acta Theriol.*, 5 : 185-202.

PETROV, B. M., 1961. "K sistematike i vozrostnoi izmenchivosti surka Menzbira (*Marmota menzbieri* Kasch)" ["On the Taxonomy and Growth Variability of Marmot (*Marmota menzbieri* Kasch)"], *Zool. Zh.*, 40 : 93-105.

PHILLIPS, J. C., 1920. "Skull Measurements in the Northern Virginia Deer," *J. Mamm.*, I : 130-133.

PIKHAREV, G. A., 1941. "Tyuleni Yugo zapadnoi chasti Okhotskogo morya" ("Seals of Southwest Part of the Okhotsk Sea"), *Izv. Tikh Nauchno-Issled. Inst. Ryb. Khoz. i Okeanogr.* (Vladivostok), 20 : 68-76.

PLOCHINSKII, N. A., 1960. *Biometriya* (Biometrics). Novosibirsk : Izdatel'-stvo Sibirsk. Otdel. Akd. Nauk SSSR.

POKROVSKII, A. V., 1962. "Individual'naya izmenchivost' skorosti polovogo sozrevaniya samok stepnoi pestrushki (*Lagurus lagurus*)" ("Individual Variability in the Rate of Sexual Maturity in Female *Lagurus lagurus*"), *Trudy Inst. Biol. Uralsk Fil. Akad. Nauk SSSR*, 29 : 121-123.

POKROVSKII, A. V., V. S. SMIRNOV and S. S. SCHWARTZ, 1962. "Kolorimetri-cheskoe izuchenie izmenchivosti okraski gryzunov v eksperimental'nykh usloviyakh v svyazi s problemoi gibridnykh popyulyatssii" ("Colorimetric Study of Variability of Coloration of Rodents under Experimental Conditions in Connection with the Problem of Hybrid Populations"), Ibid., 29 : 15-28.

POLYAKOV, G. D., 1961. "Prisposobitel'noe znachenie izmenchivosti priznakov i svoistv popyulyatsii ryb" ("The Adaptive Significance of Traits and the Nature of Fish Populations"), *Trudy Soveshch. Ikhtiol Kommissii*, 13 : 158-172.

POLYAKOV, G. D., 1962. "Prisposobitel'naya vzaimosvyaz' izmenchivosti popyulyatsii ryb s usloviyami pitaniya" ("Adaptive Relations of Vari-ability of Fish Populations with Feeding Conditions"), *Trudy Inst. Morfol. Zhivotnykh im. A. N. Severtsova,* 42 : 5-63.

PONOMAREV, A. L., 1944. "Reaktsiya nekotorikh khishchnykh (*Mustelidae*) na gradient temperatury" ["Reaction of Some Carnivora (*Mustelidae*) to a Temperature Gradient"], *Zool. Zh.*, 23 : 51-55.

POPOV, L. A., 1959. "Osobennosti polovogo dimorfizma tyulenya-khokhlacha" ("Characteristics of the Sexual Dimorphism of the Hooded Seal"), *Trudy l Konf. Mosk. Morf. Labor.*, Moscow.

POPOV, L. A., 1961. "Materialy k obshchei morfologii khokhlacha Grenlandskogo morya" ("Materials on the General Morphology of the Greenland Seal"), *Trudy Soveshch. Ikhtiol. Kommissii*, 12 : 180-191.

POPOV, V. A., 1959. "Materialy po ikologii norki (*Mustela vison* Br.) i rezultaty akklimatizatsii ee v Tatarskoi SSSR" ["Data on the Ecology of Minks (*Mustela vison* Br.) and the Results of Its Acclimatization in the Tatar USSR"], *Trudy Kaz. Fil. Akad. Nauk SSSR*, 2 : 3-140.

Popov, V. A., 1960. *Mlekopitayushchie Volzhsko-Kamskogo kraya : Nasekomy-adnie, rukokril'e, gryzuny* (Mammals of the Volga-Kamsk Region : Insectivores, Pinnipeds, Rodents). Kazan' : Izdatelstvo Akad. Nauk SSSR.

Popova, E. T., 1941. "Rezultaty metiztisii kuchugurovskikh ovets linkol'nami i puti dalneishego napravleniya selektsionnoplemennoi raboty s metisami" ("Results of Crossing Kuchugurov Ewes with Lincolns and the Direction of Future Trends in Selection and Breeding Work with Crossbreeds"), *Trudy Mosk. Zootekhn. Inst.*, 1 : 186-210.

Potelov, V. A., 1963. "K kharakteristike shonnokh skoplenii khokhlacha v Grinlandskom morye" ("On the Density of the Hooded Seal in the Greenland Sea"), *Sb. Rabot Sev. Otd. Polyarnogo Inst. Ryb. Khoz. i Okeanogr.* (Arkhangelsk), 1962, pp. 53-63.

Potelov, V. A., and A. V. Yablokov, 1966. "Novoe v morfologicheskoi kharakteristike khokhlacha (*Cystophora cristata* Erxl.)" ["New Data on the Morphological Characters of the Hooded Seal (*Cystophora cristata* Erxl.)"], *Zool. Zh.*, 45 : 1222-1228.

Prakash, I., 1964. "Cyto-morphology of Adrenal Gland of Indian Desert Gerbil," *J. Anat. Soc. India,* 13 : 76-79.

Prakash, I., and C. G. Kumbkarni, 1962. "Eco-toxicology and Control of Indian Desert Gerbil, *Meriones hurriane* (Jerdon) : I. Feeding Behavior, Energy Requirements, and Selection of Bait," *J. Bombay Natur. History Soc.*, 59 : 800-806.

Prout, T., 1962. "The Effect of Stabilizing Selection on the Time of Development in *Drosophila melanogaster*," *Genet. Res.*, 3.

Prout, T., 1964. "Observations on Structural Reduction in Evolution," *Amer. Naturalist*, 48 : 239-249.

Pšenička, P., and J. Jurin, 1964. "Pozorovani 100 pripadu utvareni circulus arteriosus (Willisi) u opice *Macaca mulatta*," *Ceskosl. Morfol.*, 12 : 321-326.

Puček, Zd., 1956. "Untersuchungen über die Veränderlichkeit des Schädels im Lebenszyklus von *Sorex araneus araneus* L.," *Ann. Univ. M. Curie-Slodowska*, Sect. C, 9 : 163-208.

Puček, Zd., 1962. "The Occurrence of Wormian Bones (*Ossicula vormiana*) in Some Mammals," *Acta Theriol.*, 6 : 1-51.

Puček, Zd., 1963. "Seasonal Changes in the Braincase of Some Representatives of the Genus *Sorex* from the Palearctic," *J. Mammal.*, 44 : 523-536.

Puček, Zd., and G. Markov, 1964. "Seasonal Changes in the Skull of the Common Shrew from Bulgaria," *Acta Theriol.*, 9 : 363-366.

Purohit, K. G., 1965. "Effect of Sexual Activity on the Adrenal Gland in the Northern Palm Squirrel, *Funambulus pennanti* Wroughton," *Experientia*, 19 : 1-4.

Raicu, P., 1960. "Die gerichtete Variabilität und die Anpassungsfätigkeit der Organismen," *Arb. Fragen Evolution,* Jena, 1959, pp. 113-120.

RASMUSSEN, B., 1957.   "Exploitation and Protection of the East Greenland Seal Herds," *Norsk. Hvalfangs-tidende,* 46 : 45-59.

RASMUSSEN, B., 1960.   "Om klappmyssbestanden i det nordlige Atlanterhav," *Fisk. og Hevet.,* 1: 1-23.

RASMUSSEN, B., and T. ORITSLAND, 1964.   "Norwegian Tagging of Harp Seals and Hooded Seals in North Atlantic Waters," *Fiskdirector Skr.,* 13 : 43-55.

RAUSCH, R. L., 1963.   "Geographic Variation in Size in North American Brown Bears, *Ursus arctos* L., as Indicated by Condylobasal Length," *Canad. J. Zool.,* 41 : 33-45.

RAZORENOVA, A. P., 1952.   "Vozrostnaya izmenchivost' u krsnokhvostnoi polevki *(Clethrionomys)*" ["Age Variability of the Red-tailed Vole *(Clethrionomys)*"], *Bull. Mosk. Obshch. Ispyt. Prir. (Biol.),* 57: 23-28.

READING, A. J., 1966.   "Effect of Maternal Environment on the Behavior of Inbred Mice," *J. Compar. and Physiol. Psychol.* , 62 : 437-440.

REED, S. C., 1936.   "Harelip in the House Mouse : I. Effect of the External and Internal Environments," *Genetics,* 21 : 339-360.

REINIŠ, ST., 1964.   "Kvantitativni analisa morfologichych zmen v mozkove kure v prubehu ontogeneza krysy," *Ceskosl. Morfol.,* 12 : 283-291.

REMANE, A., 1960.   "Die Beziehungen zwischen Phylogenie und Ontogenie," *Zool. Anz.,* 164 : 306-337.

REMANE, A., 1961.   "Gedanken zum Problem : Homologie und Analogie, Pre-adaptation und Parallelität," *Zool. Anz.,* 166 : 447-465.

ROBERTSON, F. W., and E. C. R. REEVE, 1952.   "Heterozygosity, Environmental Variation, and Heterosis," *Nature,* 170 : 286.

ROBSON, G. S., and O. W. RICHARDS, 1936.   *The Variation of Animals in Nature.*   New York : Longman and Green.

ROGINSKII, YA. YA., 1954.   "Velichina izmenchivosti izmeritel'nykh priznakov cherepa i nekotorie zakonomernosti ikh korrelyatsii u cheloveka" ("Magnitude of Variability of Measurable Traits of the Skull and Some Regularities of Their Correlations in Man"), *Uch. zap. Moskovskii Gos. Univ.,* No. 16.

ROGINSKII, YA. YA., 1959.   "O Nekotorykh rezul'tatakh primeneniya kolichestvennogo metoda k izucheniyu morfologicheskoi izmenchivosti" ("Some Results of Using the Quantitative Method to Study Morphological Variability"), *Arkhiv Anat. Gistol. Embriol.,* 36 : 83-89.

ROGINSKII, YA. YA., 1960.   "Nekotorye zakony izmenchivosti i korelyatsii izmeritel'nykh priznakov u cheloveka i grugikh mlekopitayushchikh" ("Some Rules of Variability and Correlation of Measurable Traits of Man and Other Mammals"), *Antropologicheskie Dokl. na VI Mezhdunor. Kongr. Antropol. i Etnogr. Nauk,* pp. 23-28.   Izdatelstvo Moskovskii Gos. Univ.

ROKITSKII, P. F., 1961. *Osnovy variatsionnoi statistiki dlya biologov* (Fundamentals of Variation Statistics for Biologists). Minsk : Izdatelstvo Belorus. Gos. Univ.

ROKITSKII, P. F., 1964. "K voprosu o matematicheskikh metodakh analiza vnutrividovykh razlichii" ("On the Question of Mathematical Methods of Analysis of Intra-species Variation"), *Materialy Soveshch. Sovrem. Probl. Izucheniya Dinamiki Chislennosti*, pp. 86-87.

ROMASHOV, D. D., 1931. "Ob usloviyakh 'ravnovesiya' v popyulyatsii" ("On the Conditions of 'Balance' in a Population"), *Zh. Eksperim. Biol.*, 8 : 442-454.

ROMASHOV, D. D., and E. D. IL'INA, 1943. "Ob aberrativnoi izmenchivosti v popyulyatsiyakh pyshnykh zverei" ("On Aberrant Variability in Populations of Fur Animals"), *Zh. Obshch. Biol.*, 4 : 286-312.

ROMER, A. S., 1960. Phylogeny and Morphology. Lecture, XIII Annual Meeting Soc. Study of Evolution.

ROOS, T. B., and R. M. SHACKELFORD, 1955. "Some Observations on the Gross Anatomy of the Genital System and Two Endocrine Glands and Body Weights in the Chinchilla," *Anat. Rec.*, 123 : 301-311.

ROSSOLIMO, O. L., 1962. "O vnutrividovoi izmenchivosti krasnoi polevki (*Clethrionomys rutilus* Pall.)" ["On the Intra-species Variability of the Red Vole (*Clethrionomys rutilus* Pall.)"], *Zool. Zh.*, 41: 443-452.

RUSSELL, W. M. S., 1958. "Evolutionary Concepts in Behavioral Science," *General Systems Yearbook*, 3 : 18-28.

SAINT GIRONS, M. C., and P. J. H. VAN BREE, 1962. "Recherches sur la systématique de *Apodemus sylvaticus* (Linnaeus, 1758) en Afrique du Nord," *Mammalia*, 26: 478-488.

SARYCHEVA, T. G., 1948. "Opyt primenenia graficheskovo metoda v izuchenii izmenchivosti produktid" ("An Experiment on the Use of Graphical Methods in the Study of Variability of Productids"), *Izv. Akad. Nauk SSSR, Ser. Biol.*, 1948 (2): 205-212.

SAUER, M. E., and CH. T. RUBLE, 1946. "The Number of Nerve Cells in Mysenteric and Submucous Plexuses of the Small Intestine of the Cat," *Anat. Rec.*, 96 : 373-382.

SAWIN, P. B., 1937. "Preliminary Studies of Hereditary Variations in the Axial Skeleton on the Rabbit," *Anat. Rev.*, 69 : 407-428.

SAWIN, P. B., 1945. "Morphogenetic Studies of the Rabbit : I. Regional Specificity of Hereditary Factors Affecting Homeotic Variations in the Axial Skeleton," *J. Exper. Zool.*, 100 : 301-329.

SCHEFFER, V. B., 1958. *Seals, Sea Lions and Walruses.* Oxford: Oxford University Press.

SCHEFFER, V. B., 1962. "Pelage and Surface Topography of the Northern Fur Seal," *North Amer. Fauna*, 64 : 1-206.

SCHEFFER, V. B., 1964. "Hair Patterns in Seals (Pinnipedia)," *J. Morphol.*,

115 : 291-303.

SCHMALHAUSEN, I. I. (SHMAL'GAUZEN), 1935. "Opredelenie osnovnykh ponyatii i metodika issledovaniya rosta" ("Determination of Basic Concepts and Methods of Investigations of Growth"), Sb. *Rost zhivotnykh*, pp. 8-60. Moscow, Leningrad : Biomedgiz.

SCHMALHAUSEN, I. I. (SHMAL'GAUZEN), 1939. *Puti i zakonomernosti evolyutsionnogo protsessa* (Paths and Regularities of Evolutionary Processes). Moscow, Leningrad : Izdatelstvo Akad. Nauk SSSR.

SCHMALHAUSEN, I. I. (SHMAL'GAUZEN), 1940. "Izmenchivost' i smena adaptivnykh norm v protsesse evolyutsii" ("Variability and Changes of Adaptive Norms in the Process of Evolution"), *Zh. Obshch. Biol.*, 1 : 9-24.

SCHMALHAUSEN, I. I. (SHMAL'GAUZEN), 1943. "Temp evolyutsii i faktory ego opredelyayushchie" ("The Rate of Evolution and Factors Determining It"), *Zh. Obshch. Biol.*, 4 : 253-285.

SCHMALHAUSEN, I. I. (SHMAL'GAUZEN), 1946. *Faktory evolyutsii* (*Factors of Evolution*). Moscow, Leningrad : Izdatelstvo Akad. Nauk SSSR. (Translated 1949, Philadelphia : Blakiston).

SCHMALHAUSEN, I. I. (SHMAL'GAUZEN), 1947. *Osnovy sravnitel'noi anatomii* (Fundamentals of Comparative Anatomy). Moscow : Izdatelstvo 'Sov. Nauka'.

SCHMALHAUSEN, I. I. (SHMAL'GAUZEN), 1958. "Kontrol' i regulyatsiya v evolyutsii" ("Control and Regulation in Evolution"), *Bull. Mosk. Obshch. Ispyt. Prir.* (*Biol.*) 13 (5) : 93-121.

SCHMALHAUSEN, I. I. (SHMAL'GAUZEN), 1959. "Perspektivy primeneniya tochnykh metodov dlya izucheniya faktorov evolyutsii" ("Prospects for the Use of Exact Methods for the Study of Evolutional Factors"), *Vestnik Leningradskii Gos. Univ.*, 1959 (9) : 108-118.

SCHMALHAUSEN, I. I. (SHMAL'GAUZEN), 1965. "Evolyutsiya v svete kibernetiki" ("Evolution in the Light of Cybernetics"), *Problemy Kibernetiki*, 13 : 195-199.

SCHMIDLY, D. J., 1971. "Population Variation in *Dipodomys ordii* from Western Texas," *J. Mammal.*, 52 : 108-120.

SCHULTZ, A. H., 1917. "Variations in Man and Their Evolutionary Significance," *Amer. Naturalist*, 60 : 297-323.

SCHULTZ, A. H., 1926. "Studies on the Variability of Platyrrhine Monkeys," *J. Morphol.*, 7 : 286-304.

SCHULTZ, A. H., 1958. "Cranial and Dental Variability in Colobus Monkeys," *Proc. Zool. Soc. London*, 130 : 79-105.

SCHUMACHER, G. H., E. WOLFF, and E. JUTZI, 1965. "Quantitative Untersuchungen über das postnatale Organwachstum des Goldhamsters (*Mesocricetus auratus* Wrth)," *Morphol. Jb.* : I. Korpergewicht-Herz, 107 : 550-567. II. Lunge-Leber-Milz, 108 : 18-40. III. Thymus-Schilddrüse, 108: 41-66. IV. Besprechung der Ergebnisse, 108: 123-138.

SCHWARTZ, S. S. (SHWARTZ), 1959. "Nekotorye voprosy problemy vida u nazemnykh pozvonochnykh zhivotnykh" ("Some Questions on the Species Problem in Terrestrial Vertebrate Animals"), *Trudy Inst. Biol. Uralsk Fil. Akad. Nauk SSSR*, Vol. 11.

SCHWARTZ, S. S. (SHWARTZ), 1959. "Nekotorye zakonomernosti ekologicheskoi obuslovlennosti interernykh osobennostei nazemnykh pozvonochnykh zhivotnykh" ("Some Regularities of Ecological Relationships of Inner Characters of Terrestrial Vertebrate Animals"), Ibid., 14 : 113-177.

SCHWARTZ, S. S. (SHWARTZ), 1962. "Izuchenie korrelyatsii morfologicheskikh osobennostei gryzunov so skorostyu ikh rosta v svyazi s nekotorymi voprosami vnutrividovoi sistematiki" ("Study of the Correlation of Morphological Characters of Rodents with Their Rate of Growth in View of Some Questions of Intra-species Taxonomy"), Ibid., 29 : 5-14.

SCHWARTZ, S. S. (SHWARTZ), 1962a. "Morfologicheskie i ekologicheskie osobennosti zemlerosek na krainem severnom predele ikh rasprostraneniya" ("Morphological and Ecological Peculiarities of Shrews on the Extreme Northern Borders of Their Distribution"), Ibid., 29 : 45-51.

SCHWARTZ, S. S. (SHWARTZ), 1963. "Vnutrividovaya izmenchivost' mlekopitayushchikh i metody ee izucheniya" ("Intra-species Variability of Mammals and Methods of Its Study"), *Zool. Zh.*, 42 : 417-433.

SCHWARTZ, S. S. (SHWARTZ), 1964. "Ekspiremental'nye metody issledovaniya v teoreticheskoi sistematike" ("Experimental Methods of Investigation in Theoretical Taxonomy"), Sb. *Vopr. Vnutrividovoi Izmenchivosti*, pp. 146-152. Sverdlovsk.

SCHWARTZ, S. S. (SHWARTZ), 1965. "Uchenie o mikroevolyutsii i teoreticheskie voprosy sistematiki ptits" ("The Study of Micro-evolution and Theoretical Problems of the Taxonomy of Birds"), Sb. *Sovremennye Problemy Ornitologii*, pp. 65-86. Frunze, Izdatelstvo 'Ilim'.

SCHWARTZ, S. S. (SHWARTZ), K. I. KOPEIN and A. V. POKROVSKII, 1960. "Sravnitel'noe izuchenie nekotorykh biologicheskikh osobennostei polevok *Microtus gregalis gregalis* Pall., *M. g. major* Ogn. i ikh pomesei" ["Comparative Study of Some Biological Characteristics of Field Voles (*Microtus gregalis gregalis* Pall., *M. g. major* Ogn) and Their Crosses"], *Zool. Zh.*, 39 : 912-926.

SCHWARTZ, S. S. (SHWARTZ), A. V. POKROVSKI, V. G. ISTCHENKO, V. G. OLENJEV, N. A. OVTSCHINNICOVA, and O. A. PJASTOLEVA, 1964. "Biological Peculiarities of Seasonal Generations of Rodents, with Special Reference to the Problem of Senescence in Mammals," *Acta Theriol.*, 0 : 11-13.

SCORKOWSKI, ED., 1958. "Die dreiartige Variabilität im der Natur," *Arch. Tierzucht*, 1 : 283-293.

SEALANDER, J. A., 1961. "Hematological Values in Deer Mice in Relation to Botfly Infection," *J. Mammal.*, 44 : 57-60.

SEARLE, A. G., 1954. "Genetical Studies on the Skeleton of the Mouse : IX. Causes of Skeletal Variation within Pure Lines," *J. Genet.*, 52 : 68-102.

SEARLE, A. G., 1954a. "Genetical Studies on the Skeleton of the Mouse : XI. The Influence of Diet Variation within Pure Lines," *J. Genet.*, 52 : 413-424.

SEGAL', A. N., 1962. "Opyt perevoda i akklimatizatsii v Karelii tundrovykh olenei iz murmanskoi oblasti" ("Experiment in Rearing and Acclimatization of Deer in the Tundra of the Murmansk Region"), *Severnyi olen' v Karel'skoi ASSR,* pp. 58-80. Moscow : Izdatelstvo Akad. Nauk SSSR.

SEKHLYANU, V., 1960. "O Primenenii matematiki v biologii i meditsine" ("On the Use of Mathematics in Biology and Medicine"), *Vopr. filosofii,* 1960 (10) : 100-109.

SERAFINSKI, W., 1965. "The Sub-specific Differentiation of the Central European House Mouse (*Mus musculus* L.) in the Light of Their Ecology and Morphology," *Ecolog. Polska,* Ser. A, 13 : 304-335.

SERGEANT, D. E., 1963. "Harp Seals and the Sealing Industry," *Canad. Audubon,* 25 (2) : 29-35.

SEWERTZOFF, A. N., 1931 (1927). "Über die Beziehungen zwischen der Ontogenese und Phylogenese der Tiere," *Jen. Ztschr.,* 63 : 51-180.

SEVERTSOV, A. N., 1912 (1945). "Etyudi po teorii evolyutsii" ("Studies on the Theory of Evolution"), *Sobr. Soch.,* Vol. III, pp. 19-216. Moscow, Leningrad : Izdatelstvo Akad. Nauk SSSR.

SEVERTSOV, A. N., 1914. *Soveremennye zadachi evolyutsionnoi teorii* (Current Problems of Evolutionary Theory). Moscow : Izdatelstvo Akad. Nauk SSSR.

SEVERTSOV, A. N., 1939. *Morfologicheskie zakonomernosti evolyutsii* (Morphological Regularities of Evolution). Moscow, Leningrad : Izdatelstvo Akad. Nauk SSSR.

SHARMAN, G. B., H. J. FRITH, and J. H. CALABY, 1964. "Growth of the Pouch, the Young, Tooth Eruption, and Age Determination in the Red Kangaroo, *Megaleia rufa,*" *CSIRO Wildlife Res.,* 9 : 20-49.

SHAW, A. M., 1929. "Variations in the Skeletal Structure of the Pig," *Sci. Agric.,* 10 : 23-27.

SHNOLL', S. E., 1964 (Ed.). *Biologicheskie chasy.* Predislovie k russkomu izdaniyu (Biological Clocks. Introduction to the Russian Edition), pp. 5-10. Izdatelstvo 'Mir'.

SHPET, G. I., and V. K. IVANKO, 1940. "Dannye ob izmenchivosti geologicheski, drevnykh i molodykh form nasekomykh" ("Data on Variability of Geologically Old and Young Forms of Insects"), *Zh. Obshch. Biol.,* 1 (2).

SHUSTOV, A. P., and A. V. YABLOKOV, 1967. "Sravnitel'no-morfologi-cheskaya kharakteristika grenlandskogo i polosatogo tyulenei (materialy k popyulyatsionnomu analizu lastonogikh)" ["Comparative Morphological Characteristics of the Greenland and Striped Seals (Materials on the Population Analysis of Seals)"], *Trudy Polyar. Inst. Ryb. Khoz. i Okeanogr.*, 21 : 51-59.

SIDORKIN, V. I., and M. V. MIKHALEV, 1964. "Kolichestvennoe Sootno-shenie belkovykh fraktsii syvorotki krovi u dvukh vidov serykh polevok" ("Quantitative Correlation of Protein Fractions of Blood Plasma in Two Species of Gray Field Voles"), Sb. *Voprosy Vnutrividovoi Izmenchivosti i Mikroevolyutsiya,* pp. 119-120. Sverdlovsk.

SIGMUND, L., 1964. "Relative Wachstum und intraspezifische Allometrie der Grossmausohr (*Myotis myotis* Borkh.)," *Acta Univ. Carolinae Biol.*, 3 : 235-303.

SIKORSKA-PIVOVSKA, Z., 1965. "The Variability of Structure of the Lacrimal Bone in the Lacrimal Sac Fossa of Primates," *Zool. Polon.*, 15 : 147-158.

SIMPSON, G. G., 1944. *Tempo and Mode in Evolution.* New York : Columbia Univ. Press.

SIMPSON, G. G., 1948. *Tempy i formy evolyutsii* (Tempo and Mode in Evolution). Moscow : Izdatelstvo Inostrannoi Literatury.

SIMPSON, G. G., 1951. "The Role of the Individual in Evolution," *J. Wash. Acad. Sci.,* 31 : 1-20.

SIMPSON, G. G., 1953. *The Major Features of Evolution.* New York : Columbia Univ. Press.

SIMPSON, G. G., and A. ROE, 1939. *Quantitative Zoology.* New York : McGraw-Hill.

SINSKAYA, E. N., 1948. *Dinamika vida* (Dynamics of the Species). Moscow : Sel'khozgiz.

SKAREN, UOLENI, 1964. "Variation of Two Shrews, *Sorex unguiculatus* Dobson and *S. a. araneus,* L.," *Ann. Zool. Fennica,* 1 : 94-124.

SKOCZEŇ, ST., 1962. "Age Structure of Skulls of the Mole, *Talpa europaea* (Linnaeus, 1758) from the Food of the Buzzard (*Buteo buteo*)," *Acta Theriol.,* 6 : 1-9.

SKOPAKOFF, CHRISTO VON, 1965. "Über die Variabilität der Abzweigung der A. subclavia und ihrer Hauptaste," *Anat. Anz.,* 116 : 73-91.

SLENTSOV, M. M., 1939. "O rudimentakh zadnykh lastov u chornomors-kogo del'fina *D. delphis*" ["On the Rudimentation of the Posterior Flippers of the Black Sea Dolphin (*D. delphis*)"], *Zool. Zh.,* 18 : 361-366.

SLENTSOV, M. M., 1955. *Kitoobraznye dal'nevostochnykh morei* (Cetaceans of the Far East Seas). Vladivostok.

SLENTSOV, M. M., 1961. "Rezul'taty vzveshivaniya krupnykh i melkikh kitoobraznykh dobivaemykh na Dal'nem Vostoke" ("Weights of Large and Small Cetaceans Found in the Far East"), *Trudy Inst. Morfol. Zhivot. Akad. Nauk SSSR.*

SLIJPER, E. J., 1962. *Whales.* London : Hutchinson Publ.

SMIRNOV, N. A., 1927. "Diagnostical Remarks about Some Seals (*Phocidae*) of the Northern Hemisphere," *Troms Mus. Aarb.*, 48 : 1-23.

SMIRNOV, N. A., 1927. "Issledovanie nad belomorskim tyulenyem. Noveishie nablyudeniya nad belomorskim lysunom" (Studies on White Sea Seals : Recent Observations on White Sea Seals"), *Izv. Otd. Prikl. Ikhtiol.*, 6 : 5-27.

SMIRNOV, N. A., 1935. "Morskie zveri arkhticheskikh vorei" ("Sea Animals in the Arctic Seas"), *Zveri Arktiki*, Leningrad : Izdatelstvo 'Glavsevmorput'.

SMIRNOV, V. S., 1962. "K taksonomicheskoi kharakteristike pestsa Yamala i Grenlandii" ("On Taxonomic Characters of the Arctic Fox from Yamel and Greenland"), *Trudy Inst. Biol., Uralsk. Fil. Akad. Nauk USSR*, 29 : 71-80.

SOKAL, R. R., 1962. "Some Stages in the Development of the Concept of Natural Selection," *Univ. Kansas Sci. Bull.*, 42 (Suppl.) : 129-151.

SOKAL, R. R., and P. H. A. SNEATH, 1963. *Principles of Numerical Taxonomy.* San Francisco : Freeman.

SOKOLOV, E. A., 1941. "Emkost' pishchevaritel'nogo trakta i pokazateli perevarivaemosti u pushnykh zverei" ("Volume of the Digestive Tract and the Digestive Indices in Fur Animals"), *Trudy Mosk. Zootekhn. Inst.*, 1 : 72-83.

SOKOLOV, I. I., 1960. *Morfologiya porod domashnykh ovets* (Morphology of Domestic Sheep Breeds). Moscow, Leningrad : Izdatelstvo Akad. Nauk SSSR.

SOKOLOV, I. I., and V. L. RASHEK, 1961. "Razvitie zubov i cherepa kak pokazatel' vozrosta u saigi (*Saiga tatarica*)" ("The Development of Teeth and Skull as Growth Parameters in *Saiga tatarica*"), *Bull. Moskov. Obshch. Ispyt. Prir. (Biol.)*, 66 (6) : 77-98.

SPARKES, R. S., and D. T. ARAKAKI, 1967. "Intra-subspecific and Inter-subspecific Chromosomal Polymorphism in *Peromyscus maniculatus* (Deer Mouse), *Cytogenetics*, 5 : 411-418.

SPITZ, F., 1963. "Croissance en élévage de la longeur tête et corps chez le campagnol des champs (*Microtus arvalis* Pallas) de San-Michel-en-l' Herm (Vendée)," *Mammalia*, 27 : 111-118.

STEBBINS, G. L., 1950. *Variation and Evolution in Plants.* New York : Columbia Univ. Press.

STECHER, R. M., 1961. "Numerical Variation in the Vertebrae of the Prjevalesky Horse," *Mammalia*, 25 : 192-194.

STEIN, G. H. W., 1963. "Anomalien der Zahnzahl und ihre geographische Variabilität bei Insectivora, I. Maulwurf, *Talpa europaea* L.," *Mitt. Zool.*

Mus. Berlin, 39 : 223-244.

STOCKHAUS, K., 1965. "Metrische Untersuchungen an Schadëln von Wolfen und Hungen," *Zeit. Zool. Syst. Evolutionsforschung,* 3: 157-258. [Cited from Long (1968)].

STRAKA, F., 1963. "Za nyakoi osobennosti v morfologiyata na lalugera (*Citellus citellus*) v Bulgariya" ("On the Morphological Characteristics of Bulgarian *Citellus citellus*"), *Priroda,* 12 (4) : 100-101.

STRANDSKOV, H. H., 1942. "Skeletal Variations in Guinea Pigs and Their Inheritance," *J. Mammal.,* 23 : 65-75. [Cited from Long (1968)].

STRAUS, W. L., JR., 1962. "The Mylohyoid Groove in Primates," *Biblioth. Primatol.,* 1 : 197-216.

STROGANOV, S. U., 1948. "Sistematika krotovykh (*Talpidae*)" ("Taxonomy of *Talpidae*"), *Trudy Zool. Inst. Akad. Nauk SSSR,* 8 : 286-405.

STUGREN, B., and N. POPOVICH, 1961. "Analiz izmenchivosti vneshnykh priznakov zherlyanok Rumenii" ("Analysis of Variability of External Traits of Zherlyanika in Rumania"), *Zool. Zh.,* 41 : 569-576.

STURTEVANT, A., 1961. *Genetics and Evolution.* San Francisco : Freeman.

STURTEVANT, A., and TH. DOBZANSKY, 1936. "Geographical Distribution and Cytology of 'Sex Ratio' in *Drosophila pseudoobscura*," *Genetics,* 21 : 475-510.

SUEYOSHI, AKIRA, 1964. "Arteries of the Gluteal Region in *Macacus cyclopsis,*" *Acta. Med. Nagasakiensis,* 8 : 49-62.

SUMNER, F. B., 1909. "Some Effects of External Conditions upon the White Mouse," *J. Exper. Zool.,* 7 : 97-155.

SUMNER, F. B., 1915. "Some Studies of Environmental Influence, Heredity, Correlation and Growth in the White Mouse," *J. Exper. Zool.,* 18 : 325-432.

SUMNER, F. B., 1920. "Geographic Variation and Mendelian Inheritance," *J. Exper. Zool.,* 30 : 369-402.

SUMNER, F. B., 1921. "Desert and Lava-dwelling Mice and the Problem of Protective Coloration in Mammals," *J. Mammal.,* 2 : 75-86.

SUMNER, F. B., 1923. "Results of Experiments in Hybridizing Sub-species of *Peromyscus,*" *J. Exper. Zool.,* 38 : 245-292.

SUMNER, F. B., 1924. "The Stability of Sub-species under Changed Conditions of Environment," *Amer. Naturalist,* 58 : 475-481.

SUMNER, F. B., 1926. "An Analysis of Geographic Variation in Mice of the *Peromyscus polionotus* Group from Florida and Alabama," *J. Mammal.,* 7 : 149-184.

SUMNER, F. B., 1927. "Linear and Colorimetric Measurements of Small Mammals," *J. Mammal.,* 8 : 177-206.

SUMNER, F. B., 1928. "Observations on the Inheritance of a Multifactor Color Variation in White-footed Mice (*Peromyscus*)," *Amer. Naturalist,* 62 : 193-206.

SUMNER, F. B., 1932. "Genetic, Distributional and Evolutionary Studies of the Sub-species of Deer Mice (*Peromyscus*)," *Bibl. Genet.*, 9 : 1-106.

SUROVIAK, J., 1965. "Influence of UV Radiation on the Post-embryonal Development of the Testes of the White Mouse (*Mus musculus* L.)," *Vest. Ceskosl. Spolec. Zool.*, 29 : 255-281.

SWINDLER, D. K., J. A. GAVAN, and W. M. TURNER, 1963. "Molar Tooth Size Variability in African Monkeys," *Human Biol.*, 35 : 104-122.

TAKAYOSHI, INO, and SADAO ISHIGAKI, 1966. "Comparison of Hemoglobin Quantities in Two Inbred Strains of Mice and Reciprocal Hybrids," *Nat. Inst. Animal Health Quart.*, 6 : 101-108.

TALBOT, LEE M., and J. S. G. McCULLICH, 1965. "Weight Estimations for East African Mammals from Body Measurements," *J. Wildlife Manag.*, 29 : 84-89.

TATARINOVA, O. M., 1964. "Osobennosti okraski mekha trekh podvidov stepnoi pestrushki" ("Characters of the Color of the Fur of Three Sub-species of Gerbil"), Sb. *Voprosy Vnutrividovoi Izmenchivosti i Mikroevolyutsiya*, pp. 125-126. Sverdlovsk.

TERENT'EV, P. V., 1957. "O primenimosti ponyatiya 'podvid' v izuchenii vnutrividovoi izmenchivosti" ("On the Use of the Concept of 'Sub-species' in the Study of Intra-species Variability"), *Vestnik Leningradskii Gos. Univ.* 1957 (21) [Ser. Biol. 1957 (4)] : 78-79.

TERENT'EV, P. V., 1959. "Metod korrelyatsionnykh pleyad" ("The Method of Correlation Pleiades"), *Vestnik Leningradskii Gos. Univ.* 1959 (9) : 137-141.

THORPE, W. H., 1940. "Ecology and the Future of Systematics," in *The New Systematics* (J. S. Huxley, ed.), pp. 341-364. Oxford : Clarendon Press.

TIKHOMIROV, E. A., 1961. "Raspredelenie i migratsii tyulenei v vodakh Dal'nego vostoka" ("Distribution and Migration of Seals in the Waters of the Far East USSR"), *Trudy Soveshch. Ikhtiol. Kommissii*, 2 : 204-207.

TIMIRYAZEV, K. A., 1937. *Darvinizm i selektsiya* (*Darwinism and Selection*). Moscow : Sel'khozgiz.

TIMOFEEV-RESSOVSKII, N. V. (TIMOFEEFF-RESSOVSKY), 1927. "Genetische Analyse einer freilebenden *Drosophila melanogaster* Population," *Roux. Arch. Entwicklungsmech. Organismen*, 109 : 70-109.

TIMOFEEV-RESSOVSKII, N. V. (TIMOFEEFF-RESSOVSKY), 1939. "Genetik und Evolutionforschung," *Verh. Deutsch. Zool. Ges.*, 41 : 157-169.

TIMOFEEV-RESSOVSKII, N. V. (TIMOFEEFF-RESSOVSKY), 1958. "Mikroevolyutsiya, elementarnye yavleniya, material i faktory mikroevolyutsionnovo protsessa" ("Micro-evolution, Elementary Phenomena, Materials, and Factors of Micro-evolutional Process"), *Bot. Zh.*, 43 : 317-336.

TIMOFEEV-RESSOVSKII, N. V. (TIMOFEEFF-RESSOVSKY), 1965a. "O mikro i makrofilogenii u polovykh perekestnooplodotvoryayushchikhsya organizmov" ("On Micro- and Macro-phylogeny in Cross-fertilizing Organisms"), *Trudy Inst. Biol., Uralsk Fil. Akad. Nauk SSSR,* 44 : 5-10.

TIMOFEEV-RESSOVSKII, N. V. (TIMOFEEFF-RESSOVSKY), 1965b. "K teorii vida" ("On the Theory of Species"), Ibid., 44 : 11-26.

TIMOFEEV-RESSOVSKII, N. V. (TIMOFEEFF-RESSOVSKY), and YU. M. SVIREZHEV, 1966. "Ob adaptatsionnom polimorfizme v pop_ulyat-siyakh *Adalia bipunctata* L." ("On the Adaptive Polymorphism in Populations of *Adalia bipunctata* L."), *Problemy Kibernetiki,* 16 : 137-146.

TOMILIN, A. G., 1954. "Prisposobitel'nye tipy otryada kitoobraznykh" ("Adaptive Types of the Order Cetacea"), *Zool. Zh.,* 33 : 667-692.

TOMILIN, A. G., 1957. *Kitoobraznye zveri SSSR (Cetaceans of the USSR).* Vol. IX. Moscow : Izdatelstvo Akad. Nauk SSSR.

TRIBE, D. E., and L. PEEL, 1963. "Body Composition of the Kangaroo (*Macropus* sp.)." *Austral. J. Zool.,* 11 : 273-289.

TROYER, J. R., 1965. "Neurosecretion in the Hibernating Bat," *Anat. Rec.,* 151 : 77-91.

TRYUBER, I. F., 1937. "Izmenchivost' cherepa chernomorskogo delfina" ("Variability of the Skull of Black Sea Dolphin"), *Bull. Moskov. Obshch. Ispyt. Prir. (Biol.)* 46 : 17-24.

TSALKIN, V. I., 1956. "Izmenchivost' i sistematika turov zapadnogo Kavkaza (*Caprinae, Artiodactyla*)" ["Variability and Taxonomy of the tur (*Caprinae, Artiodactyla*) of the West Caucasus"], Ibid., 60 : 17-33.

TSALKIN, V. I., 1960. "Izmenchivost' metapodii i ee znachenie dlya izucheniya krupnogo rogatogo skota drevnosti" ("Variability of Meta-podia and Its Significance in the Study of Ancient Cattle"), Ibid., 45 : 109-126.

TU CHIN, 1963. "A. Femoralis and Its Branches in *Macacus cyclopsis,*" *Acta Med. Nagasakiensis,* 7 : 87-114.

TUMURZHAV, M., 1964. Sravnitel'noe izuchenie gistologii kozhi i razvitiya volosyannykh follikullov u mongolskikh ovets (A Comparative Study of the Histology of Skin and the Development of Hair Follicles in Mongolian Sheep). *Avtoref. Diss. na Soisk. Uch. St. Kand. Biol. Nauk.,* Inst. Morf. Zhivot., Akad. Nauk SSSR, Moscow.

URSIN, E., 1956. "Geographical Variation in *Apodemus sylvaticus* and *Apodemus flavicollis (Rodentia, Muridae)* in Europe, with Special Reference to Danish and Latvian Populations," *Biol. Skr. Dansk. Vidensk. Selsk.,* 8 (4) : 1-46.

USHAKOV, B. P., 1959a. "Teploustoichivost' tkanei-vidovoi priznak poikilotermnykh zhivotnikh" ("Heat Resistance of Tissues—A Charac-teristic of Poikilothermal Animals"), *Zool. Zh.,* 38 : 1292-1301.

USHAKOV, B. P., 1959b. "Fiziologiya kletki i problema vida v zoologii" ("Cell Physiology and the Problem of Species in Zoology"), *Tsitologiya,* 1 : 541-545.

VAN VALEN, L., 1962. "A Study of Fluctuating Asymmetry," *Evolution,* 16 : 125-141.

VAN VALEN, L., 1962a. "Growth Fields in the Dentition of *Peromyscus,*" *Evolution,* 16 : 272-277.

VAN VALEN, L., 1963. "Selection in Natural Populations : Human Fingerprints," *Nature,* 200 : 1237-1238.

VERHEYEN, R., 1969. "Adaptation to Environment," *Gerfaut,* 49 : 235-237.

VINOGRADOV, A. P., 1964. "Provinces biogéochimiques et leur role dans l'évolution organique," *Advances Organ. Geochem.,* pp. 317-337. Paris : Pergamon Press.

VOIPIO, PAAVO, 1962. "Color Variation in the Marten (*Martes martes*)," *Ann. Soc. Zool. Vanamo,* 24 (6) : 1-14.

VORONTSOV, N. N., 1958. "Znachenie izucheniya khromosomnykh naborov dlya sistematiki mlekopitayushchikh" ("The Significance of the Study of Chromosomal Units for the Taxonomy of Mammals"), *Bull. Moskov. Obshch. Ispyt. Prir.* (*Biol.*) 63 (2) : 5-36.

VORONTSOV, N. N., 1961. "Neravnomernost' tempov preobrazovaniya organov pishchevaritel'noi sistemy u gryzunov i printsip kompensatsii funktsii" ("Non-uniformity of the Rate of Formation of the Organs of the Digestive System in Rodents and the Principle of Compensation of Function"), *Dokl. Akad. Nauk SSSR,* 135 : 1494-1497.

VORONTSOV, N. N., 1963. "Neravnomernost' tempov preobrazovaniya organov i printsip kompensatsii funktsii" ("Non-uniformity in the Rate of Reformation of Organs and the Principle of Compensation of Functions"), *Zool. Zh.,* 42 : 1289-1305.

WADDINGTON, C. H., 1942. "Canalization of Development and the Inheritance of Acquired Characters," *Nature,* 50 : 563-565.

WASILEWSKI, W., 1952. "Badania nad morfologia *Clethrionomys glareolus glareolus* Schreb.," *Ann. Univ. M. Curie-Slodowska,* Sect. C, 7 : 119-212.

WASILEWSKI, W., 1956. "Untersuchungen über die morphologische Veränderlichkeit der Erdmaus *Microtus agrestis* Linne)," Ibid., 9 : 261-305.

WASILEWSKI, W., 1956a. "Untersuchungen über die Veränderlichkeit des *Microtus oeconomus* Pall. in Bialowieza," Ibid., 9 : 355-384.

WEBB, D. S., 1965. "The Osteology of *Camelops.*" *Bull. Los Angeles Co. Mus. Sci.,* 1 : 1-54.

WENK, P., 1964. "Die topographische Anatomie des lymphatischen Systems der Baumwollratte *Sygmodon hispidus* Say et Ord.," *Z. Versuchstierkunde,* 4 : 80-97.

WHITAKER, J. O., JR., 1963. "A Study of the Meadow Jumping Mouse, *Zapus hudsonius* (Zimmerman) in Central New York," *Ecol. Monographs,* 33 : 215-254. [Cited from Long (1968)].

WHITTAKER, H. M., and M. J. DELANY, 1969. "Variation in the Skull of the Long-tailed Field Mouse, *Apodemus sylvaticus*, in Mainland Britain," *J. Zool.*, 157 : 147-157.

WITHERS, R. F. J., 1964. "Morphological Correspondence and the Concept of Homology," *Form and Strategy in Science* (J. R. Gregg and F. T. C. Harris, eds.), pp. 378-394. Dordrecht : D. Reidel.

WOOD, A. J., T. McCOWAN, and M. J. DANIEL, 1965. "Organ Weight-Body Weight Relations in the Family *Mustelidae*, the Mink (*Mustela vison*)," *Canad. J. Zool.*, 43 : 55-68.

WRIGHT, S., 1926. "Effects of Age of Patterns on Characteristics of the Guinea Pig," *Amer. Naturalist*, 60 : 552-560.

WRIGHT, S., 1931. "Evolution in Mendelian Populations," *Genetics*, 16 : 97-159.

WRIGHT, S., 1952. "The Genetics of Quantitative Variability," *Quantitative Inheritance*, pp. 5-41. London : Agricultural Research Council.

WRIGHT, S., and H. B. Chase, 1936. "On the Genetics of the Spotted Pattern of the Guinea Pig," *Genetics*, 21 : 758-787.

YABLOKOV, A. V., 1956. "Interesnaya funktsiya beloi okraski" ("An Interesting Function of White Coloration"), *Priroda*, 1956 (6) : 92-94.

YABLOKOV, A. V., 1958a. "O stroenii zubnoi sistemy i tipakh zubov u kitoobraznykh" ("Structure of the Dental System and Types of Teeth in Cetaceans"), *Bull. Moskov. Obshch. Ispyt. Prir.* (*Biol.*) 63 (2) : 37-48.

YABLOKOV, A. V., 1958b. "K morfologii pishchevaritel'nogo trakta zubatykh kitoobraznykh" ("Morphology of the Digestive Tract of Toothed Whales"), *Zool. Zh.*, 37 : 601-611.

YABLOKOV, A. V., 1959a. Morfologicheskie osobennosti belukhi *Delphinapterus leucas*) kak predstavitelya zubatykh kitoobraznykh [Morphological Characteristics of the White Whale (*Delphinapterus leucas*) as a Representative of Toothed Whales]. *Avtoref. Diss. na Soisk. Uch. St. Kand. Biol. Nauk.* Moscow.

YABLOKOV, A. V., 1959b. "Nekotorye osobennosti stroeniya skeleta belukhi kak predstavitelya zubatykh kitoobraznykh" ("Some Characteristics of the Skeletal Structure of the White Whale as a Representative of Toothed Whales"), *Trudy i konf. Melodykh nauch. Sotr. Morf. Labor.*, Moscow, pp. 137-140.

YABLOKOV, A. V., 1961a. "Funktsional'naya morfologiya organov dykhaniya zubatykh kitoobraznykh" ("Functional Morphology of the Respiratory Organs of Toothed Whales"), *Trudy Soveshch. po ekologii i promyslu morskikh mlekopitayushchikh*, pp. 79-87. Moscow : Izdatelstvo Akad. Nauk SSSR.

YABLOKOV, A. V., 1961b. "Nekotorye osobennosti mochepolovoi sistemy kitoobraznykh" ("Some Features of the Urogenital System of Cetaceans"), *Bull. Moskov. Obshch. Ispyt. Prir.* (*Biol.*), 46 (2) : 33-38.

YABLOKOV, A. V., 1961c. "O znachenii stepeni razvitiya muzhskoi matki kak taksonomicheskogo priznaka u kitoobraznykh" ("Significance of the Degree of Development of the Male Uterus, as a Taxonomic Trait in Cetaceans"), Ibid., 46 (6) : 149-150.

YABLOKOV, A. V., 1961d. "Osbennosti stroeniya popyulyatsii kitoobraznykh kak evolusionnyi faktor" ("Features of the Population Structure in Cetaceans as an Evolutionary Factor"), *Vsesoyuznoe Soveshch. po Mlekopit.*, Vol. II : 111-112. Moscow : Izdatelstvo Moskovskii Gos. Univ.

YABLOKOV, A. V., 1962. "Sud'ba grenlandskogo tyulenya" ("Fate of the Greenland Seal"), *Priroda,* 1962 (2) : 66-72.

YABLOKOV, A. V., 1963a. "Nekotorye predvaritel'nye materialy k morfologicheskoi kharakteristike grenlandskogo tyulenya Belogo i Grenlandskogo morei" ("Some Preliminary Data on the Morphological Characters of Greenland Seals of the White and Greenland Seas"), *Sb. Nauchno-Issled. Rabot Sev. Otd. Polyarnogo Inst. Ryb. Khoz i Okeanogr.* (Arkhangelsk), pp. 24-36.

YABLOKOV, A. V., 1963b. "Materialy k morfologicheskoi kharakteristike khokhlacha Grenlandskogo morya" ("Data on Morphological Characters of Hooded Seals of the Greenland Sea"), Ibid., pp. 64-72.

YABLOKOV, A. V., 1963c. "Problema rudimentarnykh organov" ("The Problem of Vestigial Organs"), *Zool. Zh.,* 42 : 441-450.

YABLOKOV, A. V., 1963d. "Morfologicheskie kriterii v opredelenii samostoyatel'nosti popyulyatsii nekotorykh lastnogikh" ("Morphological Criteria in Determination of the Independence of Populations of Some Pinnipeds"), *Tezisy Dokl. Vtorogo Vsesoyuzn. Soveshch. po Izucheniyu Morskikh Mlekopitayushchikh,* Leningrad, p. 50.

YABLOKOV, A. V., 1963e. "O tipakh kitoobraznykh" ("On the Types of Cetaceans"), *Bull. Moskov. Obshch. Ispyt. Prir. (Biol.),* 68 (6) : 27-41.

YABLOKOV, A. V., 1964. "Konvergentsiya ili parallelizm v razvitii kitoobraznykh ?" ("Convergence or Parallelism in the Evolution of Cetaceans ?"), *Paleontol. Zh.,* 1946 (1) : 97-106.

YABLOKOV, A. V., 1964a. "O nekotorykh elementarnykh tendentsiyakh izmenchivosti priznakov mlekopitayushchikh i popytka klassifikatsii razlichnykh proyavlenii individual'noi izmenchivosti" ("On Some Elementary Tendencies of Variability of Mammalian Traits and an Attempt at Classification of Different Kinds of Individual Variability"), Sb. *Voprosy Vnutrividovoi Izmenchivosti i Mikroevolyutsiya,,* pp. 153-155. Sverdlovsk.

YABLOKOV, A. V., 1968. "Popyulyatsionnaya morfologiya zhivotnykh" ("Population Morphology of Animals"), *Zool. Zh.,* 47 : 1749-1765.

YABLOKOV, A.V., 1968. "Morfologicheskaya izmenchivost' v popyulyatsiyakh mlekopitayushchikh" ("Morphological Variability in Populations of Mammals"), *Itogi Nauki Zoologiya,* 1966 : 48-85.

YABLOKOV. A. V., 1970. "Morfologiya i mikroevolyutsiya" ("Morphology and Microevolution"), *Zhur. Obshch. Biol.*, 31 : 3-13.

YABLOKOV, A. V., and T. V. ANDREEVA, 1965. "Age Determination in Baleen Whales (*Mystacoceti*)," *Nature*, 205 : 412-413.

YABLOKOV, A. V., and V. YA. ETIN, 1965. "Analiz vnutrividovykh razlichii v okraske tela mlekopitayushchikh (na primere grenlandskogo tyulenya)" ["An Analysis of the Intra-species Differences in Body Color of Mammals (with an Example from the Greenland Seal)"], *Zool. Zh.*, 44 : 1094-1097.

YABLOKOV, A. V., and V. YA. ETIN, 1968. "Izmenchivost' morfologicheskikh priznakov nutrii Azerbaidzhana i Tadzhikistana" ("Variability of Morphological Features of the Coypu in Azerbaidzhan and Tadzhikistan"), *Zool. Zh.*, 47 : 116-121.

YABLOKOV, A. V., and G. A. KLEVEZAL', 1964. "Vibrissy kitoobraznykh i lastonogikh, ikh raspredelenie, stroenie, znachenie" ("Vibrissae of Cetaceans and Pinnipeds : Their Distribution, Structure, and Importance"), Sb. *Morf. Osobennosti Vodnykh Mlekopitayushchikh*, pp. 48-81. Moscow : Izdatelstvo 'Nauka'.

YABLOKOV, A. V., and D. E. SERZHENT (SERGEANT), 1963. "Morfologicheskaya kharakteristika izmenchivosti kraniologicheskikh priznakov grenlandskogo tyulenya" ("Morphological Characteristics of Variability of Craniological Traits of the Greenland Seal"), *Zool. Zh.*, 42 : 1857-1865.

ZARAPKIN, S. R., 1934. "Zur Phänoanalyse von geographischen Rassen und Arten," *Arch. Naturgesch.* (N. F.), 3 : 161-186.

ZARAPKIN, S. R., 1937. "Phänoanalyse von einigen Populationen der *Epilachna chrysomelina*," *Zschr. Indukt. Abstammungs- und Vererbungslehre*, 78 : 282-331.

ZARAPKIN, S. R., 1939. "Das Divergenzprinzip in der Bestimmung kleiner systematischer Kategorien," *VII Internat. Kongr. Entomol.*, pp. 494-518.

ZAVADSKII, K. M., 1958. "K ponimaniyu progressa v organicheskoi prirode" ("On the Understanding of Progress in Nature"), Sb. *Razvitie v Prirode i Obshchestve*, pp. 79-120. Leningrad.

ZAVADSKII, K. M., 1961. *Uchenie o vide* (The Concept of Species). Izdatelstvo Leningradskii Gos. Univ.

ZEJDA, J., 1960. "The Influence of Age on the Formation of the Third Upper Molar in the Bank Vole, *Clethrionomys glareolus* (Schreber, 1780) (*Mammalia, Rodentia*)," *Zool. Listy*, 9 : 159-166.

ZEJDA, J., 1965. "Zur Variabilität der Molarenwurzeln des Oberkiefers vier *Apodemus* Arten (Mammalia), " *Z. Morphol. Ökol. Tiere*, 54 : 699-706.

ZEMSKII, V. A., 1960. "Byli li u kitoobraznykh zadnie konechnosti" ("Did the Cetaceans Have Posterior Extremities ?"), *Okhrana Prirody i Ozelenenie*, 3 : 105-107.

ZEMSKII, V. A., and A. A. BERZIN, 1961. "O redkom yavlenii atavisma u kashalota (*Physeter catadon* L.)" ("The Rare Phenomena of Atavism in *Physeter catadon* L."), *Nauchnye Dokl. Vysshei Shkoly, Seriya Biol. Nauki*, pp. 56-60.

ZHDANOV, D. A., and B. A. NIKITYUK, 1964. "Vozrastnye izmeneniya dlinny i vesa tela i okruzhnosti grudnoi kletki u sovremennogo vozroslogo naseleniya g. Moskvy" ("Growth Variation in Length and Weight of the Body and the Circumference of the Thoracic Cavity in the Modern Adult Population of Moscow"), *Arkhiv Anat. Gistol. Embriol.*, 16 (3) : 28-42.

ZSCHIESCHE, W., and H. HEINECKE, 1964. "Biometrische Untersuchungen äusseres Körpermasse au Mauseinzuchtstammen," *Z. Versuchstkunde*, 5 (1-3) : 78-87.

ZUBCHANINOVA, E. V., 1962. "O geograficheskoi izmenchivosti burundu-kov (*Eutamias sibirica* Laxm.)" ("Geographical Variability of *Eutamias sibirica* Laxm."), *Z. Versuchstkunde*, 5 (4) : 41-45.